STRONG SOLIDS

BY

A. KELLY F.R.S.

DEPUTY DIRECTOR, NATIONAL PHYSICAL LABORATORY

SECOND EDITION

CLARENDON PRESS · OXFORD

1973

Oxford University Press, Ely House, London W. 1

GLASGOW   NEW YORK   TORONTO   MELBOURNE   WELLINGTON
CAPE TOWN   IBADAN   NAIROBI   DAR ES SALAAM   LUSAKA   ADDIS ABABA
DELHI   BOMBAY   CALCUTTA   MADRAS   KARACHI   LAHORE   DACCA
KUALA LUMPUR   SINGAPORE   HONG KONG   TOKYO

ISBN 0 19 851350 X

FIRST EDITION 1966
SECOND EDITION 1973

TEXT SET IN 11/13 pt. MONOTYPE MODERN, PRINTED BY LETTERPRESS,
AND BOUND IN GREAT BRITAIN AT THE PITMAN PRESS, BATH

PREFACE TO THE SECOND EDITION

THE first edition of this book was written seven years ago. Since that time the topic of Strong Solids has become very well known because of the growth in technology of fibrous composites and because of a quickened interest in the Universities in the envelope of possible strengths of solids and how this is related to the understanding of many problems in the science of materials, e.g. the coherence of second phase particles, and the essential distinction between a brittle and a ductile solid.

The science of controlling cracks—fracture mechanics—is now firmly established and applied, and so the parts of the book dealing with this topic have been rewritten and updated. Beautiful experiments have confirmed the essential correctness of the methods for estimating the strengths of ideal crystals and attempts to calculate some plastic properties of crystals have been pushed a little farther. The pressure reached under an indenter remains the largest statically-maintained pressure on the surface of this planet. A small section has been included on the effects of shock waves on materials because those interested in understanding the constitution of this and other planets need to consider the limiting strengths of materials under high pressures.

Some improvements have been made in our understanding of the strength of ductile metals and these have required the revision of Chapter IV. As usually occurs when a scientific problem is explored in depth, a straightforward view requires numerous qualifications but the advantages of an over-all view are, I hope, still clear.

Activity in the field of fibre reinforcement has increased enormously, due mainly to the use in engineering structures of high strength boron and carbon fibres. The reasons for this high strength are not quantitatively understood. The section on fibre reinforcement has been rewritten and enlarged to take account of this growth because it is believed that advance in this field, particularly in the behaviour of cracks, can illuminate other problems in the science of materials.

The large scientific effort devoted to understanding the behaviour of organic polymers has begun to produce polymers with strength and stiffness equal to those of metals. The few remarks made in the first edition on theoretical estimates of stiffness and strength of these materials have therefore been amplified.

The problem of which units to use in writing, or revising a book of this type remains. SI units predominate in this revision because of their increasing acceptance everywhere and because of my own official position. Pounds per square inch, the choice for the first edition, remain, alone in some places, but usually related to SI units. Some facility in conversion remains necessary for all of us!

Chapter V of this revised edition owes much to the preparation of a review article with Mr D. K. Hale, and I am very grateful to him for permission to use some of the unpublished material. I am also very grateful to other colleagues who have, by their efforts and example, maintained my interest in these subjects. I would particularly mention Mr J. Aveston, Dr G. A. Cooper, Dr N. H. Macmillan, and Dr K. N. Street.

A. K.

Thames Ditton
November, 1972

PREFACE TO THE FIRST EDITION

THERE is currently a good deal of interest in the production and use of materials which are very strong, very stiff, and very light in weight. A number of articles have recently appeared adumbrating the principles to be used in the design of such solids. The main suggestion made is that reinforcement of a weak material with strong fibres or with whisker crystals will provide a new type of material which may replace conventional strong metals and their alloys in a number of applications. Many conferences have been devoted to this topic.

This small book aims to review the basic theory behind these suggestions and to see how well supported it is by experiment. Some consideration is given to the properties of strong solids which are available today and to materials which can be used at elevated temperatures. These are principally the metals and glass-reinforced plastics. A consideration of their properties leads to many suggestions for improvement in the light of the basic principles.

I was first introduced to this subject by Professor A. H. Cottrell and I am very grateful to him for this and to him and to Dr N. Kurti for suggesting that I write this book. A number of my colleagues have read chapters of the book and commented helpfully upon them. These are L. M. Brown (Chapter 3), A. H. Cottrell (Chapter 4), G. J. Davies (Chapter 6), J. D. Eshelby (Chapters 1 and 2), and W. R. Tyson (Chapter 1). I am most grateful to all of them. I would also like to thank the Interservices Metallurgical Research Council of the Ministry of Aviation who invited me to write a review of the principles of fibre reinforcement on which Chapter 5 is based.

The field of research into strong materials is currently a very rapidly developing one and for this reason this monograph can only appear in some respects similar to an interim report. It makes no claim to originality or to completeness but aims to bring together into one convenient compass results and ideas which are currently widely scattered in the literature. My own work in this field has been done completely in collaboration with my research students and I am very grateful to all of those who have worked with me over the last few years in the fields of ceramic materials and precipitation-hardening and lately on fibre reinforcement. Many of the ideas in the field of strong materials have been discussed with Mr J. E. Gordon and Dr W. R. Tyson and I am particularly grateful to these two colleagues for the stimulation and help which they have always so readily provided.

Cambridge
November 1965

ACKNOWLEDGEMENTS

GRATEFUL acknowledgement is made to the following people for providing the Plates: J. D. Embury (Plate 1), F. D. Lemkey (Plate 2), G. A. Cooper (Plates 3 and 5), and I. G. Palmer (Plate 4); and to the following societies and publishers for permission to reproduce illustrations: The Royal Society; J. Wiley and Sons Inc.; *Journal of Applied Physics*; The Cambridge Philosophical Society; *Physical Review*; The Institute of Physics and the Physical Society; *Acta Metallurgica*; The National Gas Turbine Establishment; Pergamon Press; The Society of Plastics Engineers; The General Electric Company.

I would like to thank Mrs M.E. Harper, Mrs D. N. Beall, and Mrs Y. F. Mears for typing the manuscript of the first edition.

CONTENTS

CONTENTS

LIST OF PLATES

INTRODUCTION

THIS book is about solids which are strong in tension. The stress required to break a solid depends upon the type of stress system applied. In most cases throughout this book we will be considering that the solid is subject to a simple uniaxial tensile pull.

Any solid has in principle a theoretical failure stress determined solely by the chemical binding forces between the constitutive atoms, and the temperature. This theoretical failure stress applies to a notional specimen of the substance which is completely perfect in the sense that it is everywhere homogeneous and contains no cracks, inclusions, foreign atoms or dislocations or other definable imperfections. Thirty years or so ago there was great interest in the theoretical failure stress because the highest observed strengths of solids (with one or two exceptions such as quartz fibres) fell short of the theoretically expected value by at least two orders of magnitude. This discrepancy was emphasized and was an important link in the argument that solids (principally crystals) contained imperfections. Those imperfections known to influence the breaking strengths of most crystals have been directly observed during the last ten years and the intensive study of these, principally the dislocation, has led to a decrease in interest in the theoretical strength.

However, in the meantime many solids have been made with a strength equal to or greater than 10 GN m^{-2} (10^{11} dyn cm^{-2} or 1·45 × 10^6 lbf in^{-2}). These strengths approach the theoretical values. They have been observed principally in whiskers but large specimens of silica glass or sapphire have been made with strengths greater than this value. Two important questions then arise. The first is to enquire whether our estimates of the theoretical strength are accurate and if so, whether the experimental values of the strengths of very strong materials are explained in terms of them. The rough answer to this question is yes. It is examined quantitatively, as far as is possible at present, in Chapter I and in general the observed strengths of the strongest solids are found to be about one-third of the theoretical value, though some metal crystals have been made which appear to fail at the theoretical stress.

The second question of importance is to ask whether these very large *observed* strengths can be approached in practice in a usable material. If the answer to this question is yes, then many technological changes are possible because new materials of greater strength to weight ratio and, more importantly, of greater Young's modulus to weight ratio, will be made available to the engineer. In addition, materials for use at higher temperatures can then be made. The obvious application of such materials, at present, is in the field of transportation, e.g. in rocket motor cases or in helicopter rotor blades, and in gas turbines, e.g. in vanes and blades. If the adoption of new materials in the field of engines and transport becomes widespread we can expect to see them used in conventional civil engineering and in architecture.

The use of a strong material in practice depends on many factors. Cost is one of the most important. Further, when considering the use of new stronger solids it has to be clearly realized that resistance to fracture is not solely a property of the material but that the specimen shape and dimensions and the state of stress must all be taken into account. The subject matter of this book is confined to the problem of understanding at an elementary level what materials will be strong in uniaxial tension and how their strength can be obtained in a piece sufficiently large to handle easily and which does not lose its strength immediately that the surface is scratched.

The plan of this book is as follows. Estimates of the theoretical strength are made in Chapter 1 and where possible compared with experiment. The discussion of the theoretical strength enables one to set down the chemical constitution of the strongest materials. High strength is not realized in practice because crystals usually contain imperfections. The two most important of these are the crack and the dislocation. The way in which cracks reduce the strength is outlined in Chapter 2 and dislocations are discussed in Chapter 3. The present-day strong solids in widest use are the metals. The microstructure of a metallic specimen which produces the greatest strength without extreme fragility is discussed in Chapter 4 and examples of how strong and versatile metals can be are pointed out. The relatively new principle in man-made materials of copying nature and designing a fibrous microstructure to provide high strength without extreme notch sensitivity is described in Chapter 5. Finally, in Chapter 6 some of the possible ways of making strong fibres and incorporating them into a matrix are discussed.

When writing a book of this nature the problem of what units to use to measure the strength is a real one. I have tended to use pounds per square inch. This is because from observation, the many people working on strong solids, polymer scientists, physicists, metallurgists, engineers, seem most able to convert their own natural units into these. The c.g.s. equivalent is often given throughout the book. Appendix D relates currently used units. In the other appendices some data on strong materials are collected.

The relation between breaking strength and microstructure of a solid is a problem in the science of materials which is not completely solved. For this reason most of the arguments in this book can only be of a qualitative nature. A survey of the kind presented here points up some serious gaps in our knowledge. Examples of these are our ignorance of the way in which the theoretical cleavage stress or theoretical shear stress depends on other superposed stresses, our ignorance of the nature of the state of affairs at the tip of a true crack, our inability to understand from first principles the ductile to brittle transition. Most of these problems are connected with understanding the nature of a crack. The amount of scientific interest in the dislocation has perhaps diverted interest in the last few years from the problem of understanding and controlling the motion of cracks.

1
THE IDEAL STRENGTH

A SOLID can be broken in two distinct ways; it can cleave as
does mica, or it may flow apart as does pitch. We usually assume
that breaking will occur when a certain tensile stress is applied
to the solid. It follows, then, that whichever mode of breaking
requires the smallest stress will be the one observed. A perfect
crystal is expected to be the strongest form of a solid and so its
strength sets an upper limit to the envelope of attainable
strengths. In this chapter, we first make some general remarks in
section 1.1 upon the significance of calculations of the strength
of ideal, i.e. perfect crystals. We then consider estimates of the
theoretical cleavage stress in sections 1.2 and 1.3. In section 1.4,
we comment on calculations of the elastic modulus and of the
ideal strength of linear polymers. The theoretical shear stress,
which is more difficult to calculate exactly, is considered in
section 1.5, and effects of temperature in section 1.6. Experimental results are compared with the theoretical estimates in
section 1.7. Section 1.8 details the chemical constitution of the
strongest solids and 1.9 describes how some quantitative
information on the plastic yield stress of a strong solid can be
deduced from a hardness test. Finally in section 1.10 we make
some remarks upon the notion of the ideal strength of a solid
under conditions of hydrostatic compression.

1.1. Introduction

Since a perfect crystal is expected to be the strongest form of
solid, calculations of the strength from theoretical models of the
interatomic forces are important in order to define the upper limit
of attainable strengths. Such calculations involve choosing
models for the interatomic forces which it is hoped will be accurate when the interatomic distances are altered by a few per cent

from those in the unstrained crystal. The calculations have application to other problems in the science of materials, which we can list briefly. The width of a dislocation in a crystal is related to the ideal shear strength. The emission of dislocations from an interface in the absence of dislocation sources may be controlled by the ideal shear strength. The emission of dislocations under these conditions is of importance in understanding the stresses around a growing inclusion in a solid, and whether or not such an inclusion or inhomogeneity is able to retain coherence with the host crystal in the sense that the Bravais lattice of the inclusion and host remain continuous. The generation of dislocations at or near an interface also sets limits to the elastic stresses produced in heterogeneous crystals due to changes of temperature, to the stresses between grains in a polycrystal, and to the attainable stresses at the tip of a sharp crack. Some of these problems are considered further in this book. However, mention of them is important because one may note that these other problems always involve large gradients of stress and strain within a solid. We do not know whether the mode of failure or instability which limits the stresses in these cases is in fact governed by the attainment of a certain stress. The notion of stress implies that the traction per unit of area be constant over a sufficiently large number of atoms and hence the notion of an ideal strength supposes a large crystal uniformly stressed. Such an assumption may be unrealistic. It may be that the stability of the deformed crystal under stress is what governs its strength. This point is considered further in section 1.3.

1.2. Theoretical cleavage stress

A simple way of estimating the expected cleavage stress of a perfect solid is due to Orowan (1949). It is only a crude estimate but has the advantage of being applicable to all solids, whatever the detailed nature of the interatomic forces. If we attempt to pull a perfect solid apart at absolute zero the restraining force per unit area between two adjacent atomic planes must vary with distance as in Fig. 1.1. At the equilibrium separation of the atomic planes a_0 the force is zero. It must rise to a maximum and then fall to zero. The exact form of the curve can only be calculated for the solid if the interatomic forces are known in detail. This can be done in some cases as we describe in outline in section 1.3. In general it cannot, and so to make a rough estimate we note that the area under the curve must represent the work of fracture. The work of fracture cannot be less than

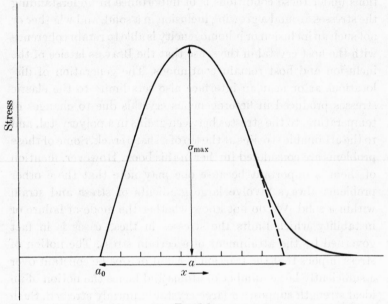

FIG. 1.1.

the surface energy of the two new surfaces created when the solid breaks. If we are carrying out a tensile test on a rod, this work is equal to 2γ times the initial area of cross-section of the rod, where γ is the surface energy. We do not expect the breaking strength of the rod to depend upon its length, and so we equate the stored elastic energy *between adjacent atomic planes* to the minimum work of fracture.

A simple form to assume for the variation of restraining force with distance is to write the stress σ as

$$\sigma = K \sin \frac{\pi}{a}(x - a_0). \tag{1.1}$$

We find the constant K as follows. When $(x-a_0)$ is very small,

$$a_0 \frac{\mathrm{d}\sigma}{\mathrm{d}x} = K\pi \frac{a_0}{a} \cos \frac{\pi}{a}(x-a_0) = E,$$

where E is Young's modulus for the appropriate direction in the solid. Hence

$$K = \frac{E}{\pi}\left(\frac{a}{a_0}\right).$$

We do not know the value of a, which is a measure of the 'range of the interatomic forces'. To evaluate a, following Orowan, we set

$$\int_{a_0}^{a_0+a} \sigma \, \mathrm{d}x = 2\gamma, \tag{1.2}$$

whence,

$$a = \pi\gamma/K.\dagger \tag{1.3}$$

The 'theoretical breaking stress' σ_{max} is given by the maximum value of σ in equation (1.1), i.e.

$$\sigma_{max} = K = \frac{E}{\pi}\left(\frac{a}{a_0}\right). \tag{1.4}$$

Substituting for a from equation (1.3) we have

$$\sigma_{max} = \sqrt{\left(\frac{E\gamma}{a_0}\right)}. \tag{1.5}$$

The breaking strain is

$$\varepsilon_{max} = \frac{a}{2a_0} = \frac{\pi}{2}\sqrt{\left(\frac{\gamma}{Ea_0}\right)}. \tag{1.6}$$

---

† This assumption is clearly a very rough one since in a uniformly stressed crystal the work done by the applied forces will be equal to that necessary to separate the crystal into a uniformly and widely spaced stack of monatomic planes and not equal to twice the surface energy. The assumption has been considered in detail by Macmillan and Kelly (1972).

According to this simple model the surface energy of a solid is given from equation (1.3) as

$$\gamma = \frac{Ka}{\pi} = \frac{E}{a_0}\left(\frac{a}{\pi}\right)^2. \tag{1.7}$$

Since a will be approximately equal to a_0 this gives as a very rough estimate of the surface energy,

$$\gamma = Ea_0/10. \tag{1.8}$$

According to equation (1.5) the breaking strength at absolute zero of a perfect solid should increase with an increase in Young's modulus and with an increase in the surface energy, and decrease with increase in the spacing of the atomic planes. When looking for strong solids we therefore look for substances of high elastic modulus and high surface energy, and with the largest number of atoms per unit volume.

In using equation (1.5) one must take into account the anisotropy of the physical properties. For a crystal, E will be replaced by $1/S'_{11}$, where S'_{11} is the elastic compliance for the direction considered. $1/S'_{11}$ is taken and not C'_{11}, the relevant elastic constant, since we are considering the breaking strength of a rod of which the sides are *not constrained*. Also, the values of γ and of a_0 will depend on the particular planes of the crystal across which fracture occurs. Data for a number of crystals and for silica glass are collected in Table 1.1 and the theoretical breaking stress evaluated using equation (1.5). The data are appropriate to a temperature of 20°C. They have not been corrected to 0 K since the derivation of equation (1.5) and the accuracy of estimating γ, the surface energy, do not justify this.

The greatest uncertainty in using equation (1.5) is in the value of γ because this is difficult to measure in absolute units for a solid. The values of the surface energy given in Table 1.1 come from a number of sources. They are accurate only to two significant figures at most and have not been corrected to apply at a particular temperature since the accuracy of doing this is very uncertain. Those for zinc, silicon, sodium chloride, and magnesium oxide come from experiments on cleaving crystals at low temperatures; those for silver, copper, and iron from high temperature measurements on the creep of wires. Those for tungsten, sodium, and silica glass were obtained by extrapolation from the liquid state. The first value for aluminium oxide was obtained from sessile drop experiments involving the equilibrium with liquid nickel; the second from the equilibria of drops and the third from the equilibrium with liquid platinum. The value for graphite was calculated from experiments on heats of immersion and that for diamond computed from the bond energy of the C—C bond.

In face-centred cubic metals the variation of surface energy with orientation is not large, being less than 15 per cent (Sundquist 1964); in body-centred cubic metals it is somewhat bigger, about 25 per cent. For these metals the principal variation of σ_{max} with direction then arises from the variation of the elastic moduli. The values of surface energy of the metals are usually high and equation (1.5) predicts breaking strengths of several million pounds per square inch, and large breaking strains (20–30 per cent). Zinc and graphite are representative of the layer structures with low values of the surface energy parallel to cleavage planes and with small elastic moduli for stretching normal to these planes. The theoretical cohesive strengths are of course very low compared to those of the other crystals. Diamond apparently has a large surface energy so that if this value is correct the theoretical breaking strain is about 20 per cent. The values for the other non-metallic crystals in Table 1.1 show that in such materials planes of low surface energy can be exposed by cleavage and so the theoretical fracture strengths do not exceed 15 per cent of Young's modulus.

Comparison of the values of σ_{max} for diamond and for sodium chloride with those computed for these crystals in a more exact fashion in section 1.3 shows that Orowan's estimate (equation (1.5)), though giving the right order of magnitude for the theoretical breaking strength, appears to *overestimate* it by a factor of up to 2 for a crystal. For silica glass the estimate is quite close to the observed (temperature independent) strength at low temperature (section 2.5).

Table 1.1

Values of the theoretical cleavage stress derived from equation (1.5)

Substance	Direction	†E (GN m^{-2})	Surface energy (mJ m^{-2})	σ_{max} (GN m^{-2})	σ_{max} (10^6 psi)
Silver	$\langle 111 \rangle$	121	1130[a]	24	3·4
Gold	$\langle 111 \rangle$	110	1350[a]	27	3·9
Copper	$\langle 111 \rangle$	192	1650[a]	39	5·7
Copper	$\langle 100 \rangle$	67	1650[a]	25	3·6
Tungsten	$\langle 100 \rangle$	390	3000[b]	86	12·5
α-Iron	$\langle 100 \rangle$	132	2000[c]	30	4·4
α-Iron	$\langle 111 \rangle$	260	2000[c]	46	7·6
Zinc	$\langle 0001 \rangle$	35	100[d]	3·8	0·55
Sodium	$\langle 100 \rangle$	0·16	228[1]	0·9	0·13
Graphite	$\langle 0001 \rangle$	10	70[g]	1·4	0·2
Silicon	$\langle 111 \rangle$	188	1200[d]	32	4·6
Diamond	$\langle 111 \rangle$	1210	5400[f]	205	29·8
Silica glass	—	73‡	560[h]	16·0	2·3
Sodium chloride	$\langle 100 \rangle$	44	115[e]	4·3	0·62
Magnesium oxide	$\langle 100 \rangle$	245	1200[d]	37	5·4
Aluminium oxide	$\langle 0001 \rangle$ §	460	1000[1]	46	6·7
			600[j]	35	5·2
			770[k]	40	5·9

† See Appendix C, Table 1.

‡ The value increases somewhat with strain, F. P. MALLINDER and B. A. PROCTOR (1964). *Physics Chem. Glasses* **5**, 91.

§ Hexagonal cell.

a. *The Structure and Properties of Solid Surfaces* (1952). Eds. R. GOMER and C. S. SMITH. University of Chicago Press.

b. B. C. ALLEN (1963). *Trans. Am. Inst. Min. metall. Petrol. Engrs.* **227**, 1175.

c. A. T. PRICE, M. A. HALL, and A. P. GREENOUGH (1964), *Acta metall.* **12**, 49. The surface energy of body-centred cubic metals will be determined by first and second nearest neighbour interactions. To allow for this a_0 in equation (1.5) has been taken equal to a for the (100) plane and $\sqrt{3}a/2$ for (111). a is the lattice parameter. On this assumption $\gamma_{100} \approx \gamma_{111}$ (Sundquist 1964).

d. J. J. GILMAN (1960). *J. appl. Phys.* **31**, 2208.

e. W. CLASS (1964). Ph.D. Thesis, Columbia University.

f. W. D. HAWKINS (1941). *J. chem. Phys.* **10**, 269.

g. R. J. GOOD, L. A. GIRIFALCO, and G. KRAUS (1958). *J. phys. Chem.* **62**, 1418.

1.3. More exact calculations

The force between two atoms bound by covalent bonds can be well described by a Morse function. We use this to investigate the strength of a carbon to carbon bond, following an early method due to de Boer (1936). The Morse function is shown in Fig. 1.2.

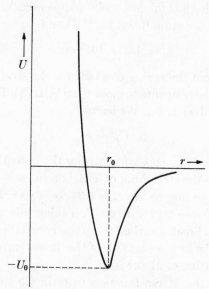

FIG. 1.2. The Morse function.

The energy of interaction U, between two atoms of separation r is given by

$$U = U_0[\exp\{-2a(r-r_0)\}-2\exp\{-a(r-r_0)\}]. \quad (1.9)$$

The maximum attractive force between the atoms is $U_0 a/2$ and this occurs at a separation

$$r_{\max} = (ar_0 + \ln 2)/a. \quad (1.10)$$

h. A. A. GRIFFITH (1920). Phil. Trans. R. Soc. A221, 163.
i. W. D. KINGERY (1954). J. Am. ceram. Soc. 37, 42.
j. Value found at melting point, R. N. MCNALLY, H. C. YEH, and N. BALASUBRAMANIAN (1968). J. mater. Sci. 3, 136.
k. M. MCLEAN and E. D. HONDROS (1971). J. mater. Sci. 6, 19.
l. J. W. TAYLOR (1955). Phil. Mag. 46, 867.

The value of the parameter a is related to the curvature of the curve at the equilibrium separation, r_0, as

$$\left(\frac{d^2 U}{dr^2}\right)_{r=r_0} = 2a^2 U_0. \tag{1.11}$$

The bond energy of an aliphatic carbon to carbon bond is 83 kcal per mole (332 kJ per mole) (Appendix A, Table 5) or $5 \cdot 8 \times 10^{-12}$ ergs per atom ($5 \cdot 8 \times 10^{-19}$ J) and

$$r_0 = 1 \cdot 54 \times 10^{-8} \text{ cm}.$$

We obtain a from the spring constant for the stretching of the C—C bonds in the neopentane molecule ($C(CH_3)_4$). This is known from spectra (Silver 1940). We have

$$2a^2 U_0 = k_{cc}, \tag{1.12}$$

where k_{cc} is the force constant relating the potential energy of the molecule to the stretching of a carbon to carbon bond. The value of k_{cc} according to Silver is $5 \cdot 2 \times 10^5$ dyn cm^{-1} ($5 \cdot 2 \times 10^2$ N m^{-1}), whence $a = 2 \cdot 12 \times 10^8$ cm^{-1}. Taking this value of a we find the force to break a carbon to carbon bond is $6 \cdot 1 \times 10^{-4}$ dyn. The bond breaks at a separation of the atoms corresponding to a tensile elongation of 21 per cent.

We can use the Morse function to estimate the theoretical fracture strength of diamond. Between the widely separated {111} planes in diamond (see the drawing of the structure in Fig. 3.2) there are $1 \cdot 82 \times 10^{15}$ bonds per square centimetre. The force to break a single bond, estimated above, is $6 \cdot 1 \times 10^{-4}$ dyn. The breaking strength of diamond in the $\langle 111 \rangle$ direction is then 11×10^{11} dyn cm^{-2} (110 GN m^{-2} or 16×10^6 psi).

Zwicky (1923) attempted an exact calculation of the breaking strength of rock-salt. The method is to consider a rod of NaCl with a force applied along the [100] direction parallel to the axis of the rod and to write the total electrostatic energy of the crystal U in terms of x, the separation of neighbouring (100) planes. For a rod of unit area of cross section dU/dx is a measure of the tensile stress in the [100] direction. Breaking will occur when $d^2 U/dx^2 = 0$, at a specific value of x, x_R. Zwicky finds that breaking will occur at a tensile strain of 0·14. The tensile strain normal to [100] is −0·023 at this point. The breaking stress is then found by evaluating dU/dx at a value of x_R of $1·14a/2$, where a is the lattice parameter. Zwicky obtains a value of 2×10^{10} dyn cm^{-2} (2GN m^{-2}) for the breaking stress of NaCl in the [100] direction.

Zwicky's calculation is based on finding U, the electrostatic energy of the crystal, from Born's orginal lattice theory of crystals, and using for the potential energy ϕ between a pair of ions in the crystal of separation r,

$$\phi = \pm \frac{e^2}{r} + \frac{A}{r^9}, \qquad (1.13)$$

where A is a constant independent of the type of ion considered. The value of 2×10^{10} dyn cm^{-2} for the breaking stress of a perfect rock-salt crystal pulled in the direction [100] is within a factor of close to 2 of that found from the simple calculation of section 1.1 (see Table 1.1). However, it is lower.

de Boer repeated Zwicky's calculation for sodium chloride using a somewhat simpler method and obtained $2·4 \times 10^{10}$ dyn cm^{-2} for the breaking stress at a tensile strain of 0·17. de Boer also attempted to estimate the contribution to the theoretical strength of the van der Waals' forces. This calculation was less accurate but increased the value of the theoretical breaking stress to $2·6 \times 10^{10}$ dyn cm^{-2} (2·6 GN m^{-2} or 380 000 psi). Tyson (1966) has also repeated Zwicky's calculation using a computer and considering van der Waals' forces. He has used the lastest figures for the polarizabilities of the ions to evaluate these. The term A/r^9 in the expression for ϕ is replaced by terms taking into account the difference in the repulsive forces between ions of different type and the van der Waals' forces—the so-called Born–Meyer model for sodium chloride. Tyson's value of σ_{max} for sodium chloride pulled parallel to [100] is $2·7 \times 10^{10}$ dyn cm^{-2} (2·7 GN m^{-2} or 390 000 psi), or $E/21$ at 0 K. The observed maximum strength of a whisker of sodium chloride at room temperature when pulled parallel to ⟨100⟩ is very close to one-third of this value (Appendix A, Table 1).

Born and Fürth (1940) carried through a calculation of the tensile strength of a face-centred cubic lattice in order to investigate the soundness of one of Zwicky's assumptions which has also been made in the later work. Zwicky's condition for the breaking of the crystal, viz. $\mathrm{d}^2 U/\mathrm{d}x^2 = 0$, is that the point of instability of the lattice against further deformation in the

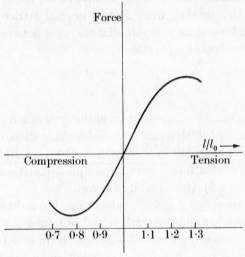

FIG. 1.3. The force–elongation curve for a face-centred cubic Lennard–Jones crystal stressed along [100] according to Born and Fürth (1940).

direction of the stress is reached, but Born and Fürth point out that there will be other small forces actually acting on a crystal and so perhaps a better condition is that the lattice, strongly stressed in the direction of one of the axes, becomes unstable against a small deformation in an arbitrary direction. Born and Fürth assume central forces and a simple power law for the potential between two atoms, viz.

$$\phi(r) = U \frac{mn}{n-m} \left[-\frac{1}{m}\left(\frac{r_0}{r}\right)^m + \frac{1}{n}\left(\frac{r_0}{r}\right)^n \right]. \qquad (1.14)$$

r_0 is the equilibrium distance of two isolated atoms and U is the energy required to bring them to an infinite distance. For their numerical calculations Born and Fürth take the values $m = 6$

and $n = 12$ (the so-called Lennard–Jones potential) and find as follows. If a single tensile force is applied along the [100] direction Hooke's law is well obeyed up to a tensile strain of 10 per cent (see Fig. 1.3). At larger strains the deviation from Hooke's law becomes more marked and fracture should occur at a tensile strain of close to 25 per cent, at a stress of $0 \cdot 16E$. If small additional deformations are allowed to act on the crystal the critical strain is reduced to about 15 per cent and the stress to about $0 \cdot 14E$.

Calculations of the type carried through originally by Zwicky and those of the type introduced by Born and Fürth have been extended by Macmillan and Kelly (1972) using a computer. These authors carried out calculations of the ideal cleavage stress for sodium chloride, using essentially the model of interatomic forces used by Tyson with only small modifications, and calculated the cleavage stresses of argon using the Lennard–Jones potential with modern values of the constants. These materials were chosen because they obey quite closely the Cauchy relation $C_{12} = C_{44}$ and so might be represented by central-force models which involve only the distance between ions to determine the potential energy, with no angular dependence. Many orientations of the tensile axis were chosen and calculations performed for unconstrained tension (i.e. the crystal is allowed to relax sideways) and also for various forms of constrained tension.

Using the Zwicky condition for fracture, i.e. that the tensile force should reach a maximum, these authors find that the constrained values are larger than the unconstrained in the case of uniaxial tension of sodium chloride, but that in the case of argon the constrained values are the smaller. In the case of sodium chloride, for example, the difference between constrained and unconstrained values is 14 per cent for [100] tension and 40 per cent for [111] tension. Using the constants appropriate to room temperature,† sodium chloride in triaxial

† Small numerical differences arise between the values reported by Tyson and those given by Macmillan and Kelly for the case of sodium chloride, because the latter authors used the lattice parameter appropriate to 25°C and Tyson used values extrapolated to 0 K.

tension is calculated to fail at $4 \cdot 28$ GN m^{-2}, and in uniaxial unconstrained [100] tension at $2 \cdot 4$ GN m^{-2}. For argon the difference between constrained and unconstrained values in uniaxial tension is always less than 10 per cent. The ideal failure stress in triaxial tension is calculated as $2 \cdot 54 \times 10^{8}$ N m^{-2} and in unconstrained [100] tension as $3 \cdot 45 \times 10^{8}$ N m^{2}.

By exploring the variation with orientation of the constrained ideal tensile strength Macmillan and Kelly find that the observed plane of easy cleavage in sodium chloride, viz. (100), lies normal to a pronounced minimum (probably a cusp) in a polar plot of σ_{max} against direction in the crystal. No pronounced minimum was found in the case of argon, and argon shows no plane of easy cleavage. These calculations suggest that if a crystal is known to possess a well-defined tendency to cleave then calculation of the ideal strength normal to this direction is likely to yield the lowest value.

For both sodium chloride and argon Macmillan and Kelly investigate the reduction in ideal tensile strength which is found if Born's stability condition is employed to define the ideal tensile stress, rather than Zwicky's condition that the force per unit area passes through a maximum. The reductions in ideal tensile strength when the former condition is taken to define failure are never more than 20 per cent. This means that calculating the maximum tensile force that a crystal can withstand does not lead to a gross overestimate of the expected strength of a perfect crystal. It is not known at present, however, that the Born condition for failure provides a lower limit to the ideal tensile strength of a crystal. The Born condition is that the crystal, strongly stressed in one direction, fails when a vanishingly small additional deformation leads to no increase in the total potential energy of the system of crystal plus applied forces. Born's method as applied by Macmillan and Kelly and by most others examines the crystal for stability against small additional *homogeneous* deformation, i.e. in physical terms against lattice vibrations having a wavelength large compared with the atomic dimensions. However, while under some conditions stability against a small homogeneous deformation guarantees stability against any combination of small atomic displacements, such is not true in general and has been shown to be untrue in particular cases (Wallace 1968). This theoretical worry is not settled at present.

There have been two lattice calculations of the ideal tensile strengths of *metals*. The difficulty here is to find an approximation to the ion–ion interaction which can be used to carry out lattice sums to find the potential energy of the strained crystal, and which can be used at large strains, while successfully predicting the physical properties such as elastic constants and surface energies at vanishingly small strains. Milstein (1970, 1971) pioneered the application of the Born stability criterion, but treated the case of iron using a Morse potential which he had previously shown to give a rather poor representation of a body-centred cubic metal. His predicted strength of an ideal crystal of iron is less than the observed strength (section 1.7). Calculations of the ideal tensile strength of sodium, again using the Born criterion for failure, have been given by Basinski, Duesbery, and Taylor (1971), using a central-force model for the ion–ion interaction involving a Coulombic term and an oscillating term of the form $(\sin qr)/qr$, where r is the ion–ion separation. Sodium departs from the Cauchy relation $C_{12} = C_{44}$ (which must be obeyed by a crystal bound by central forces only) by about 15 per cent. The ideal tensile strength for a crystal pulled along [100] is found to be $1 \cdot 8 \times 10^{-2}$ of the Young's modulus in that direction. For crystals stressed along [110] and [111] the values are respectively $5 \cdot 6 \times 10^{-2}$ and $6 \cdot 0 \times 10^{-2}$ of the corresponding Young's modulus. The ideal tensile strength is much the least along [100] since the Young's modulus is much smaller in this direction than in any other. Sodium is not a typical metal in its elastic behaviour, since it is extremely anisotropic.†

---

† Anisotropy in *cubic* materials is often assessed by the ratio $2C_{44}/(C_{11} - C_{12})$ which is unity for an isotropic material. For sodium the ratio is 8·4 compared with iron: 2·4; tungsten: 1·0; diamond: 1·6; copper: 3·2; NaCl: 0·7.

Basinki, Duesbery, and Taylor's estimate for sodium of $\sigma_{\max}$ along [100] of $1 \cdot 8 \times 10^{-2}(1/S_{11})$ or $2 \cdot 5 \times 10^{8}$ dyn cm^{-2} $(2 \cdot 5 \times 10^{7}$ N m$^{-2})$ is only 2·5 per cent of the estimate made using the Orowan criterion (equation (1.5)). For [111] their estimate is 25 per cent of the corresponding estimate according to equation (1.5).

The estimate of the theoretical fracture strength of diamond, using a Morse function gives a value of 11×10^{10} N m^{-2}. This is less than that obtained by Orowan's estimate (equation (1.5)), and corresponds to a value of $0.09E$; Orowan's estimate gives $0.17E$. A discrepancy of the same order is found between Orowan's elementary estimate and the much more accurate ones for sodium chloride. We conclude that for covalently bound solids and for ionic solids, Orowan's estimate is too large by a factor of between 2 and 4.[†] No reliable comparison can be made for metals.

The assumption of a Lennard–Jones potential leads to a calculated cleavage stress of $0.16E$ and taking this in conjunction with the estimates for diamond and for sodium chloride we conclude that for non-metallic crystals σ_{max} is between 5 and 16 per cent of Young's modulus, the exact value depending on the type of binding and the crystal orientation.

1.4. Stiffness and strength of polymers

Linear organic polymers consist of carbon and some other atoms joined by strong covalent bonds to form a long chain, and the solid consists of these long chains variously coiled and intertwined, with the bonding between the chains accomplished by van der Waals' forces. In principle if all chains were aligned and broken simultaneously a very strong material would result. Interest attaches to the idea, however, that in this case alignment of the chains would produce a material of much greater stiffness than is usually observed.

Diamond may be regarded as a three-dimensional organic polymer. A simple estimate of the Young's modulus can be made assuming a simple valence-force field and nearest neighbour interactions, so that the interaction energy between two atoms is increased by $(k_r/2)(\Delta r)^2$ for a change in separation of Δr and by $(k_\theta/2)(r_0\Delta\theta)^2$ for a change in angle $\Delta\theta$. As an example, taking $k_r = 4.74 \times 10^2$ N m^{-1} and $k_\theta = 0.32 \times 10^2$ N m^{-1} with $r_0 = 1.54$ Å, we obtain for the modulus C_{11} in the $\langle 111 \rangle$ direction

---

[†] See N. H. MACMILLAN and A. KELLY (1972). *Mater. Sci. and Eng.* **10**, 139.

900 GN m^{-2} (9×10^{12} dyn cm^{-2}). The experimental values lie between 11 and 12×10^3 GN m^{-2}. The simple valence-force field gives an estimate reliable to better than an order of magnitude, and so can be applied to estimating the expected stiffness of fully aligned linear polymers. Simple estimates for common polymers have been given by Lyons (1958) and by Treloar (1960). For instance, for linear polythene (—[CH_2]—) the modulus of a single chain E' can be deduced by considering the bending and stretching of the bonds in Fig. 1.4. One finds

$$E' = (r_0 \cos \alpha)/\{(\cos{}^2\alpha/k_r) + (\sin{}^2\alpha/4k_\theta)\}, \qquad (1.15)$$

where $\alpha = (\pi - \theta)/2$ with θ the bond angle, and r_0 is the carbon to carbon separation. If the aligned chains are packed as in the

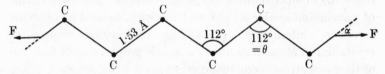

FIG. 1.4. The arrangement of the carbon atoms (—[CH_2]— groups) in a single chain of polyethylene. In calculating the modulus a force F is supposed applied at each end of the chain at the mid-point of a bond.

crystal structure, there are 5.5×10^{18} chains per unit area normal to the axis of the chains. Taking $r_0 = 1.53$ Å, k_r and k_θ as for diamond, and $\theta = 112°$ we predict a modulus of 184 GN m^{-2} (1.84×10^{12} dyn cm^{-2} or 26.3×10^6 psi). Predicted values for this and other polymers are given in Table 1.2. Since the densities ρ of these polymers are all less than 2×10^3 kg m^{-3}, very large values of the ratio E/ρ are predicted, e.g. 178×10^{12} m^{-2} s^{-2} for nylon 66. The large difference between the estimates for polythene arises from the neglect of repulsive forces by Treloar and this author. Shimanouchi, Asahina, and Enomoto (1962) find, according to their model, that these are very important. The experimentally observed moduli measured in short times at low temperatures are all between one and two orders of magnitude less than the theoretical values for an aligned polymer, e.g. even for highly stretched nylon 66 the value is only 5 GN m^{-2} (7×10^5 psi). In the case of cellulose, the most common of all biopolymers, the theoretical value is not more than an order of magnitude larger than the Young's modulus of a stiff wood.

Taking the force to break a carbon to carbon bond as 6×10^{-4} dyn or 6×10^{-9} N—section 1.3—the stress required to break all of the primary bonds simultaneously in aligned polyethylene would be 6×10^{-9} N $\times 5 \cdot 5 \times 10^{18}$ m^{-2} or 33 GN m^{-2} (33×10^{10} dyn cm^{-2} or $4 \cdot 8 \times 10^6$ psi). This is enormously greater than the observed breaking strength of $0 \cdot 2$–$0 \cdot 5$ GN m^{-2} (2–5×10^9 dyn cm^{-2}). Even stretched polythene broken at 77 K has a strength of $1 \cdot 52$ GN m^{-2} ($1 \cdot 52 \times 10^{10}$ dyn cm^{-2} or 200 000 psi) (Vincent 1964) which is very small compared with the theoretical value.

The strengths of polymers are normally time-dependent because the microstructures consist of coiled and branched chains of varying molecular weight and tacticity, as well as different forces of interaction, all leading to varying degrees of crystallinity. Measurement of the elastic properties as a function of time and stress is one tool used to deduce the structure of the solid (e.g. Ward 1971). A model of aligned chains may, therefore, seem highly artificial. However, this is not the case. There is currently much interest in attaining alignment (see e.g. Frank 1970); X-ray and ultrasonic measurements confirm over very small volumes the large values of stiffness which are predicted (e.g. Sakurada, Ito, and Nakamae 1964). In addition, fibres of an organic polymer have recently been produced which has a Young's modulus of 134 GN m^{-2}, a density of $1 \cdot 45 \times 10^3$ kg m^{-3}, and an average tensile breaking stress of $2 \cdot 8$ GN m^{-2} (Kwolek 1968); this appears to be a polymer based on parabenzamide. The stiffness and strength are both larger than those of glass fibres and the polymer loses strength less than glass on weaving and its strength is not so sensitive to handling. It also has a high mechanical damping capacity but a low strength in compression— 60 per cent that of glass.

An estimate of the tensile strength of silica glass—a three-dimensional glassy polymer—can be made by the same methods as used here for diamond (Náray-Szabó and Ladik 1960) by employing a Morse function to describe the interaction between an oxygen ion and an SiO_3 group. These authors use the expression $U_0a/2$ for the maximum strength of the bond (section 1.3), and they estimate U_0 from the difference in energy of formation of an SiO_4 ion and an SiO_3 group, obtaining 3.46×10^{-12} erg (3.46×10^{-19} J) which is only 40 per cent of the value required to dissociate an Si—O bond given in Appendix A, Table 5. They then calculate a from spectral data and obtain $a = 1.14 \times 10^8$ cm^{-1} and hence a force of 2×10^{-4} dyn (2×10^{-9} N). According to Náray-Szabó and Ladik (1960) there are 8×10^{16} bridging oxygen ions (oxygen ions linking silicon atoms) per square centimetre in pure silica. Assuming all of these to be broken simultaneously predicts an ideal tensile strength of 2.47×10^{11} dyn cm^{-2} (24.7 GN m^{-2} or 3.6×10^6 psi). This value is no more than 50 per cent greater than the measured breaking strength of silica glass at 4.2 K and agrees within a factor of less than 2 with the simple estimate in Table 1.1.

TABLE 1.2

Theoretical Young's modulus of linear polymers

Polymer	Constitution	Predicted modulus (GN m^{-2})	Reference
Polyethylene	—[CH_2]—	184	This author, and Treloar (1960)
Polyethylene	—[CH_2]—	340	Shimanouchi *et al.* (1962)
Nylon (66)	—[CH_2]$_6$NHCO—	196	Treloar (1960)
Polyethylene terephthalate	—CO⟨ ⟩CO—O— [CH_2]$_2$—O—	122	Treloar (1960)
PTFE	—[CF_2]—	160	Shimanouchi *et al.* (1962)
Cellulose parallel to chain	—	56·5	Treloar (1960)
Cellulose parallel to chain	—	56·5	Jaswon, Gillis, and Mark (1968) These authors calculate all of the moduli in addition to that parallel to the chain.

1.5. Theoretical shear stress

The simplest calculation of the theoretical shear stress of a crystal is due to Frenkel (1962). Consider two neighbouring planes in a crystal with a repeat distance b in the direction of shear (Fig. 1.5), and suppose them to remain *individually*

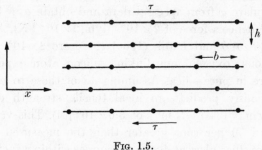

FIG. 1.5.

undistorted as a shear stress τ is applied. We assume that as the shear displacement x varies we can write

$$\tau = k \sin 2\pi x/b. \qquad (1.16)$$

For small x, $h\, d\tau/dx$ is equal to G, the shear modulus, so k equals $Gb/2\pi h$. The maximum restoring force then occurs when $x = b/4$ and hence

$$\tau_{\max} = Gb/2\pi h. \qquad (1.17)$$

For face-centred cubic metals we take $b = a/\sqrt{6}$ and $h = a/\sqrt{3}$, where a is the lattice parameter, so $\tau_{\max}/G \approx 1/9$. For a layer structure such as graphite $b/h = 0.4$, for b equal to the slip vector of a partial dislocation, and $\tau_{\max}/G \approx 1/15$.

A more extended discussion of the theoretical shear strength has been given by Mackenzie (1949). In Frenkel's calculation the variation of potential energy $U(x)$ between two neighbouring planes varies with the relative displacement x as

$$U(x) = \frac{Gb^2}{4\pi^2 h}\left(1 - \cos 2\pi \frac{x}{b}\right). \qquad (1.18)$$

This is equivalent to considering just the first term in a Fourier series for $U(x)$ and Mackenzie showed how to take further terms

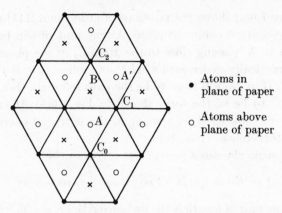

FIG. 1.6(a). A plan of the atomic positions projected on to (111) in a face-centred cubic crystal. The letters ABC denote atoms in successive (111) planes in the crystal.

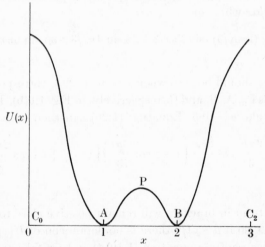

FIG. 1.6(b). The predicted variation of $U(x)$ along the line $C_0 C_2$ in Fig. 1.6(a).

into consideration. He attempted to deduce the coefficients from general arguments peculiar to the crystal structure involved, and he considered in detail a face-centred cubic crystal with one atom at each lattice point. This will be appropriate for noble metals and noble gases, and will also apply to certain hexagonal metals.

Figure 1.6(a) shows the positions of atoms in a {111} plane of the face-centred cubic structure. A true unit of slip takes the atom A to A′ passing close to the atom C_1 in the plane below. An energetically easier path would be to follow A to B and then B to A′. If we take B to A′ to be the path followed, then $U(x)$ is expected to be of the form shown in Fig 1.6(b). If only two planes are considered, of spacing h, the potential energy at B will be the same as that at A.

Mackenzie chooses a convenient origin so that

$$U(x) = K(\cos 2\pi x/3 + \alpha \cos 4\pi x/3 + \beta \cos 6\pi x/3) \qquad (1.19)$$

where the unit of length is the distance AB, i.e. $a/\sqrt{6}$, where a is the conventional lattice parameter of a face-centred cubic crystal. We call this distance b'. The restoring force per unit area τ when the planes are sheared by a displacement x is equal to $- dU/dx$ which gives

$$\tau = (2\pi K/3)\,(\sin 2\pi x/3 + 2\alpha \sin 4\pi x/3 + 3\beta \sin 6\pi x/3).$$
$$(1.20)$$

This force should be zero when $x = 0, 1, 2, 3$, corresponding to the points C_0, A, B, and C_2 respectively, in Fig. 1.6(b). To ensure this we take $\alpha = 0.5$. Equation (1.20) can then be written as

$$\tau = \frac{2\pi K}{3} \sin \frac{2\pi x}{3} \left(1 + 2 \cos \frac{2\pi x}{3}\right)\left(1 - 3\beta + 6\beta \cos \frac{2\pi x}{3}\right).$$
$$(1.21)$$

The last term in brackets will remain positive close to $x = 1.5$ if $\beta \leqslant 1/9$, so if $\beta \leqslant 1/9$ there is no depression of $U(x)$ at P. If $\beta = 1/8$ we see from equation (1.19) that $U(x)$ falls at P to the same value as at A and B. Therefore, the choice of the value of β is somewhat critical. The shear modulus G is equal to

$$\frac{h}{b'} \left(\frac{d\tau}{dx}\right)_{x=1} = \frac{2\pi^2}{3} K \frac{h}{b'} (1 - 6\beta). \qquad (1.22)$$

For any value of β the critical displacement can be found by solving the equation $d\tau/dx = 0$ and then substituting in equation (1.20) to find the value of τ_{max}. The corresponding critical shear strain is

$$\gamma_{max} = (b'/h)\,(x_{max}-1). \tag{1.23}$$

Values of τ_{max} calculated from Mackenzie's results are given in Table 1.3. Written in terms of b'/h they can be applied to a number of crystal structures. For face-centred cubic metals $b'/h = 0.707$ and the values of τ_{max}/G become 0.039 and 0.028 for $\beta = 1/9$ and $\beta = 1/8$, respectively. In face-centred cubic metal crystals the resolved shear stress is taken in a $\langle 110 \rangle$ direction, i.e. along AA' in Fig. 1.6(a). Since in the present calculation we assume slip to occur by the zig-zag path A to B followed by B to A', the value of $\tau_{max}/\cos 30°$, that is $(2/\sqrt{3})\tau_{max}$, should be taken as the theoretical strength when comparison is to be made with values of the critical resolved shear stress of single crystals. The lower limit of $(2/\sqrt{3})\tau_{max}$ with $\beta = 1/8$ is 0.032 G. This is the basis of the frequently quoted assertion that the theoretical shear strength is $G/30$, which is actually the lower limit for a face-centred cubic metal. The value $\beta = 1/9$ gives $(2/\sqrt{3})\tau_{max} = G/22$. The values of τ_{max}/G in Table 1.3 for close-packed planes can be used directly for face-centred cubic metals setting $b'/h = 0.707$; for the hexagonal metals b'/h can be obtained from the axial ratio; it is $2/\sqrt{(3)}\,a/c$. The result of Mackenzie's calculation with $\beta = 0$ and $\alpha = 0.5$ is also included in Table 1.3. This will apply to graphite slipping on the basal plane. For graphite $c/a = 2.72$ and so $\tau_{max} \approx G/20$.

Mackenzie also calculated τ_{max}/G for slip in the direction AA' in Fig. 1.6(a) using a series with $\beta = 0$ and obtained a value of 0.114. The author has used a method similar to Mackenzie's to calculate the theoretical shear strength of a body-centred cubic crystal slipping on a $\{110\}$ plane in a $\langle 111 \rangle$ direction. Taking a two-term series the values for τ_{max}/G are given in Table 1.3 for two values of α.

For slip on $\{110\}$ in the $\langle 1\bar{1}0 \rangle$ direction in the rock-salt structure inspection of a model suggests that Frenkel's estimate with $b = h$ in equation (1.17) is likely to be the best approximation using Mackenzie's method.

In evaluating estimates of τ_{max} from Table 1.3 account must be taken of the value of G. It is assumed in calculating the theoretical shear strength by Mackenzie's method that the slip planes do not distort. In a real case the planes will distort and it seems

TABLE 1.3

Ratios of shear strength to shear modulus using Mackenzie's method

Model	γ_{max}	τ_{max}/G
Close-packed planes ($\alpha = 0.5$)		
$\beta = 0$	$0.229\,b'/h$	$0.117\,b'/h$
$\beta = 1/9$	$0.125\,b'/h$	$0.055\,b'/h$
$\beta = 1/8$	$0.092\,b'/h$	$0.0395\,b'/h$
b.c.c. lattice		
$\alpha = 0.25$	0.204	0.13
$\alpha = 1.0$	0.17	0.107
Sodium chloride structure Equation (1.17)	0.25	0.16

best to allow this and use the values of G' given in Table 1.4. These are values of $1/S'_{44}$ for the particular crystal planes and directions listed.

Values of the theoretical shear strength calculated by Mackenzie's method are listed in Table 1.5 for a number of crystals using values of the physical properties measured at room temperature. For the face-centred cubic metals of low stacking fault energy (Cu, Ag, Au) and the body-centred cubic metals (Fe, W) the appropriate values underlined in Table 1.3 have been used to find τ_{max}/G.

When slip occurs from A to B in Fig. 1.6(a) a stacking fault of energy γ per unit area will be produced in a face-centred cubic metal. This means that the depth of the potential well at A and at B will not be the same. We neglect this difference because we are using a two-layer model of the crystal, and obtain a value for $\tau_{\max}$ of about $G/25$. If the value of γ is large it may not be energetically favourable for slip to occur from A to B and then from B to A′ but rather slip may occur directly from A to A′. We may expect the value of $\tau_{\max}$, appropriate to the path A to B, to

TABLE 1.4

Appropriate values of the shear modulus in calculating the theoretical shear stress

Crystal system	Slip system		G'
Cubic	$\{111\}$	$\langle \bar{2}11 \rangle$	$\dfrac{3\,C_{44}(C_{11}-C_{14})}{4C_{44}+C_{11}-C_{12}}$
,,	$\{111\}$	$\langle 1\bar{1}0 \rangle$	,,
,,	$\{1\bar{1}0\}$	$\langle 111 \rangle$	,,
,,	$\{110\}$	$\langle \bar{1}10 \rangle$	$\frac{1}{2}(C_{11}-C_{12})$
,,	$\{110\}$	$\langle 001 \rangle$	C_{44}
Hexagonal	On (0001) in any direction		C_{44}

be seriously in error if the stress required to extend the stacking fault is comparable with $\tau_{\max}$, i.e. if

$$\gamma/b_{\mathrm{p}} = G/25,$$

where b_{p} is the Burgers vector of a partial dislocation. This corresponds to a value of γ of about $Gb/50$ where $b(= \sqrt{3}b_{\mathrm{p}})$ is the Burgers vector of a total dislocation. The values of the stacking fault energies of the face-centred cubic metals are not very well-established. For copper, silver, and gold values of much less than $Gb/50$ are usually estimated for γ. However, the value of γ for aluminium is usually taken to be about 200 mJ m^{-2}, or $Gb/35$. For aluminium, therefore, the displacement to be considered in estimating $\tau_{\max}$ may be that from A to A′ in Fig. 1.6(a), which requires a stress of $0\cdot114G$ instead of from A to B, requiring a stress of $0\cdot039G$. These two values are given for aluminium in Table 1.5. For zinc the face-centred cubic metal case has been followed in arriving at the value given in Table 1.5, allowing for the value of $c/a(1\cdot855)$ and assuming a low stacking fault energy.

A value for the theoretical shear strength for aluminium oxide slipping on the basal plane is also included in Table 1.5. A diagram of the slip plane of sapphire is shown in Fig. 3.3. If

TABLE 1.5

Values of the theoretical shear stress

Material	Appropriate elastic constant (G') $(GN\ m^{-2})$	τ_{max}/G'	τ_{max} $(GN\ m^{-2})$	τ_{max} (psi)
Diamond†	505	0·24	121·0	$17\cdot6\times10^6$
Cu (at 10 K)	33·2	0·039	1·29	$1\cdot8\times10^5$
Cu (20 °C)	30·8	0·039	1·2	$1\cdot75\times10^5$
Au	19·0	0·039	0·74	$1\cdot07\times10^5$
Ag	19·7	0·039	0·77	$1\cdot11\times10^5$
Al	23	0·039	0·9	$1\cdot3\times10^5$
Al	23	0·114	2·62	$3\cdot8\times10^5$
Si†	57	0·24	13·7	$2\cdot0\times10^6$
Fe	60	0·11	6·6	$1\cdot0\times10^6$
W	150	0·11	16·5	$2\cdot4\times10^6$
NaCl†	23·7	0·120	2·84	$4\cdot1\times10^5$
Al_2O_3	147	0·115	16·9	$2\cdot5\times10^6$
Zn	38	0·034	2·3	$1\cdot9\times10^5$
Graphite	2.3	0·05	$11\cdot5\times10^{-2}$	$1\cdot7\times10^4$

† The values for diamond and NaCl are direct calculations due to Tyson (1966). For NaCl the calculation applies at absolute zero. For silicon the value of τ_{max}/G' has been taken as that for diamond. This is likely to be an overestimate for silicon.

the aluminium ions are neglected the similarity to Fig. 1.6(a) is obvious. In deriving the value of τ_{max} in Table 1.5 for Al_2O_3 only the oxygen ions, which are in contact in this structure, have been considered. Mackenzie's method has been used, as for a face-centred cubic metal of high stacking fault energy (the presence of the aluminium ions in octahedral interstices will lead to this). Taking account of the departure from close-packing of the oxygen ions, the value of τ_{max}/G' is 0·115; this is obviously only a crude estimate of the theoretical shear strength.

Mackenzie's method of estimating the shear strength of a perfect crystal is open to the objection that it is by no means certain that the potential curve $U(x)$ can be represented adequately by a Fourier series of which only the first few terms are significant. Thus we have no guarantee that $U(x)$ does not possess sharp corners. The experimental evidence reviewed in section 1.7 indicates that Mackenzie's method gives reasonable values for the theoretical shear strength of face-centred cubic metals. In addition, it predicts correctly to within 10 per cent, the critical shear strain of a dislocation-free raft of bubbles on a soap solution. (The predicted value of $\gamma_{\max}$ is 0·144 and the observed value for bubbles of 1·2 mm diameter is 0·135).

Mackenzie himself worried about the justification of the Fourier method and calculated $\tau_{\max}$ for a number of assumed interatomic force laws. These are of little general application but the Lennard–Jones potential function represents approximately the interatomic force law for the noble gases. Using this approximation Mackenzie found that for slip on $\{111\}$ in $\langle 11\bar{2}\rangle$ $\gamma_{\max} = 0\cdot129$ and $\tau_{\max}/G = 0\cdot062$.

A calculation of the theoretical shear strength of diamond has been carried out by Tyson (1966), working with the present author. This is for shear on (111) in $[1\bar{1}0]$. The arrangement of atoms in a (111) plane of diamond is similar to that shown in Fig. 1.6(a) but the stacking of the planes is different. The stacking arrangement is shown in Fig. 3.2. Slip is assumed to occur between the widely spaced planes in Fig. 3.2, say between those marked C_1 and C_2. An atom in C_1 has three nearest neighbours in B_2 and one in C_2. We take an atom in C_1 to be the atom marked 2 in Fig. 1.7. A unit of slip is accomplished if the atom marked 1 in Fig. 1.7 is moved in the direction x so that it lies above the atom marked 6. Tyson calculates the shearing force (F) required to move atom 1 in the x-direction. $\tau_{\max}$ is taken to be the maximum shearing force per unit area required to move n atoms of type 1 simultaneously, where n is the number of atoms per unit area in a (111) plane of the type C_2 (Fig. 3.2). The atoms marked 2, 3, 4, 5, 6, 7, and 8 in Fig. 1.7 are assumed to remain stationary whilst this occurs. To find the force F, Tyson calculates the increase in potential energy U of atom 1 with respect to atoms 2 to 8 as it moves. U is written in terms of the bending and stretching of the atomic bonds as this occurs, i.e. in terms of the change of distances r_{12} and r_{16} (Fig. 1.7) and the change in the angles 1,2,4; 1,2,3; 1,2,5; 1,6,3; 1,6,7; and 1,6,8 and the corresponding angles for the bonds above atom 1. The interaction energy dependent on r_{12} and r_{16} is represented by a

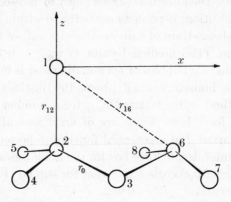

FIG. 1.7. The atomic positions in diamond. Each atom has four nearest neighbours. The nearest neighbours of atom 2 are those designated 1, 3, 4, and 5.

Morse function, equation (1.9). The constant a is derived from the bond-stretching constant for nearest neighbours of the neopentane molecule following Musgrave and Pople (1962). The part of U due to bond bending (U_θ) is assumed to be of the form

$$U_\theta = (\tfrac{1}{2} r_0^2 k_\theta) \theta^2 \frac{U_r}{U_0}. \tag{1.24}$$

The constant k_θ is the bond-bending constant derived by Musgrave and Pople and the quantity U_r/U_0 is used to allow for the fact that k_θ must decrease as the separation between atoms is increased.

The computation is carried out on a computer in a step-by-step fashion. Atom 1 is assumed displaced by a distance dx, so

$$dU = \left(\frac{\partial U}{\partial z}\right) dz + \left(\frac{\partial U}{\partial x}\right) dx.$$

The value of dz is found for which $(\partial U/\partial z)$ is equal to zero, corresponding to no force normal to (111). dU is then found at this value of dz. The shearing force F equals (dU/dx). Another small displacement dx is then assumed and so on. It is found that the (111) planes move apart as shearing proceeds and that

$$\tau_{max} = G'/4,$$

where G' is the shear modulus for (111) [1$\bar{1}$0] shear. The shear strain when τ_{max} is reached is 28·6 per cent. If Frenkel's estimate (equation (1.17)) were used for diamond a value of $G'/3·9$ would be obtained for τ_{max} and the limiting shear strain would be 41 per cent.

Tyson (1966) has also made a detailed estimate of the theoretical shear stress of sodium chloride subject to a *uniform* shear on (1$\bar{1}$0) in a [1$\bar{1}$0] direction. The computation was carried out on a computer in the same fashion as that for diamond. The van der Waals' attraction between ions has been taken into account and the latest values of the constants used to evaluate closed-shell repulsive forces between ions. The value for τ_{max} at absolute zero is $2·84 \times 10^9$ N m^{-2} or $G'/8·3$. This happens to be quite close to the estimate made above of $G'/2\pi$.

The estimates so far made of the theoretical shear strength of a crystal assume that the crystal is subject to a simple shear, and that there is no traction normal to the slip plane. A superposed tensile or compressive stress may greatly affect the value of τ_{max}. The quantitative evaluation of the dependence of τ_{max} on other applied stresses is of great importance in answering the question whether slip at the theoretical shear stress or cleavage will occur at the tip of a crack (see section 2.4). In the case of sodium chloride Tyson has estimated the effect of a tensile stress along [110] on the value of τ_{max} for shear on (110) in [1$\bar{1}$0]. He finds a linear decrease of τ_{max} with increase in tensile traction, σ, so that

$$\frac{d\tau_{max}}{d\sigma} = -0·5.$$

A similar decrease is found in a van der Waals' solid. Macmillan (1969) finds the value of

$$\frac{d\tau_{max}}{d\sigma} = -0.172.$$

Macmillan and Kelly (1972) have explored the variation of ideal shear strength with orientation for sodium chloride and for argon. They proceed, as in all previous calculations of τ_{max}, to postulate that the crystal is subject to a simple shear and then from the calculated increase in potential energy of the crystal, calculate the required shear stress. τ_{max} is identified with the maximum shear stress found. Macmillan and Kelly also calculated the unrelaxed stresses upon the crystal which must arise using this procedure. These are very large and often of the order of τ_{max}. Macmillan and Kelly suggest that τ_{max} is not estimated to better than an order of magnitude unless at least the largest of these stresses is relaxed. This is usually the stress normal to the plane on which shear occurs. Because of the lack of symmetry of a crystal subject to a simple shear, there are in general at least five stresses to be relaxed in order to carry out calculations of the unconstrained ideal shear strength.

To carry out an accurate calculation of the ideal shear strength, perhaps the best way to proceed is by the method used by Basinski et al. (1971). These authors, having first calculated the elastic compliance (inverse of the elastic modulus), then calculate the strains produced in the crystal by an assumed (small) shearing stress. Using these strains to describe the new positions of the ions, they then calculate the new compliance. Following this an additional shearing stress is assumed to be applied to the crystal and so on. Failure is taken to occur when the model lattice becomes unstable against a small, arbitrary, homogeneous deformation (the Born condition). They have used this method to calculate τ_{max} for sodium. Sodium is extremely elastically anisotropic and the shear mode $\{110\}$ $\langle 1\bar{1}0 \rangle$ encounters little resistance from this lattice. The shear modulus on $\{110\}$ $\langle 1\bar{1}0 \rangle$ is very small (Table 1·4 and Appendix C, Table 3). Basinski et al.

find that for sodium the ideal shear strength for a crystal sheared on ($\bar{1}$01) in a [101] direction is $0 \cdot 036 G''$, where G'' is the ($\bar{1}$01)[101] shear modulus. Failure at this stress corresponds to failure on the observed glide system of ($\bar{1}$01)[111] at a resolved shear stress of $0 \cdot 021 G'$, where G' is the shear modulus for ($\bar{1}$01)[111] shear. This is calculated by taking the cosine of the angle between [101] and [$\bar{1}$11] as $\sqrt{(2/3)}$, the anisotropy factor as 8·4 (Appendix C, Table 3), and using Table 1.4 to relate the two shear moduli. The value of $0 \cdot 021 G'$ is only one-fifth of the value found for the body-centred cubic lattice employing Mackenzie's method (see Table 1.3) but in view of the extreme elastic anisotropy of sodium the application of this calculation to body-centred cubic metals in general is not clear.

1.6. Temperature dependence of the theoretical strength

Both the theoretical cleavage stress and the theoretical shear stress of perfect crystals will depend upon temperature, because of the variation with temperature of the physical parameters involved. These are principally the elastic constants, the lattice parameters, and the surface energy. More importantly, however, both estimates will be affected by thermal fluctuations. No reliable estimate has been given of the effect of thermal fluctuations on the cleavage stress. An approximate calculation due to Zwicky (1923) indicates a reduction in σ_{max} proportional to the r.m.s. amplitude of the atomic vibrations. In this section we consider the temperature dependence of the theoretical shear stress.

The figures given in Table 1.5 for the theoretical shear stress of a crystal apply in the absence of thermal fluctuations. At temperatures greater than 0 K there is a finite probability of dislocations being produced in a crystal by an applied stress aided by thermal agitation, and of these being expanded and subsequently multiplied by the applied stress. The energetics of this process have been considered by Frank (1950). If a semi-circular loop of dislocation of radius R is formed on its slip plane at the surface of a crystal, under a shear stress τ applied parallel to the Burgers vector b of the dislocation, the energy of the crystal is increased by

$$U = \frac{\pi R^2}{2}(\gamma - \tau b) + \frac{1}{4}Gb^2R \ln\left(\frac{2R}{r_0}\right); \tau > \frac{\gamma}{b}. \quad (1.25)$$

The Burgers vector of the dislocation is assumed parallel to the surface of the crystal, since this represents the case of easiest activation. We have neglected the difference between screw and edge dislocations and also the energy of the dislocation core. γ is the energy of the fault produced if the dislocation is a partial. With increasing R the energy U increases to a maximum value given by

$$\frac{U_c}{Gb^3} = \frac{R_c}{8b}\left(\ln\frac{2R_c}{r_0} - 1\right), \quad (1.26)$$

which occurs at

$$\frac{R_c}{b}\left(1 - \frac{\gamma}{\tau b}\right) = \frac{G}{4\pi\tau}\left(\ln\frac{2R_c}{r_0} + 1\right). \quad (1.27)$$

A loop of radius smaller than R_c will shrink and one of larger radius will expand. U_c therefore represents an activation energy. This can be evaluated for different values of G/τ. If γ is small compared to Gb, say less than $Gb/50$, a partial dislocation will be nucleated and b must be set equal to the partial Burgers vector b_p; the value of $(1 - \gamma/\tau b)$ in equation (1.27) is then negligibly different from unity.

If γ is greater than $Gb/50$ a total dislocation will be nucleated and so we set γ equal to zero and take b as that for a total dislocation. $Gb/50$ is typically 200 mJ m^{-2} for metals.

Figure 1.8 is a plot of U_c/Gb^3 against G/τ according to equations (1.26) and (1.27). The value of r_0 has been taken so that the theoretical shear stress, τ_{max}, is equal to $G/20$, which corresponds approximately to the case of face-centred cubic metals and nucleation of a partial dislocation, following the analysis of the theoretical shear strength in section 1.5. For materials of high stacking fault energy the theoretical strength at 0 K will be somewhat higher. However, the variation of U_c with G/τ will be as shown in Fig. 1.8 but the values of the ordinates will be increased.

The maximum value of the energy which can be supplied by thermal fluctuation is proportional to the absolute temperature. We can thus take U_c as proportional to the absolute temperature and use Fig. 1.8 to estimate the temperature dependence

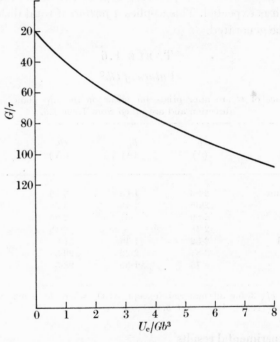

FIG. 1.8.

of the theoretical strength. To do this we first take the appropriate value of Gb^3 or Gb_p^3 from Table 1.6.

For instance, in the case of copper we have $Gb^3 = 0·63$ eV, and if we suppose that thermal fluctuations can supply an energy of up to 50 kT at any temperature, we take $U_c = 50\ kT$. Then at 27°C U_c/Gb^3 equals 2·1 and at 900°C it equals 8·1. From Fig. 1.8 a decrease of the theoretical shear strength from $G/55$ to $G/110$, i.e. by a factor of 2, is predicted between these temperatures. Figure 1.8 is thus a plot of the temperature dependence of the theoretical shear strength with a scale factor which depends on Gb^3 for each material. If thermal fluctuations generate total dislocations in copper the values of U_c/Gb^3 are 0·4 and 1·6 at 27°C and 900°C respectively. The ratio of the theoretical shear strength at the lower temperature to that at higher would be about 1·6. The values of Gb_p^3 for the non-metals in Table 1.6 are very large and little temperature dependence of the theoretical strength is expected. This applies *a fortiori* if total dislocations are to be generated.

TABLE 1.6
Values of Gb^3

The values of G are appropriate for shear on the slip plane in the slip direction and are taken from Table 1.5.

Material	b (Å)	b_p† (Å)	Gb^3 (eV)	Gb_p^3 (eV)
Aluminium	2·86	1·65	3·36	0·65
Copper	2·56	1·48	3·28	0·63
Silver	2·89	1·67	2·96	0·57
Iron	2·48	—	6·48	—
Diamond	2·52	1·46	51·0	9·8
Silicon	3·84	2·22	20·3	3·9
Alumina	4·75	1·59	98·5	3·7

† $b_p = b/\sqrt{3}$ for all materials except Al_2O_3 where $b_p = b/3$. See M. L. Kronberg (1957), *Acta metall.* **5**, 507.

1.7. Experimental results

Before proceeding further it is pertinent to enquire whether experimental tests are available of the theoretical maximum strength of solids deduced in sections 1.2 to 1.6. These are estimates of the strengths of perfect solids and so to check them directly flaw-free solids must be produced. This means essentially producing specimens with atomically smooth surfaces which contain no internal cracks, inclusions, or dislocations. Accurate tensile tests must then be carried out on the specimens. The only experiments of this nature are due to Brenner (1956) and to Crump and Mitchell (1970).

Brenner has performed accurate tensile tests on very small whiskers of iron, copper, and silver. These crystals have strengths approaching the theoretical shear strength. The breaking strengths σ_{uw} at room temperature of the strongest whiskers Brenner found are shown in Table 1.7. τ_{uw} is the corresponding resolved shear stress. Many other whiskers were tested and found to have lower strengths.

TABLE 1.7

Brenner's experiment on very strong metal whiskers

Whisker	Axis	Diameter (μm)	σ_{uw} (GN m^{-2})	Slip	System	τ_{uw} (GN m^{-2})	τ_{uw}/G'
Fe	[111]	1·6	13·1	(011)	[1$\bar{1}$1]	3·56	0·052
Cu	[111]	1·25	2·94	(1$\bar{1}$1)	[011]	0·84	0·027
Ag	[001]	3·80	1·73	(1$\bar{1}$1)	[011]	0·71	0·036

Comparison of the values of the theoretical cleavage stress in Table 1.1 with the theoretical shear stresses in Table 1.5 shows that the former is always larger by a factor of greater than 4 for the metals Brenner examined. It is then expected that the theoretical shear strength of these crystals will be reached before the cleavage strength when a continuously increasing tensile load is applied. In the face-centred cubic crystals the theoretical cleavage strength is an order of magnitude greater than the theoretical shear strength.

The values of τ_{uw}/G' in Table 1.7 are in each case somewhat lower than those given for τ_{max}/G' in Table 1.5. The values in Table 1.5 were never exceeded. (Actually the values in Table 1.5 for copper and silver should be multiplied by $2/\sqrt{3}$ to compare with the value in Table 1.7). If crystals are yielding and fracturing at the theoretical shear strength then one expects to find the slope of the stress–strain curve continuously decreasing before failure. One would also expect to observe a characteristic shear type of fracture. This last will be difficult to observe because the crystal may break again in other places due to the large amounts of elastic energy released on failure. Brenner found a stress–strain curve of decreasing slope (see Fig. 1.9). The form of the fracture was difficult to determine. The silver whiskers showed plastic deformation. It is noteworthy that the iron whiskers fail at shear stresses of a little over half the calculated theoretical shear strength and the tensile stress on the

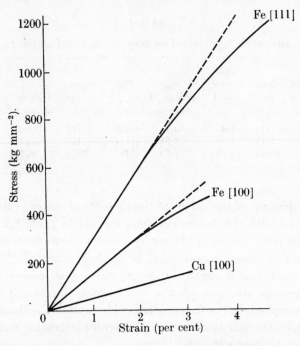

Fig. 1.9. Stress–strain curves of iron and copper whiskers pulled in tension in the directions shown. (S. S. Brenner (1958). *Growth and Perfection of Crystals* (Editors R. H. Doremus *et al.*), Wiley, New York).

whisker resolved normal to the (100) cleavage plane, viz. $4 \cdot 35 \times 10^{10}$ dyn cm^{-2} ($4 \cdot 35$ GN m^{-2}) is only about one-seventh of the calculated theoretical fracture strength according to Orowan's estimate. In the case of copper the maximum tensile stress is only one-twentieth of the Orowan estimate of the cohesive strength.

For whiskers pulled along [111] the factor resolving the applied stress on to the most highly stressed member of either the $\langle 111 \rangle$ $\{10\bar{1}\}$ glide system or of the $\langle 10\bar{1} \rangle$ $\{111\}$ slip system has its smallest possible value of 0·272. Thus this orientation of tensile stress gives the largest possible ratio of tensile stress to resolved shear stress. In view of the large ratio of σ_{max} to τ_{max} the face-centred cubic metals are therefore certainly expected to fail by slip at the theoretical shear strength instead of cleaving. However, this is only predicted for iron provided the Orowan estimate for σ_{max} is accurate to better than an order of magnitude.†

From this discussion and bearing in mind the temperature dependence of the theoretical shear strength it seems that Brenner's results are consistent with his strongest whiskers failing at or close to the theoretical shear strength, within the accuracy of estimation of this quantity. Brenner held a copper whisker for two hours at 900°C under a shear stress of one-sixth that found to produce failure at room temperature. No flow was observed. This again is completely consistent with the crystals failing at the theoretical shear strength and with the variation of the theoretical shear strength with temperature calculated in section 1.6. These results then give confidence in the applicability to metals of Mackenzie's method of estimating the theoretical shear strength.

Using an electron microscope, Crump and Mitchell (1970) selected flaw-free crystals of cadmium which were then subject *in situ* to stress parallel to the [$\bar{2}110$] direction. In a series of beautiful and amazingly reproducible experiments, they showed that such crystals failed either by brittle fracture normal to $\{10\bar{1}0\}$ planes, or by shear upon $\{\bar{1}011\}$ planes when the tensile strain along the [$\bar{2}110$] axis of tension reached values between 3·8 and 4·5 per cent. The stress–strain curves were linear to failure. The calculated shear stresses on the glide systems observed in cadmium (other than those corresponding to shear

† It is not known if Brenner's whiskers failed by twinning, which might reduce the theoretical shear strength, nor do we know how τ_{max} depends on a superposed tensile stress for this material.

on the basal plane) vary between $G'/11$ and $G'/15$, where G' is the appropriate shear modulus for the system. These authors conclude that Mackenzie's method of using the crystal structure as a guide to the choice of coefficients in the Fourier expansion of the variation of lattice potential energy during shear adequately estimates the ideal shear strength.

Gane (1970) has studied the plastic deformation, under the electron microscope, of small crystals of gold. Four types of experiment were performed: (a) the metal surface was indented with a hard stylus, e.g. titanium carbide, and the load to produce permanent deformation measured; (b) a soft metal tip was pushed against a hard surface and the load to produce a flattening noted; (c) individual crystals of diameter down to $0.5 \mu m$ were deformed in compression; and (d) thin filaments of unknown orientation and of dimensions $\sim 1 \mu m$ by $10 \mu m$ were bent elastically until they kinked. In (d) large surface stresses were always obtained $\sim 2 \times 10^{10}$ dyn cm^{-2} (2 GN m^{-2}) but the actual value is uncertain because of lack of knowledge of the orientation. In the other experiments large stresses to produce plastic flow were consistently obtained, provided the surface of the metal contained a layer of unidentified polymeric contaminant. Gane believes this contaminant removes the large shear stresses otherwise generated at the interface between the two surfaces of different elastic moduli (see section 2.6) and provided it is present, the true yield stress of the metal crystal or surface may be observed. He found that very large tensile forces up to 3.0 GN m^{-2} (3×10^{10} dyn cm^{-2} or 430 000 psi) were necessary to produce plastic shear. There is some uncertainty in deriving the true value of the maximum shear stress in these unique experiments, but Gane concludes that it could be as large as $G'/20$, which is larger than the estimate for gold in Table 1.5, and even larger than τ_{max} if it is supposed that thermal fluctuations might assist generation of dislocations (section 1.6). However, the true value of the shear stress is not known, and in particular the effects of elastic anisotropy of the gold crystals are not clear. These beautiful experiments are the only ones to suggest that (neglecting thermal effects) the calculations of the ideal shear strengths of crystals in section 1.5 are *too low*.† Nonetheless, they again confirm the accuracy of the estimates to better than a factor of two.

1.8. Strong solids

From the results of the calculations in sections 1.2, 1.3, 1.4, and 1.5 we can make some general remarks upon the relation between the ideal strength of materials and the chemical constitution. From equation (1.5), materials with the largest breaking strength require a high Young's modulus, large surface energy, and small separation of atoms. The three properties required are, of course, interrelated. Covalently bound crystals and metallic crystals yield the highest values of σ_{max}, principally because in ion solids electicrically neutral planes can function as cleavage planes of low surface energy. Among the metals the transition metals have higher values of σ_{max} than the noble metals and aluminium, because of the higher values of E and smaller values of a_0.

The theoretical tensile cleavage stress is usually greater than the theoretical shear strength.‡ Physically this is clearly because when atoms slide along the slip plane their bonds with neighbours across the plane are renewed periodically as successive neighbours are approached. No new surface is created, except for steps at the end of the plane. The process is thus less drastic than cleavage and so τ_{max} is less than σ_{max}. Inspection of the estimates of σ_{max} and of τ_{max} (Tables 1.1 and 1.5 and the values discussed in sections 1.2, 1.3, and 1.5) reveals that metals as a class are distinguished by low values of the ratio τ_{max}/σ_{max}. For diamond and rock-salt the value of this ratio is close to one, while for the noble metal copper it is about one-thirtieth. The value for body-centred cubic transition metals is a good deal larger than that

† Some less direct experiments on the generation of dislocations in a copper crystal containing growing particles of a face-centred cubic form of cobalt, at the interface between the precipitates and the matrix, also suggest this. (L. M. BROWN and G. R. WOOLHOUSE (1970). *Phil. Mag.* **21**, 329).

‡ For example for a Lennard–Jones potential for which both σ_{max} and τ_{max} can be calculated, the ratio of the cleavage stress normal to (100) to the theoretical shear stress for (111) [$\bar{2}$11] slip is 2·6 E/G (see sections 1.3 and 1.5).

for the face-centred cubic metals, but nevertheless is smaller than for typical covalently bound and ionically bound solids.

Crystal anisotropy should always be taken into account. However, speaking generally, provided τ_{max} is less than $\sigma_{max}/4$† one one does not expect to observe a strength as high as σ_{max} under uniaxial tension; shear will occur at lower stresses. For metals τ_{max}/σ_{max} is less than one-quarter and hence perfect crystals of metals are expected to fail by shear and to have their maximum attainable strengths limited by τ_{max}. For these materials a lower limit to the attainable tensile strength at low temperature should be between two and four times the value of τ_{max} (Table 1.5). The spread between two and four arises from the possible variation of crystal orientation.

Metals show low values of τ_{max}/σ_{max} because of the low value of τ_{max}/G and the small ratio of G to E compared to other crystal types. The small ratio of G/E implies a correspondingly large value of Poisson's ratio in an elastically isotropic solid. Some values of Poisson's ratio are collected in Appendix C, Table 2. Metals as a class are distinguished by values of about one-third or greater. Covalently bound crystals have values of about one-quarter or less. Poisson's ratio in a particular solid reflects the ratio of the ability to resist volume change to the ability to resist shear deformation (which occurs without volume change). A large value of Poisson's ratio means that the solid resists an elastic change of volume much more than a shear deformation. This is typical of a metallic crystal. A small value of Poisson's ratio means that shear and volume change are both strongly resisted as is the case, say, for diamond.‡

† The value 1/4 here comes from noting that the maximum ratio of σ/τ, where σ is an applied tensile stress and τ the corresponding resolved shear stress on any slip system is 3·7 when τ is on a slip system of high multiplicity (say $\{111\}$ $\langle 10\bar{1} \rangle$ in a cubic crystal).

‡ The volume change occurring in uniaxial tension is $(1-2\nu)$ times the uni- axial strain, where ν is Poisson's ratio. For gold, as example, $(1-2\nu)$ is only 0·16 whereas for diamond it is 0·8 (using figures given in Appendix C). The difference between the properties of solids of high and low values of Poisson's ratio emerges most clearly if the velocities of uniaxial compressional waves and of shear waves is considered. The square of the velocity is equal to an elastic modulus divided by the density. The relevant moduli are the modulus

An ideally strong solid will possess a large value of both σ_{max} and of τ_{max}. We have dealt with the properties which ensure that σ_{max} will be large. To ensure a large value of τ_{max} both the shear modulus G and the value of τ_{max}/G must be as large as possible. This is found in solids in which the interatomic forces are of a directed nature. These are the covalently bound solids and materials with strongly polarized ionic bonds. To ensure a large value of the elastic modulus in a covalently bound solid requires small atoms with small bond lengths so that a large density of bonds per unit volume is produced. A covalence of three or four is required to ensure a three-dimensional network of covalent bonds and to produce molecular crystals instead of molecules. The elastic modulus of ionic crystals increases as the valence increases and is inversely proportional to the fourth power of the interionic distance (Gilman 1961). A small ion of high charge possesses great polarizing power so that ionic solids of high elastic modulus will necessarily possess strongly polarized bonds. The distinction between ionic and covalent binding will then be artificial if we are seeking very strong solids. We may say simply that we require materials with the highest density of strong directional bonds. Bond dissociation energies are listed for some strong bonds in Table 5 of Appendix A. A three-dimensional network of bonds must be formed so that a valence of at least two is required of all atoms and as short a bond-length as possible. The elements possessing the required properties are beryllium, boron, carbon, nitrogen, oxygen, aluminium, and silicon. The strongest materials always contain one of these elements and frequently only these.

Several important consequences flow from this definition of the chemical constitution of the strongest solids. The requirement of small atoms ensures that the lighter elements are present and the directional binding implies non-close-packed crystal structures. The densities of the strongest materials will

---

for uniaxial tension without lateral contraction, i.e. $E(1-\nu)/(1+\nu)(1-2\nu)$, where E is the Young's modulus and G, the shear modulus, equal to $E/2(1+\nu)$. If we call the former E' we see that E'/G is 7 for gold and 2·25 for diamond.

therefore be low. Further, a large elastic modulus involves a large binding energy of the solid, which in turn implies a high melting point and low coefficient of thermal expansion†. Thus the strongest solids will possess high elastic moduli, low density, high melting points, and small thermal expansion coefficients. These are all very attractive properties to the engineer.

The measured strength of a solid is not usually close to the theoretical strength. Breaking occurs at much lower stresses by essentially one of two mechanisms. The material flows apart (plastic flow in crystals is a case of this) or it cleaves. We shall show in Chapter 3 that crystals with small values of τ_{max}/G, i.e. principally the metals, possess mobile dislocations which move at very small stresses. Such materials have their strength controlled by dislocation motion and not by the theoretical strength. The strengths attainable by restraining dislocation motion in some way are discussed in Chapter 4. Crystals which possess large values of τ_{max}/G show an inherent resistance to dislocation motion. Their strengths in tension at low temperatures are normally controlled by the presence of surface steps, cracks, and notches and not by the theoretical strength. Very similar behaviour is shown by glasses. The effects of cracks and notches are dealt with in Chapter 2.

The reasons why polymeric materials do not attain the theoretical strength are not so well understood now as they are for crystals. The microstructure of polymers has not been unravelled. The discrepancy between observed and calculated strengths is undoubtedly due to imperfections and is being rapidly reduced (section 1.4).

---

† The interrelationship of these properties can be seen in terms of the Morse function (equation (1.9)). The Young's modulus is proportional to d^2U/dr^2 and hence to $2a^2U_0$; the energy of oscillation about the equilibrium position $(r = r_0)$ can be written as

$$V = a^2U_0x^2 - a^3U_0x^3,$$

where $x = (r - r_0)$. This is the equation for an anharmonic oscillator. If we find the average displacement using Boltzmann statistics it is proportional to $(1/aU_0)$ times the temperature. It follows that the coefficient of linear thermal expansion is proportional to $(1/aU_0)$ and under the further assumption that melting occurs when a given amplitude of atomic vibration is attained, it follows that the melting temperature is proportional to (aU_0).

Despite the experimental difficulties in making very strong solids a number of crystals and glasses have been produced in a form in which they show very large values of the tensile fracture strength. The usual shape is that of a fibre, either a whisker crystal or a long thin rod. The highest observed strengths of some of these materials are listed in Appendix A, Table 1. In some cases the experimental values approach those predicted from Table 1.5, taking account of orientation. The calculated values of the theoretical shear strength have not been exceeded. Some natural fibres show large strengths and these are listed in Appendix A, Table 2, together with the strengths of silica glass and a vapour-deposited amorphous form of boron. Strong metal wires now available are listed in Appendix A, Table 4.

It is easier to prepare materials with a perfect surface than to prepare crystals free of dislocations. For this reason large specimens have been prepared of glasses and of certain crystals such as silicon, germanium, and alumina with very great strengths (see Appendix A, Table 1). This is only possible in crystals in which dislocations are very difficult to move and hence large crystals of pure metals have never been prepared with strengths approaching the theoretical strength.

Many of the materials listed in Tables 1 and 2 of Appendix A attract attention today because they possess values of Young's modulus much greater than that of steel (30×10^6 psi $= 2 \cdot 07 \times 10^{11}$ N m^{-2}) and greatly superior strengths (the breaking strength of a high tensile commercial steel is $\leqslant 0 \cdot 4 \times 10^6$ psi). In addition, the ratio of strength to specific gravity (specific strength) and the ratio of Young's modulus to specific gravity (specific modulus) is much greater than that shown by steel ($3 \cdot 8 \times 10^6$ psi). At room temperature there is then the promise of the production of very strong and stiff materials of low density. Where the melting point is much higher than that of conventionally-used metals there is promise of using such materials to replace some metals as high temperature constructional materials. In order to use such materials a large number of parallel filaments must be bound together in a matrix, such as a resin or a metal. This idea is discussed in Chapter 5.

We have deduced that directionally bound solids should always possess very high breaking strength. This great strength can only be observed in tension if the crystals are free from cracks and possess smooth surfaces. This is a difficult condition to attain. A measure of the yield stress in compression can be obtained from indentation hardness measurements. Approximate relations between indentation hardness and yield stress are given in section 1.9. Values of the yield stress deduced from measurements of hardness are shown in Appendix A, Table 3, and confirm the large values expected, which are of the same order as the whisker strengths in Table 1. The values of the yield stress in Table 3 of Appendix A and of the tensile strengths of whiskers in Table 1 can be compared with values of $2\tau_{max}$ from Table 1.5. (The factor 2 is the minimum ratio of tensile stress to shear stress in a tensile test.) Results are available for diamond and for aluminium oxide. The largest value of measured strength is about one-quarter of $2\tau_{max}$ for diamond and ~ 0.4 for alumina. It seems that the greatest measured strengths are approaching the theoretical shear strengths for these strong solids, as is also the case for metals.

1.9. Relation between yield stress and indentation hardness

The stress to produce plastic flow in materials that are apparently brittle can be found from indentation hardness tests. The most accurate of these is the Vickers test. Here a pointed diamond is pushed into the surface and the load to do this measured. Approximate relations have been established between the yield stress for plastic flow in compression Y and the Vickers Hardness number. The form of this relationship depends upon whether the ratio Y/E is greater or less than about 0.01. If Y/E is less than about 0.01 then a plastic cavity is produced under the indenter so that material flows away from under the indenter and 'piles-up' at the sides of it. The relationship between yield stress in compression and the Vickers number for this case is considered in detail by Tabor (1951). The Vickers Hardness number (VHN) can be closely identified with the yield pressure P under the indenter and for many materials P/Y is about 3.

When Y/E equals or exceeds about 0·01 different behaviour is found. The material is then displaced radially outward from the indentation. Under these conditions the material far from the indenter accommodates the displacement by deforming elastically in tension. This case has been considered by Marsh (1964). To expand a spherical cavity in an elastic–plastic solid requires a pressure which may be written

$$P/Y = C + K\left(\frac{3}{3-\lambda}\right)\ln\left(\frac{3}{\lambda+3\mu-\lambda\mu}\right),\qquad(1.28)$$

where $\mu = (1+\nu)Y/E$ and $\lambda = 6(1-2\nu)Y/E$. ν is Poisson's ratio and C and K are constants equal to 2/3. By measuring the

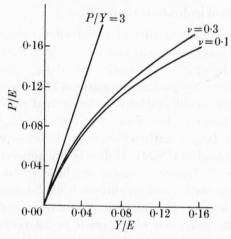

Fig. 1.10. Relation between the yield pressure under an indenter (P) and the yield stress in uniaxial compression (Y). E is Young's Modulus. (From D. M. Marsh (1964). *Proc. R. Soc.* A**279**, 420.)

VHN of various solids of known Y and E, Marsh finds empirically that $C = 0·28$ and $K = 0·60$ for the hemispherical cavity produced under an indenter. Using these values the curve in Fig. 1.10 has been made which relates P/E and Y/E. Using this curve the value of the yield stress in compression for any material can be found from the measured value of P. This is of use in estimating the yield stress of many solids, such as gem stones,

the transition metal carbides, and similar materials which we
expect to be strong from their chemical constitution but for
which we cannot measure the yield stress directly because
sufficiently large pieces with flawless surfaces have not so
far been produced. The values of yield stress given in Appendix
A, Table 3 have been derived in this way. They must be treated
with some caution since both Tabor's and Marsh's relation
between P and Y assume that the material which is indented is
plastically isotropic. This may be a good assumption for glasses
and metallic substances and other crystals which possess a high
multiplicity of slip systems but in many ceramic materials it is
a very poor approximation (see section 3.3).

1.10. Effects of hydrostatic compression

When a solid is placed under hydrostatic compression, the
principal stresses are equal and cannot be reduced by slip or
glide. The deformation is elastic, but at high pressures many
materials undergo phase transformations. The pressures produced
under a hardness indentation in a strong solid are very large, up
to between 2 and 8×10^{10} N m^{-2} (see Appendix A, Table 3) and
these are the largest static pressures produced at present on the
surface of this planet. Static high pressure apparatus can reach
2×10^{10} N m^{-2}. Larger pressures are believed to exist at the
centre of the earth† and conditions behind a shock front can
place materials under higher pressures for periods of a few micro-
seconds. The behaviour of materials under very high hydrostatic compression is explored under these latter conditions and

---

† Deduction of the central pressure of the earth requires a model for its
constitution. We know with certainty only the mass, moment of inertia, and
surface gravity. Geophysicists incline to a value of between 3 and 4×10^{11} N m^{-2}
(see e.g. Cook 1972), and stresses inside the earth are assumed to be purely
hydrostatic. If the stress at the centre is calculated assuming a *solid* earth and
admitting the consequent possibility of large shear stresses, the central pressure
is given by $10^{-1} \{(3-\nu)/(1-\nu)\} \, g\bar{\rho}a$, where g is the surface gravity, $\bar{\rho}$ is the
density (assumed constant), and a is the radius (e.g. Southwell 1941). Only one
constant needs to be guessed, namely Poisson's ratio, and this expression
gives values of 1.3×10^{11} N m^{-2} and 1.7×10^{11} N m^{-2} for $\nu = 1/3$ and $1/2$, respectively. We conclude from these various estimates that the central pressure
must be between 1 and 4×10^{11} N m^{-2} (1.5 to 6×10^6 psi).

one important use of the data is in attempts to understand the internal constitution of this and other planets.

Behind a shock wave the shock wave velocity and the particle velocity are measured and from these the pressure and specific volume (reciprocal of the density) may be determined. The pressure–density relation may then be treated in various ways to find the variation of elastic bulk modulus with pressure. In all cases the bulk modulus increases with increasing pressure although the rate of increase slows at the highest pressure. The values of the bulk modulus for a number of cubic crystals measured at atmospheric pressure are collected in Appendix C, and for some of the metals the values deduced from shock wave studies at pressures of up to 4×10^{11} N m^{-2} are given. At ambient pressures there is much less difference between the bulk moduli of solids of various types than exists between the shear moduli. This is strikingly demonstrated by comparing the values of C_{44} for diamond and for gold with the values of the bulk modulus for the same two materials. The shear moduli differ by a factor of thirteen and the bulk moduli by a factor of less than three. It has been suggested by Bullen (1949) that at very high pressures, of the order of those found at the centre of the earth, the bulk moduli of all materials become the same. The data deduced by Takeuchi and Kanamori (1966), and given in Appendix C, Table 3, show this to be a good guess for the metals, though still not strictly accurate at pressures expected to be encountered in the earth.

The phase changes which are found at high pressures in the pressure range up to 1 megabar (10^{11} N m^{-2}) produce increases in density of 25–60 per cent and similar increases in the bulk modulus. For example, α-quartz (SiO$_2$ of density 2·65 g cm^{-3} changes to stishovite of density 4·26 g cm^{-3},† forsterite, Mg$_2$SiO$_4$, changes from 3·05 to 4·24 g cm^{-3}†, and MgAl$_2$O$_4$, spinel, from 3·42 to 4·15 g cm^{-3}† (Ahrens, Anderson, and Ringwood 1969). Most close-packed metals and materials such as magnesium oxide and alumina do not undergo a phase change. These show increases in density, expressed as $((\rho/\rho_0)-1)$ of up to 40 per cent

---

† These are the deduced 'zero pressure' densities.

at 10^{11} Nm^{-2} (or rather larger, up to a doubling in the case of the softer metals such as lead or zinc) and up to 100 per cent or so at 4×10^{11} N m^{-2}. Appendix C, Table 3 indicates that at these pressures the bulk moduli are all in the range 12–18×10^{11} Nm^{-2}. The values quoted at pressures of greater than about 1×10^{11} N m^{-2} all require extrapolation. At the highets terrestrial pressures, therefore, the distinction between various materials in their resistance to hydrostatic compression begins to disappear and densities of greater than 10×10^3 kg m^{-3} become common among the elements and simple compounds.

REFERENCES

T. J. AHRENS, D. L. ANDERSON, and A. E. RINGWOOD (1969). *Rev. Geophys.* **7**, 667.

Z. S. BASINSKI, M. S. DUESBERY, and R. TAYLOR (1971). *Homogeneous Deformation of a Model Sodium Lattice*, 2nd International Conference on Metals and Alloys. Asilomar, California.

M. BORN and R. FÜRTH (1940). *Proc. Camb. phil. Soc. math. phys. Sci.* **36**, 454.

S. S. BRENNER (1956). *J. appl. Phys.* **27**, 1484.

K. E. BULLEN (1949). *Mon. Not. R. astr. Soc. Geophys. Suppl.* **5**, 355.

A. H. COOK (1972). *Proc. R. Soc.* A**328**, 301.

J. C. CRUMP and J. W. MITCHELL (1970). *J. appl. Phys.* **41**, 717.

J. H. DE BOER (1936). *Trans. Faraday Soc.* **32**, 10.

F. C. FRANK (1950). *Symposium on Plastic Deformation of Crystalline Solids*, p. 89. Carnegie Institute of Technology.

—— (1970). *Proc. R. Soc.* A**319**, 127.

J. FRENKEL (1926). *Z. Phys.* **37**, 572.

N. GANE (1970). *Proc. R. Soc.* A**317**, 367.

J. J. GILMAN (1961). *Prog. ceram. Sci.* **1**, 146.

M. A. JASWON, P. P. GILLIS, and R. E. MARK (1968). *Proc. R. Soc.* A**306**, 389.

S. KWOLEK (1968). To Dupont de Nemours Co. South African Patent Application 6813051.

W. J. LYONS (1958). *J. appl. Phys.* **29**, 1429.

J. K. MACKENZIE (1949). Ph.D. Thesis, Bristol.

N. H. MACMILLAN (1969). Ph.D. Thesis, Cambridge.

—— and A. KELLY (1972). *Proc. R. Soc.* A**330**, 291 and 309.

D. M. MARSH (1964). *Proc. R. Soc.* A**279**, 420.

F. MILSTEIN (1970). *Phys. Rev.* B**2**, 512.

—— (1971). *Phys. Rev.* B**3**, 1130.

M. J. P. MUSGRAVE and J. A. POPLE (1962). *Proc. R. Soc.* A**268**, 474.

I. NÁRAY-SZABÓ and J. LADIK (1960). *Nature, Lond.* **188**, 226.

E. OROWAN (1949). *Rep. Prog. Phys.* **12**, 185. See also *Weld. J.* **34**, 157 (1955).

I. Sakurada, T. Ito, and K. Nakamae (1964). *Bull. Inst. chem. Res. Kyoto Univ.* **42**, 77.

T. Shimanouchi, M. Asahina, and S. Enomoto (1962). *J. Polym. Sci.* **59**, 93.

S. Silver (1940). *J. chem. Phys.* **8**, 919.

R. V. Southwell (1941). *Theory of Elasticity*, Clarendon Press, Oxford.

B. E. Sundquist (1964). *Acta metall.* **12**, 67.

D. Tabor (1951). *The Hardness of Metals*, Clarendon Press, Oxford.

H. Takeuchi and H. Kanamori (1966). *J. geophys. Res.* **71**, 3985.

L. R. G. Treloar (1960). *Polymer* **1**, 95, 279, and 290.

W. R. Tyson (1966). *Phil. Mag.* **14**, 925.

P. I. Vincent (1964). *Proc. R. Soc.* A**282**, 113.

D. C. Wallace (1968). Lattice Dynamics and the Stability of Crystals. In *Adv. mater. Res.* **3**, 331.

I. M. Ward (1971). *Mechanical Properties of Solid Polymers*, Interscience–Wiley, New York.

F. Zwicky (1923). *Phys. Z.* **24**, 131.

2

CRACKS AND NOTCHES

A CRACK or fissure at the surface or in the interior of a solid is a stress-concentrating flaw. At the end of a crack the tensile stress may reach the cohesive stress of a material when quite small stresses are applied to the body as a whole. In this chapter we report the results of calculations of the stress-concentrating effects of a hole, and of a step at the surface. We then discuss the conditions under which a crack can grow and lead to fracture. Although these can be stated in general terms following the early work of Griffith there are still unsolved problems of the nature of the stress distribution at the tip of a crack. The determination of this stress distribution requires a knowledge of the interatomic cohesive forces at the crack tip. We make some remarks on this problem in section 2.4.

Apart from certain naturally occurring materials such as asbestos, glass is the material which may be most easily produced in a high strength form with a breaking stress of greater than 500 000 psi (3.5 GN m^{-2}). This is because the strength of glass is usually controlled by the presence of cracks. Nowadays it is known how these can be almost entirely eliminated and how very strong glass fibres can be produced. We discuss the strength of glass in section 2.5. Strong glass fibres can be easily damaged and their strength reduced again by introduction of cracks. This has also been studied and the results are important for preserving the strength of any strong solid. We discuss the ways in which fibres can be damaged in section 2.6.

2.1. The elliptic hole

We want to find the stresses around an elliptic hole in a stressed body, since this is an approximate model of a crack and the results can be used to represent the effect of notches. We will talk about a hole of elliptical cross-section passing through a plate (Fig. 2.1). With the origin at the centre, the equation of the ellipse is

$$\frac{x^2}{a^2}+\frac{y^2}{b^2} = 1. \tag{2.1}$$

The separation of the foci is $2c = 2\sqrt{(a^2-b^2)}$. We note that the radius of curvature (ρ) at the end of the major axis is equal to

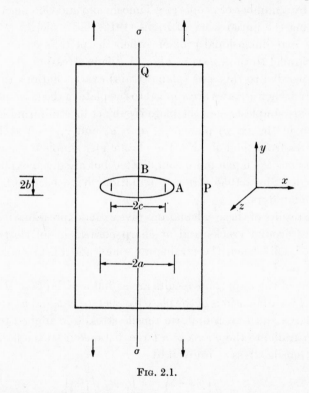

FIG. 2.1.

b^2/a and at the end of the minor axis to a^2/b. The eccentricity of the ellipse e is equal to $\sqrt{(1-b^2/a^2)}$.

If we put $x' = (x-a)/\rho$ and $y' = (y/\rho)$ the equation of the ellipse becomes

$$\left(\frac{x'+a/\rho}{a/\rho}\right)^2+\left(\frac{y'}{\sqrt{(a/\rho)}}\right)^2 = 1, \tag{2.2}$$

and it has unit radius of curvature at its tip which now falls at the origin (0, 0). Written in this form we can examine the case of a very thin sharp crack which corresponds to $\rho/a \to 0$ and yields for the form of the crack near its tip

$$y'^2 = -2x'. \tag{2.3}$$

Exact expressions for the stresses around an elliptically shaped cavity in an elastic body are very complicated. They have been given by a number of people (see Timoshenko and Goodier 1951) following the initial work of Inglis (1913) and Kolosoff (1914). In the two-dimensional problem when the plate is either very thin parallel to the z axis in Fig. 2.1 (plane stress) or else very thick parallel to this axis (plane strain) exact solutions can be obtained when stresses are applied to the plate in the (x, y) plane. These are simplest when the plate is subject to a uniform biaxial tension in the (x, y) plane, i.e. $\sigma_x = \sigma_y$ and $\tau_{xy} = 0$ at large distances from the hole. For the plate under simple tension the expressions are much more complicated but are given explicitly by Inglis. Since 1955 stress distributions have been obtained with computers.

The results of these calculations give exact expressions for the stresses around cracks and at sharp corners in an *elastically* stressed solid when the strains are small and linear elasticity can be used.

Some of the important results are as follows. Suppose that in Fig. 2.1 the dimensions of the plate parallel to the x and y axes are very large and that a uniform tensile stress σ is applied to the plate parallel to the y axis at a large distance from the hole. At A the tensile stress σ_y is given by,

$$\sigma_y = \sigma \left(1 + \frac{2a}{b}\right) = \sigma\left\{1 + 2\sqrt{\left(\frac{a}{\rho}\right)}\right\}. \tag{2.4}$$

This is the largest stress present. At B there is a compressive stress of magnitude $\sigma_x = -\sigma$. Along the x axis the value of σ_y rapidly decreases to the value $\sigma_y = \sigma$. Along BQ, σ_x changes within a distance $\sim\rho$ from a compressive stress at B to a small tensile stress and this gradually becomes zero. Near A there is a tensile stress σ_x, which is zero at A and rises to a maximum value at a distance approximately equal to b^2/a from the edge of the hole. Its maximum value is between one-fifth and one-sixth of the maximum value of σ_y, i.e.

$$\sigma_{x\,\text{max}} \approx \frac{\sigma}{5}\left(1+\frac{2a}{b}\right). \qquad (2.5)$$

The ratio of $\sigma_{y\text{max}}$ to $\sigma_{x\text{max}}$ does not depend much on a/b for an elastically isotropic material. The variation of σ_y and of σ_x along

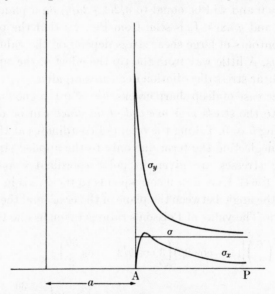

Fig. 2.2. Variation of σ_y and σ_x with distance along AP in Fig. 2.1. The curve is drawn for the case $a = 3b$.

the x axis is shown in Fig. 2.2 which is drawn accurately for the case $a = 3b$. The radius of curvature of the ellipse at A is then equal to $a/9$. After σ_x has attained its maximum values both σ_y and σ_x fall off together with a roughly constant difference between them which is equal to σ at large distances from the hole. There is also a tensile stress σ_y along BQ. This is zero at B and at a considerable distance from the hole attains the value σ. The shear stresses around the end of the crack in Fig. 2.1 on planes parallel to the z axis are shown in Fig. 2.3 for various values of a/b, viz. 10, 18, and infinity, taken from the computations of Schijve (1964), for a material of Poisson's ratio 0·33. The contours represent values of τ/σ where τ is the maximum shear stress on planes normal to the plate. The maximum shear stress, over an appreciable volume, is between 5σ and 6σ and occurs in a small volume near the tip of the crack. It falls off very rapidly with distance from the hole, being only $1\cdot5\sigma$ at a distance less than b^2/a from the tip. The greatest shear stress will be attained at the point A where $\sigma_y = \sigma(1+2a/b)$ and $\sigma_x = 0$ and will be equal to $\sigma/2(1+2a/b)$ on a plane at $45°$ to the x and y axes. It is seen from Fig. 2.3 that the positions of the contours of large shear stress depend on the value of the tip radius. A little way from the tip the effect of the tip radius on the shear stress distribution decreases rapidly.

For the case of deep sharp cracks, $b/a \ll 0\cdot1$, a good approximation to the stress *near one end of the crack* can be obtained by putting $b = 0$. Taking the origin of coordinates at the crack tip and neglecting the term due only to the applied stress, the resulting stresses are given in polar coordinates as follows (Schijve 1964). Here $\theta = 0$ corresponds to the x axis in Fig. 2.1 and β is the angle between the plane of the crack and the applied tension, σ. The value of Poisson's ratio is taken as one third.

$$\sigma_\theta = \frac{\sigma}{8}\sqrt{\left(\frac{c}{2r}\right)}\left\{(1-\cos 2\beta)\left(3\cos\theta/2 + \cos\frac{3\theta}{2}\right) - \right.$$

$$\left. -3\sin 2\beta\left(\sin\frac{3\theta}{2} + \sin\frac{\theta}{2}\right)\right\}$$

$$\sigma_r = \frac{\sigma}{8}\sqrt{\left(\frac{c}{2r}\right)}\left\{(1-\cos 2\beta)\left(5\cos\theta/2 - \cos\frac{3\theta}{2}\right) + \right.$$

$$\left. + \sin 2\beta\left(3\sin\theta/2 - 5\sin\frac{\theta}{2}\right)\right\}$$

$$\tau_{r\theta} = \frac{\sigma}{8}\sqrt{\left(\frac{c}{2r}\right)}\left\{(1-\cos 2\beta)\left(\sin\frac{\theta}{2} + \sin\frac{3\theta}{2}\right) + \right.$$

$$\left. + \sin 2\beta\left(3\cos\frac{3\theta}{2} + \cos\frac{\theta}{2}\right)\right\} \qquad (2.6)$$

From these expressions the following results emerge. The magnitude of the concentrated stresses falls off as $r^{-1/2}$. (This is seen in Fig. 2.2 as soon as r exceeds a crack tip radius.) The distribution of the values of σ_x for small θ, i.e. the value of the concentrated stress normal to the plane of the crack varies very little with β, for $\beta > 45°$. The distribution of shear stress on planes passing through the crack tip, i.e. $\tau_{r\theta}$, depends more strongly on β and as β decreases from $90°$ there is an increasing shear stress concentration along the line of the crack: this is intuitively expected.

The above calculations apply to a material which is elastically isotropic. In many strong materials and in particular in many strong fibrous materials, the elasticity is anisotropic; it is sometimes orthotropic, i.e. possessing three planes of symmetry at right angles to one another; an example is wood. Such a material possesses nine independent elastic constants. The elastic anisotropy of some woods is very marked. The elastic properties parallel to the direction of growth are very different from those normal to the direction of growth. The properties in the two directions normal to the direction of growth are quite similar. In aligned fibrous composites the properties normal to the fibre direction are often approximately isotropic so that the material possesses only five elastic constants. The relationship between these and the conventionally defined elastic moduli is given in Appendix C, Table 4.

In fibrous materials such as wood and glass-reinforced plastic the Young's modulus parallel to the fibres (or parallel to the direction of growth in wood) is very much greater than in a direction at right angles. Stress concentrations close to the end of a notch then differ from those appropriate to the isotropic case.

Green (1945) and S. M. Gilliland (private communication 1967) calculated the stress concentration close to the end of an elliptic hole in a material with elastic anisotropy appropriate to wood, and to an aligned fibrous composite, respectively. The stresses are proportional to $\sqrt{(\rho/a)}$ in a crack of half length a with radius of curvature ρ at its root. Some results taken from Gilliland's calculation for the case $(\rho/a) \to 0$ and a stress σ_∞ applied a long

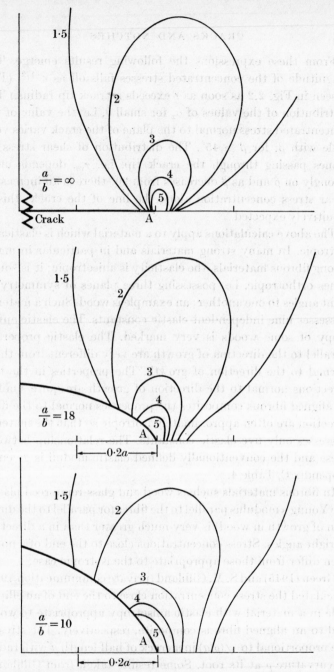

FIG. 2.3. Variation of the maximum shear stress τ, on planes normal to the plate in Fig. 2.1 with variation in the radius of curvature of the crack tip. $\tau = \frac{1}{2}|S_1 - S_2|$ where S_1 and S_2 are the principal stresses in the x, y plane. The curves locate constant values of τ/σ, where σ is the applied tensile stress. The curves are taken from Schijve (1964).

way from the crack and normal to the plane of the crack are given in Table 2.1 and compared with the isotropic case. (The effect of the applied stress alone is neglected in Table 2.1.) Gilliland's calculations are appropriate to a material with the elastic constants of an aligned composite containing 50 per cent by volume of carbon fibres in an epoxy resin matrix; these are given in Appendix C, Table 4. Compared with the isotropic case there is a much larger concentration of the stress tending to

TABLE 2.1

Values of $\sqrt{(\rho/a)(\sigma/\sigma_\infty)}$

	Anisotropic	Isotropic
Maximum tension parallel to applied stress, P_1	6·3	2·0
Maximum tension on axis normal to applied stress, P_2	0·131	0·38
Maximum shear parallel to the fibres at surface of hole, τ_{xy}	−0·57	−0·59

open the crack, and the transverse stress which tends to split the material parallel to the fibres is much reduced. The ratio P_1/P_2 (see Table 2.1) is 48 compared with a value of 5 in the isotropic case. The value of the shear stress parallel to the fibres τ_{xy} is greater than the value of P_2 in both the isotropic and the anisotropic cases, but in the latter case the ratio τ_{xy}/P_2 is larger (4·4 instead of 1·5). In the anisotropic situation $(P_1/\tau_{xy}) = 11$, and in the isotropic $(P_1/\tau_{xy}) \sim 4$. At the tip of a crack in a fibrous composite we see that there is a large concentration of the shear stress parallel to the fibres (τ_{xy}). This stress exceeds the transverse stress normal to the fibres.

2.2 Notches

Approximations to the stress distribution around the end of a notch in an elastically stressed body have been given for many forms of notch in the books by Neuber (1937) and by Savin (1961). However, for our purpose we can deduce what we need from Inglis's calculation, following that author.

An important result of Inglis's is that the stresses *at the ends* of a cavity depend almost entirely upon the length of the cavity and the form of its ends. For instance, it makes very little difference to the values of the stresses at the point A in Fig. 2.4 whether the cavity is of the exact elliptic form or whether it has the shape shown by the dotted lines. If the ends of the cavity are elliptic in form it is legitimate in calculating the stress close

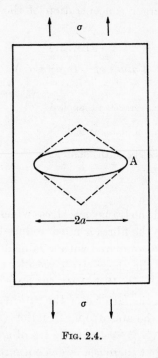

FIG. 2.4.

to the end to replace the cavity by an ellipse having the same length and the same form at the ends. The maximum tensile stress at A in Fig. 2.4 will be $\sigma\{1+2\sqrt{(a/\rho)}\}$, and this formula will apply to a cavity of any shape of length $2a$, and radius of curvature ρ at its end provided that near its end the cavity merges smoothly into an ellipse.

If the plate in Fig. 2.1 is cut in half the notched plate shown in Fig. 2.5(a) results. This plate is subject to the vertical stress σ applied a long way from the cavity and, in addition, to the surface tractions distributed along BQ and B′Q′. If these surface tractions can be annulled we have the stresses in a plate containing an elliptic notch subject to a tensile stress σ. The maximum tensile stress at A is then

$$\sigma_y = \sigma\{1 + 2\sqrt{(a/\rho)}\}, \qquad (2.7)$$

less the effect due to the distribution of normal stress along BQ and B′Q′. When the notch is narrow and deep these produce

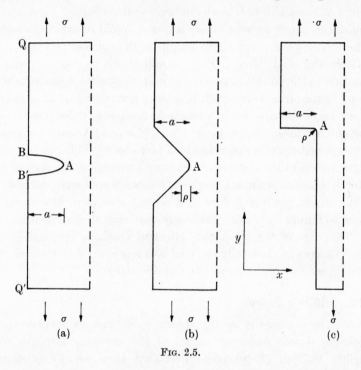

FIG. 2.5.

little effect at A. Even if the pressure σ at B were maintained all along BQ it would only amount to an additional stress of magnitude σ. This is negligible if $a/b \gtrsim 10$. Actually, this stress falls off rapidly with distance from Q Q′ and so the maximum tensile stress at the bottom of the notch lies between

$$\sigma 2\sqrt{(a/\rho)} \text{ and } \sigma\{1 + 2\sqrt{(a/\rho)}\}.$$

The former is the closer approximation for a deep sharp notch.

By similar reasoning the maximum tensile stress at A in Fig. 2.5(b) is $\sigma_y = \sigma\{1+2\sqrt{(a/\rho)}\}$. In Fig. 2.5(c) the tensile stress tangential to the surface at A is $\sigma\sqrt{(a/\rho)}$. This is strictly not the greatest tensile stress but for $a \gg \rho$ it is a very good approximation (Marsh 1963). Lastly we note that if we have a small notch in the side of a hole there will be a double magnification of stress.

The theoretical values of the concentrated stresses around the ends of holes and notches have been well confirmed by photo-elastic methods for materials such as celluloid or araldite when the stresses are everywhere small, so that strains are always within the elastic range. They should also be a good approximation to the strains at notches in materials of large modulus so long as the strains are small. It is clear from equation (2.4) that very large stresses can be present at the ends of sharp corners or notches in an elastic body. Thus, if $\rho = 30$ Å and $a = 3\mu$m the applied stress is magnified by a factor of 64. This can lead to attainment of the theoretical fracture strength at the root of a notch or step when much smaller stresses are applied to the body than would produce failure in a perfect specimen. It can also lead to failure by plastic yielding in materials such as metals.

This idea of the weakening effect of cracks, steps, notches, and fissures in elastically stressed solids is central to the use of strong materials and requires some discussion.

2.3. Griffith's theory

To account for the usually observed discrepancy between the calculated and observed values of the breaking strength of solids, Griffith (1920) postulated that they usually contain cracks and that rupture occurs by the spreading of one of these pre-existing cracks under the influence of forces applied to the body. The spreading of a crack is accompanied by an increase in energy proportional to the increase in area of the faces of the crack. The crack will not spread unless the work done as it spreads, by the forces applied to the body, is at least equal to the increase of surface energy of the solid.

If an elastic body is subject to a uniform stress, with principal stresses σ_1, σ_2, σ_3 then the presence of a very thin circular crack of radius c in a plane normal to σ_1 *increases* the elastic strain energy of the body by an amount

$$W_1 = \frac{8(1-\nu^2)\sigma_1^2 c^3}{3E}, \qquad (2.8)$$

irrespective of the value of σ_2 and σ_3 (Sack 1946), provided c is small compared to the dimensions of the body. ν is Poisson's ratio and E is Young's modulus. The crack has a surface energy,

$$W_2 = 2\pi c^2 \gamma, \qquad (2.9)$$

where γ is the surface free energy of the material. The total free energy contribution due to the presence of the crack is then

$$\Delta W = -W_1 + W_2 = 2\pi c^2 \gamma - \frac{8(1-\nu^2)\sigma^2 c^3}{3E}, \qquad (2.10)$$

writing σ for the stress normal to the crack.† The condition that the crack spreads is then that $\partial \Delta W / \partial c = 0$ which gives

$$\sigma = \sqrt{\left\{ \frac{\pi}{2(1-\nu^2)} \frac{E\gamma}{c} \right\}}. \qquad (2.11)$$

The crack cannot spread under a smaller stress than this. The same argument can be applied to an elliptical cavity of width $2c$ extending right through a plate. If the plate is stressed in plane stress,

$$\sigma = \sqrt{(2E\gamma/\pi c)}, \qquad (2.12)$$

and if in plane strain,

$$\sigma = \sqrt{\left\{ \frac{2}{\pi(1-\nu^2)} \frac{E\gamma}{c} \right\}}. \qquad (2.13)$$

† Care is needed over the definition of the sign attached to W_1 in this equation. The calculation of the change in elastic energy of a body on introducing a crack is made under the condition that the stress applied to the body at a large distance from the crack is kept constant. Then, when the crack in introduced the surface tractions do work, as the body becomes more deformable. The work done by these tractions is precisely *twice* the *increase* in elastic energy of the body due to the introduction of the crack. The change is free energy of the body is then $-W_1$.

The argument can also be applied to a thin fissure at the surface of a body. If this is of depth c the formulae (2.12) and (2.13) apply for the plane stress and plane strain cases respectively. The stresses given by (2.11), (2.12), and (2.13) differ by a factor of only 1·75 at most, for $\nu = 0·3$. This is quite within the accuracy that the calculations can be made, because at the end of the hole, which is assumed very sharp, the strain will be large and Hooke's law will not be obeyed.

In a truly brittle solid there is no question of plastic flow occurring and so at the end of a sharp deep crack under stress there will be a large stress concentration. The concentrated tensile stress will be equal to

$$\sigma\sqrt{(c/\rho)},$$

where σ is the applied stress and $c \gg \rho$. If the material is to break this must equal the theoretical rupture strength, viz. $\sqrt{(E\gamma/a_0)}$, (equation (1.5)) so giving,

$$\sigma = \sqrt{\{(E\gamma/c)(\rho/a_0)\}}. \tag{2.14}$$

Orowan (1949) has pointed out that in a truly brittle solid the *effective* value of ρ will always be of the order of the atomic spacing and cannot be less than this so $\rho \sim a_0$ and (2.14) reduces to the Griffith stress given by (2.11), (2.12), and (2.13) within the accuracy of the calculation.

However, it must be clearly borne in mind that the Griffith calculation does not involve the theoretical fracture stress of a perfect solid. Equation (2.11) is essentially a statement of the first law of thermodynamics applied to fracture and is a necessary condition for a crack to propagate. In a truly brittle solid it will also be a sufficient condition. The Griffith energy-balance relation can also be extended to include failure involving plastic flow provided γ is then understood to include all the work done in increasing the area of the fracture surface by unit amount (Irwin 1948, Orowan 1949). We return to this topic in Chapter 4.

The spread of a crack or of a notch in a brittle body requires the presence of large elastic stresses at the tip of the crack. This requires the localization of the stress. The theory does not apply to initially highly deformable elastic bodies, such as rubber, where under zero stress the molecular chains are coiled with distances of about 100 atoms, measured along a chain, between points where the chains are linked. If a slit is cut in the material under these conditions it does not produce a large stress concentration under an applied stress because the slit may be elastically widened to more than its own depth. However, rubber is brittle and a crack will run in it if introduced when the material is highly stretched so that the molecular chains are straightened.

2.4. The crack tip

In section 2.1 the results of calculations of the stresses close to the end of an elliptic hole in an elastic body under tension were presented, and the results were used in section 2.3 to present Griffith's theory of rupture. The results presented in section 2.1 will apply to a real material containing a crack at distances from the crack surface which are large compared to the radius of curvature of the surface of the crack at the crack tip. However, the stresses close to the crack tip are determined by the interatomic forces holding the body together and so the form of the crack near its tip when the body is under stress is a property of the material and may not be well represented by an elliptic surface. The nature of the interatomic forces will determine the ratio of the maximum tensile stress to the maximum shear stress and will determine whether a material will tend to cleave without any plastic flow or whether dislocations will be generated at the crack tip which may produce extensive plastic flow and under some conditions prevent brittle cleavage.

Orowan (1949), following suggestions by Rehbinder, by Mott and by Elliott (see Barenblatt 1962) first pointed out clearly that in a truly brittle material, i.e. one which is incapable of plastic flow, the appearance of a crack when the material is held at constant tensile strain between fixed grips must be as shown by the full lines in Fig. 2.6. The crack closes smoothly and around the tip there are atomic bonds at every stage of elongation and failure. Such a crack will either close up or extend under an applied tensile stress σ except for one value of the crack depth,

2c, which gives unstable equilibrium. If the crack advances by one interatomic distance each atomic bond across the face of the crack takes the strain previously held by its predecessor and the sum of all of these is just equal to the complete breaking of one interatomic bond; the work required to do this is the surface energy. This is the atomic description of the basis of

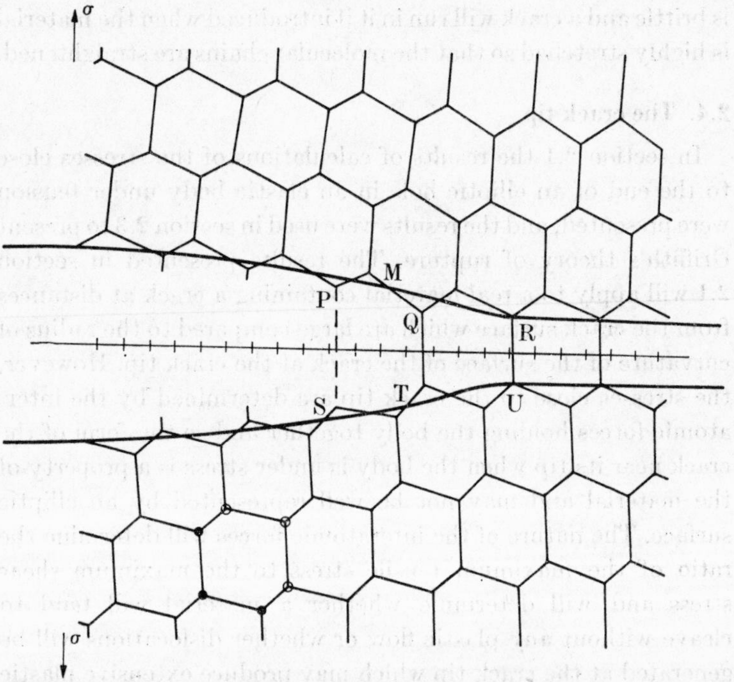

FIG. 2.6. Relaxed crack tip configuration for silicon calculated by Sinclair and Lawn (1972). The continuum solution is shown for comparison by the full lines. The view is along [0$\bar{1}$1] showing atoms in two planes separated by $\sqrt{(2/3)}\, r_0$ indicated by closed and open circles. $r_0 = $ interatomic distance.

Griffith's theory and in a truly brittle solid the Griffith condition is both necessary and sufficient for rupture.

We derived the Griffith equation in the previous section (2.3) by using results for the total increase in strain energy of an elastic body, obtained by integrating the stress field over the whole of the body, when the crack is introduced. However, the

Griffith approach can be expressed in a local form which is most important for the development of fracture mechanics (section 4.1). This extension is due to Irwin (1957). Consider an infinite body in plane strain with a plane crack of length $2c$ occupying initially the position $y = 0$, $x \leqslant 0$. Near the crack tip the stress, as x tends to zero (cf. equation (2.6)), is

$$\sigma_y(x) = \sigma\sqrt{(c/x)}, \tag{2.15}$$

where τ is the stress applied at a very large distance from the crack. Suppose the crack shown by the dotted line in Fig. 2.7

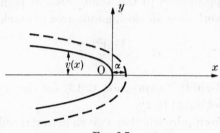

FIG. 2.7.

initially has its tip at $x = \alpha$. Now suppose stresses are applied to the edges of the crack over the region $0 < x < \alpha$ and these are gradually increased up to the values given by equation (2.15) for the various x; the crack will be closed up over the length α and its tip will be at the origin. An expression for the displacement in the y direction of the surfaces of an equilibrium crack, valid for a very thin sharp crack, with origin at $(0, 0)$ is†

$$v(x) = \pm \frac{2(1-\nu^2)}{E} \sigma\sqrt{(cx)}. \tag{2.16}$$

Since the material surrounding the crack is assumed to be linearly elastic, the work done by the stresses in closing the crack is equal

† In equation (2.16) the displacement of the crack surfaces involves the applied stress and the length of the crack, of course. This is what distinguishes a true crack from a notch. In a notch the surface opening and stress are assumed to be chosen independently of one another. The parabolic form of equation (2.16) is consistent with that of a thin deep notch (see section 2.1, equation (2.3)).

to one-half of the final stress times the initial displacement of the opposite faces of the crack. So the work done in closing the crack over a length α from equations (2.15) and (2.16) is

$$\frac{1}{2}\int_0^\alpha 2v(\alpha-x)\sigma_y(x)\,\mathrm{d}x = \int_0^\alpha \frac{2(1-v^2)}{E}\,\sigma^2 c\left(\frac{\alpha-x}{x}\right)^{\frac{1}{2}}\mathrm{d}x,$$

$$= \frac{(1-v^2)}{E}\,\sigma^2 c\pi\alpha.$$

If we consider the crack to extend all the way through a thick plate, as is appropriate to the assumption of plane strain, we have for the work done in closing unit area of crack,

$$G = \frac{(1-v^2)\pi c\sigma^2}{E} \tag{2.17}$$

which yields Griffith's expression (2.13) for the crack in plane strain if G is set equal to 2γ.

If we wish to enquire whether a given material will behave in a truly brittle manner or in a ductile fashion, when it contains a crack and is loaded in tension, the detailed nature of the stresses around a crack tip are of great importance. This problem is a difficult one and has not yet been solved completely.

Elliott (1947) first attempted an analysis of the shape of a true crack and gives some results for the stresses near a crack tip. His method is to take the asymptotic solution for the mathematical crack of zero tip radius. He finds the stresses around the crack on the assumption that no stresses act across the surface of the mathematical crack. He then calculates σ_z, the z component of stress, in the two planes which before stressing were distant $\pm a/2$ from the plane of the mathematical crack. The shape of these planes is identical with the boundary of the crack under tension provided that $f(z)$, the interatomic force per unit area when the planes are distant $(z+a)$ from one another, is the same function of z as σ_z is of $2u_z$ where u_z is the displacement of the planes in the z direction. Proceeding in this way the law of force to which the solution corresponds must be subsequently deduced. This is done by taking $f(z) = E \times 2u_z/a$ for small z, where E is Young's modulus, and requiring that the maximum value of σ_z is equal to the theoretical cohesive stress σ_{max}. The law of force is such that it corresponds to σ_z falling off as $1/u_z$ and thus tends only slowly to zero as u_z tends to infinity. Elliott's detailed procedure was approximate and led to the deduction of an initial increase in E with increasing displacement. Such an increase can occur in, for example, silica glass but is not generally expected for crystals. Recent work on the mathematical theory of the crack tip has been summarized by Barenblatt (1962).†

A detailed treatment of an equilibrium crack in diamond, silicon, and germanium has been given by Sinclair and Lawn (1972), who examined the position of atoms close to the tip of the crack by minimizing the energy of a region of the crystal (region I) within which the interatomic forces were considered explicitly, using force constants for nearest neighbour bond bending and bond stretching and a term in the expression for the total energy involving bending of a stretched bond analogous, though not similar in expression, to Tyson's assumption (equation (1.24)). The displacement at the boundary of region I was made equal to that at the inner surface of a region II within which the elastic solution for an equilibrium crack in plane strain was used. Forces are in equilibrium at the boundary between regions I and II within some specified value of the maximum residual force at the end of the calculation. Figure 2.6 shows the atom positions in silicon. The exact point of rupture is not simple to specify but from the Morse function and equation (1.10) a rupture strain of 20 per cent for silicon is calculated, and using this assumption all bonds to the left of QT in Fig. 2.6 can be taken as having broken while those to the right have not. The position of the crack tip, defined as the point half-way between the last unruptured bond and the first ruptured bond, can vary

† Barenblatt himself took into account explicitly the cohesive forces at the tip of an elastic crack and derived a criterion very similar to that of Griffith for the propagation of the crack. Willis (1967) has shown that the two approaches agree and differ only in the zero-point chosen for their definitions of the work done in separating two lattice planes. Griffith defines the work done starting from the unstrained position and Barenblatt from the strained one. For a moving crack Willis finds the difference is not a trivial one.

during the relaxation procedure. Sinclair and Lawn found no
qualitative differences between cracks in silicon, germanium or
diamond other than those predicted from continuum theory.
They found no shear instabilities during relaxation and therefore according to these calculations the diamond structure can
sustain a fully brittle crack. Figure 2.6 also shows the elastic
continuum solution for the equilibrium crack, which agrees
very closely with the atomistic calculation, the differences being
ascribable to the decrease in Young's modulus with increase
in elastic strains in the real (atomistic) case.

We can explore the stresses close to the crack tip, according
to the asymptotic solution for the mathematical crack, from
equations (2.6). If we take r very small compared to c and take
θ close to zero we see that with $\beta = 90°$ there is a state of biaxial
tension close to the crack tip, since $\sigma_r = \sigma_\theta$ and $\tau_{r\theta} = 0$. The
value of σ_r and of σ_θ is then

$$\sigma\sqrt{(c/2r)}.$$

Schijve (1964) has given alternative forms of equations (2.6)
for the case of a crack extending through a sheet. Using these
we can find the maximum value of the shear stress according to
the asymptotic solution, for $\beta = 90°$ in equations (2.6). On
planes normal to the cracked sheet the maximum shear stress
attained is one-half of the above, viz. $\sigma/2\sqrt{(c/2r)}$. This applies for
both plane stress and plane strain conditions. The maximum
value of the shear stress on planes oblique to the plane of the
sheet is

$$0.65\ \sigma\sqrt{(c/2r)}$$

for conditions of plane stress. Under conditions of plane strain
the value of the maximum shear stress on planes oblique to the
cracked sheet, depends on the value of Poisson's ratio (ν) and is
larger for smaller values of ν.

When no mobile dislocations are present in a material then
the ratio of maximum tensile stress to maximum shear stress in
the region close to the tip of the crack is of great importance,
since it must determine whether fracture will occur by cleavage

or whether the theoretical shear stress will be attained and dislocations generated in the perfect lattice (Cottrell and Kelly 1966). We see from the above discussion that the shear stress distribution close to the tip of a crack will depend on the elastic constants of the material, their relationship to the interatomic forces, and on the form of the crack. Further, the values of τ_{max} and of σ_{max} must be evaluated for the biaxial state of stress expected close to the crack tip. Our present state of knowledge is incomplete but the state of biaxial tension close to the crack tip will clearly favour cleavage if σ_{max} and τ_{max} are at all comparable. Only in the pure face-centred cubic metals is the ratio of σ_{max} to τ_{max} (see Chapter 1) so large that, despite our ignorance of the details and the uncertainty in estimating σ_{max} and τ_{max}, we can say that theory predicts that cleavage will not occur in the absence of a corrosive environment.

Kelly, Tyson, and Cottrell (1967) made the argument a little more quantitative by assuming that close to the tip of a crack in all materials the state of stress is one of biaxial tension and plane strain. The ratio of the maximum tensile stress to the maximum shear stress which they call R, then depends only on the (possibly anisotropic) value of the Poisson's ratio. Their assumption is that if R is greater than the ratio of the ideal tensile strength to the ideal shear strength for a particular material, then such a material will be brittle, whereas if R is less than $(\sigma_{max}/\tau_{max})$ such a material will be ductile in the sense that an equilibrium crack of the type discussed by Griffith could not be present in it because plastic relaxation would occur at the tip. In the course of considering various materials it became clear that the values of σ_{max} and of τ_{max} must be evaluated under the conditions of constraint appropriate to the region close to the end of a crack. For argon and for sodium chloride this could be done with some confidence (see sections 1.3 and 1.5) and it is predicted that sodium chloride at absolute zero would be brittle, and argon ductile. Other materials were considered, e.g. diamond, and various face-centred cubic and body-centred cubic metals. In these materials only the relatively crude estimates of σ_{max} and of τ_{max} reported in sections 1.2 and 1.5 of this book were available, and no estimate could be made of the effect of constraint upon these. For face-centred cubic metals the values of R are very much less than the ratio of the ideal strengths (Table 2.2), and so neglecting the (unknown) effects of constraint, the analysis successfully predicts consistent ductility for these and brittleness for diamond. The detailed analysis of the crack tip in diamond (and in silicon and germanium) carried out by Sinclair and Lawn (1972) confirms that diamond can sustain a perfectly brittle crack with no failure in shear at its tip.

For the body-centred cubic metals iron and tungsten, Table 2.2 gives values of R and of $(\sigma_{max}/\tau_{max})$ which are very close to one another and so there is obvious uncertainty in prediction because neither the value of R nor of $(\sigma_{max}/\tau_{max})$ is very certain. However, this itself is in accord with experiment on these materials since they do show a brittle to ductile transition at low temperatures and unlike diamond are not consistently brittle at low temperature. The case of potassium is interesting because it is body-centred cubic, as are tungsten and iron, and yet it is found to be ductile even at temperatures close to absolute zero (Bernstein and Gensamer 1968); the analysis predicts this.

TABLE 2.2

Material	$-S_{12}/S_{11}$	R	σ_{max}/τ_{max}†
Copper	0·416	12·6	28
Silver	0·426	14·4	30
Gold	0·457	24·7	34
Nickel	0·366	7·9	22
Iridium	0·299	4·8	10
Diamond	0·10	3·6	1·16
Iron‡	0·36	5·5	6·75
Tungsten	0·28	5·5	5·04
Potassium‡	0·45	3·3	10·0

† The values here are evaluated at 0 K, by extrapolation where necessary, and therefore may not agree with those given in Tables 1.1 and 1.5.

‡ The value of R has been found by taking a full anisotropic analysis of the ratio of maximum tensile stress to maximum shear stress for a region in a cubic crystal stressed in biaxial tension along [010] and [$\bar{1}0\bar{1}$] and in plane strain. In the original paper the Poisson contractions were less accurately evaluated. The need for this was realized in conversation with C. N. Reid.

There is general agreement that the stress required to propagate a crack through a truly brittle body is given by equation (2.14) with $\rho = a_0$. A workable definition of a truly brittle solid is one in which there is no plastic flow involved in the fracture process, and hence the work of fracture is equal to the surface energy. This is assumed in the derivation of equation (2.11) and in the estimates of the theoretical fracture stress in section 1.2. Many materials appear to be brittle to a first approximation and any plastic flow involved in the fracture process is very small if the temperature is sufficiently low. Examples are lithium fluoride, magnesium oxide, fluorite, barium fluoride, calcite, silicon, zinc, and iron (containing 3 per cent silicon). For these materials values of the surface energy have been derived from experiments on breaking them in a controlled fashion, and such values of the surface energy agree with theoretically expected ones (Gilman 1961). Silica glass at low temperatures also appears to break in a truly brittle manner under most conditions. Careful experiments on the fracture of most apparently brittle materials do, however, reveal some plastic flow; for example Johnston, Stokes, and Li (1958) found evidence of dislocation motion in germanium broken at room temperature. The truly brittle material may therefore be an abstraction. However, since many materials such as glass, bakelite, quartz, and germanium appear to behave approximately as truly brittle materials, it is a useful abstraction.

A truly brittle material will always be strong (i.e. will approach its theoretical breaking strength) if steps, notches, and fissures are removed. The breaking stress will be drastically reduced if these are present to concentrate the applied stress. Single dislocations will be unimportant stress concentrators in such solids, compared to observable surface fissures and notches, because if viewed as internal cracks the corresponding value of c in equation (2.11) will itself be of only atomic dimensions.† Truly brittle materials can then be made strong by eliminating surface defects

† If dislocations with large Burgers vectors are present some reduction in strength might be expected but experimentally in materials such as silica and sapphire cracks are not observed to propagate from them (see section 3.2) at the stress levels attained at present.

and internal holes. The strength attained when this is done must be governed by the ratio of theoretical cleavage stress to theoretical shear stress. Since silica-based glasses usually behave as brittle solids we will now discuss the strength of glass observed under a variety of conditions, since this has been very intensively studied and indicates the precautions necessary to obtain high strengths.

2.5. Strength of glass

The essential ingredients of the mineral glasses are mutually soluble oxides of elements with a valence of three or more. The most common is silica. Oxides with a valence of less than three, for instance calcium or sodium, are often introduced to prevent crystallization and to lower the softening temperature. At temperatures at which viscous flow can be disregarded, glass appears to behave as a truly brittle solid and macroscopic permanent deformation in tension is negligible, although under a hardness indenter permanent deformation is produced. The strength varies with chemical composition. There is evidence that pure silica is stronger by about a factor of 2 than the common glasses containing the oxides of calcium, sodium, boron, and aluminium but no systematic study has been made.

It has been commonly assumed in the past that thin glass fibres are stronger than thick ones. This is no longer accepted and many recent experiments have shown that there is no inherent size effect. Thomas (1960) demonstrated that E glass fibres with diameters between 5 μm and 50 μm all have a consistent short time breaking strength of 3·7 GN m^{-2} (5·3 × 10^5 psi) at room temperature in air of less than 40 per cent r.h. with a coefficient of variation (standard deviation divided by the average value) of less than 1 per cent. There is much confirmatory evidence.

In discussing the strength of glass two essentially different regimes can be considered (Proctor 1964, Gurney 1964). These are the strength of 'off the shelf' glass rods, which is normally 7–140 MN m^{-2} (1–20 × 10^3 psi) and the strength of carefully prepared specimens, usually fibres or rods, in which the surface is not damaged by abrasion with other fibres or damaged by contact with particles of dust. This high strength glass possesses a breaking stress of several hundred thousand pounds per square inch, e.g. 8×10^5 psi at room temperature, for pure silica.

The strength of 'off the shelf' glass is little changed by heating, though it may get somewhat stronger. The strength can be markedly increased by etching and this is due to the rounding-off of stress concentrating notches. If high strength glass is heated to above 300–400°C, however, the strength at room temperature is decreased permanently after heating. This decrease in strength depends on the time at temperature above 300°C and after heating for some hours a constant stress level of about one-third of the initial value is reached (Thomas 1960). It appears that flaws develop in strong glass at temperatures above 300°C and that their development is time- and temperature-dependent and may depend on applied stress. Flaws may be partly produced by crystallization which leads to volume changes and therefore the introduction of potentially stress-concentrating defects. However, the damage is closely related to the presence of water vapour, though it is still produced *in vacuo*. The cleanliness of the glass surface is most important here because particles of dust may dissolve in the glass. The glass surface is highly reactive because of the presence of unsaturated (Si—O) bonds. In many cases the loss of strength produced by heating may be eliminated by subsequent etching, which indicates clearly damage at the surface.

Below about 200°C the strength of very strong pure silica glass is reversible in the sense that fibres may be subject to a temperature within this range, returned to room temperature and exhibit an unaltered room temperature strength. The variation of breaking strength with temperature in various atmospheres below 200°C is shown in Fig. 2.8(a). The effects can be explained in general terms (Proctor, Whitney, and Johnson 1967) by a reaction occurring between silica and water adsorbed upon the surface of the glass. The reaction rate between glass and water depends upon temperature and upon the applied stress. An applied stress is necessary in the case of silica, but damage occurs

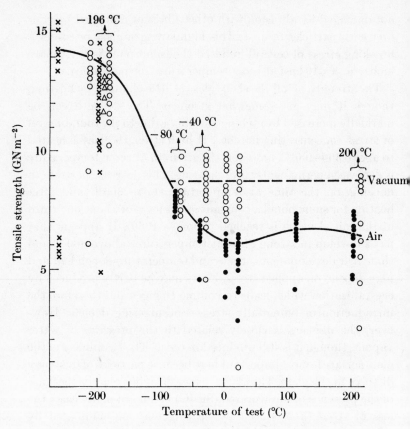

Fig. 2.8(a). Strength of silica fibres as a function of temperature from 4 K to 473 K. ×— tested in liquid helium or nitrogen; ○—tested *in vacuo*, ●— tested in air; △—tested in gaseous hydrogen. From Proctor, Whitney, and Johnson (1967).

without this in E glass (Thomas 1960). The mobility and concentration of the water depends upon the temperature. The constant strength *in vacuo* over the range −80°C to 200°C indicates the compensation of the opposing effects of increase in temperature, increasing the rate of attack but at the same time decreasing the availability of adsorbed water; in air this compensation does not occur until 0°C. Between 0°C and 200°C loss of water from the surface is the most important factor and so the strength rises. At very low temperatures the reaction with water proceeds too slowly to be observed and hence the strength increases below 77 K. At these very low temperatures the strength appears to be independent of time. Most glasses, in common with silica, show 'static fatigue' at temperatures above 77 K, i.e. the measured strength is time-dependent in the sense that failure will eventually occur provided the stress exceeds some minimum value. The static fatigue life is atmosphere-dependent and is particularly sensitive to water vapour. Static fatigue is the most easily recognised of the time-dependent effects in glass but careful experiments show that there is, in addition, a true cyclic fatigue effect which produces shorter lives if the stress is applied cyclically at a rate of about 1 s^{-1} (Whitney, Johnson, and Proctor 1966).

The measured strength in tension of carefully prepared pure silica glass immersed in liquid nitrogen averages 14 GN m^{-2} (2×10^6 psi) (with a spread of values between $11 \cdot 2$ and $16 \cdot 1$ GN m^{-2} ($1 \cdot 6 \times 10^6$ and $2 \cdot 3 \times 10^6$ psi). The strength appears independent of time and is the same at liquid helium temperatures (Morley, Andrews, and Whitney 1964). This average value is close to that calculated for the theoretical rupture stress from equation (1.5) (see Table 1.1) which should depend little on temperature, except through temperature variation of the parameters in equation (1.5). The value predicted in section 1.4 is also in agreement within a factor of 2. For a material such as silica glass in which the atoms are linked by strong covalent bonds the value of $2\tau_{max}$ may approach the value of σ_{max}. All we can say then is that the values of the breaking stress of very carefully prepared silica glass at low temperatures appear consistent with failure at the theoretical strength.

At temperatures greater than 77 K the observed discrepancy between the theoretical strength σ_{max} and the values observed has often been attributed to the presence of flaws or cracks which produce brittle fracture at a stress given by the Griffith stress (section 2.3). To account for the values shown in Fig. 2.8 cracks of width $\sim$15 Å are needed to account for the observed breaking stress at room temperature. There is some evidence for these (see Proctor for references) but equations (2.11) to (2.13) are quite unable to account for the reversible temperature dependence of the strength, shown in Fig. 2.8(a), between room temperature and 77 K.

At temperatures above 200°C the strength of silica depends on time, temperature, and atmosphere and decreases with increase in temperature. Creep occurs in periods of some hours under a stress of $\gtrsim 0\cdot7$ GN m^{-2} at temperatures above 800°C whereas

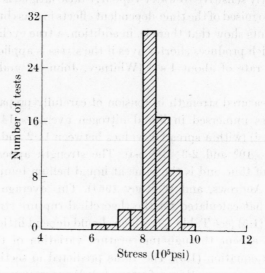

FIG. 2.8(b). Strength of fused silica fibres in air at 20°C. (Data from Morley 1964.)

apparently brittle fracture (denoted by a flat fracture surface) occurs in tensile tests of a few seconds duration at 780°C. Tensile tests up to 800°C indicate a *higher* strength at the temperature than if the material strength is measured at room temperature after heat treatment at that temperature.

Despite the central position occupied by the Griffith relation in the general theory of fracture of solids, and particularly in the fracture of glass, there have been few clear quantitative tests of its predictions, namely that the fracture stress σ is proportional to $c^{-1/2}$ and that the constant of proportionality is given by equations (2.11)–(2.13) for the various stress conditions.

Griffith (1920) burst cylindrical glass tubes and spheres containing longitudinal scratches of known length. He found that the quantity $\sigma\sqrt{c}$ at failure was a constant, and checked roughly that stresses applied parallel to the crack did not affect it. He used equation (2.12) and found quantitative agreement within 10 per cent. He measured γ, which he took to be the surface free energy, by observing the sag of thin fibres under a transverse load at temperatures between 750 and 1110°C. The value of γ extrapolated to room temperature was 550 mJ m^{-2}. The values of the applied stress used by Griffith in breaking his tubes and bulbs were about 10^3 psi.

Shand (1959) has confirmed the dependence of the breaking stress of glass on $c^{-1/2}$ and many others have verified this. Shand's methods have led to recognition that the experimental values of γ deduced using equations (2.11) to (2.13) are usually much larger than the surface energy. His method is as follows. The observation of fracture surfaces in glass has established that the appearance of the broken surface alters from a mirror-like appearance to a stippled and irregular surface when a critical maximum value of local stress is reached. This corresponds to a critical velocity of crack propagation. From the applied stress σ_a, and known dimensions of the mirror surface and knowing the appropriate stress concentration factor, it is clearly possible to write

$$\sigma_a = (\sigma'_{max}\sqrt{\rho})/f \qquad (2.18)$$

where σ'_{max} is the maximum stress and ρ an effective crack tip radius; $f/\sqrt{\rho}$ is then the appropriate stress concentration factor. f contains the radius of the mirror surface to the one-half power and the dimensions of the specimen. From this equation values of $\sigma'_{max}\sqrt{\rho}$ are found. Values found by Shand for this quantity are ~ 2000 psi(in)$^{1/2}$ or 220 kg cm$^{-3/2}$ for soda-glass at room temperature (2·2 MN m$^{-3/2}$). For a truly brittle material the maximum stress at the tip of a crack must equal the cohesive strength and we pointed out in section 2.3 that the effective value of ρ will be of the order of the atomic spacing. From equation (1.5) the value of $\sigma'_{max}\sqrt{\rho}$ should then be equal to $\sqrt{(E\gamma)}$, or $0 \cdot 14 \, \text{MN m}^{-3/2}$ for soda-glass, taking $E = 65 \cdot 5 \, \text{GN m}^{-2}$ and $\gamma = 300 \, \text{mJ m}^{-2}$. Shand's value is many times greater than this. Thus the surface energy of glass does not represent the true energy of fracture. By measuring the relation between crack depth and time to fracture Shand (1961) has shown that only when cracks propagate in air at very low velocities does the work of fracture approach the value of the surface energy. Under all other conditions the work of fracture is much larger than the surface energy being up to fifty times as great.

Marsh (1964), following a suggestion of Shand's, has proposed that the excess energy of fracture is due to plastic flow at the crack tip and that Griffith's results are largely to be explained as a result of static fatigue. Marsh has also shown that the breaking stress of strong glass fibres is closely equal to the yield stress for plastic compression under an indenter, when the values of the yield stress are obtained from the hardness number following the procedure in section 1.9. This is true over a wide range of temperature. It is necessary to take account of the rate of loading at temperatures above 77 K, in order to eliminate effects due to static fatigue. Marsh believes that the mode of plastic flow in glass is very much affected by water vapour and at temperatures above 77 K the presence of water vapour leads to a reduction in the yield stress for plastic flow and to the yield stress depending upon time and temperature.† He also accounts for the apparently catastrophic nature of the failure of a strong glass fibre because of the absence of any work-hardening in such a material.

At temperatures of 77 K and below the strength is time-independent. For soda-glass the fracture stress at 77 K is $10 \, \text{GN m}^{-2}$ or $0 \cdot 15 \, E$. The maximum shear stress is one-half this so that strong soda-glass fibres fail in shear at a shear stress of $0 \cdot 19 \, G$ where G is the shear modulus. No calculations of the theoretical *shear* strength of glass have been made but it is un-

† The fracture energy of various glasses does indeed depend on the medium surrounding the specimen. Double cantilever tests show, for instance, for Pyrex and other glasses including soda-lime, that the fracture energy per unit area of surface is largest *in vacuo* ($6000 \, \text{mJ m}^{-2}$), less in air ($4700 \, \text{mJ m}^{-2}$) and least in water ($2500 \, \text{mJ m}^{-2}$) (Linger and Holloway 1968).

likely to be greater than 0·25 G which is the value deduced in section 1.5 for covalently bound crystals. Flaw-free soda-glass fibres then could fail in shear at or close to the theoretical shear strength at low temperatures.

Because of the effect of surface condition on the strength of glass, many glass articles are treated so as to produce a state of biaxial compression in the surface. This may be done either by cooling the surface more rapidly than the interior from a temperature above the softening point (see appendix E; this is roughly the temperature for a viscosity of between $10^{7.5}$ and 10^8 poise (1 poise $= 10^{-1}$ Pa s)), or treating with sulphur at a temperature above the annealing point (temperature for a viscosity of 10^{13} poise) to remove alkali from the surface so as to reduce the coefficient of thermal expansion. While these methods raise the 'off the shelf' strength of glass objects to consistent values of about 35 000 psi or 0·24 GN m^{-2}, a much more powerful method is that of *ion* exchange, or chemical strengthening. In this, small cations originally present in the glass, e.g. sodium or lithium, are replaced by larger cations, e.g. potassium from a molten salt, at a temperature below the annealing range so that the resulting stresses are not removed. On cooling a permanently stressed layer with a thickness between 50 μm and 300 μm is obtained. A strength of more than 100,000 psi is attained which is not impaired by mild abrasion. Glass nails can be made! The equilibrium in the system has been considered by Hale (1968). As ion exchange occurs, the activities of the larger ion in the salt and the glass become equal with the appearance of a strain in the glass, and Hale gives the quantitative relation between the equilibrium concentrations of the differing ions in the glass and in the molten salt, their relative sizes, and the elastic properties of the glass.

2.6. Damage to fibres

Morley (1964) has emphasized the advantages of silica glass fibres as potentially usable strong solids, particularly to reinforce weaker matrices. Silica fibres are easy to produce in quantity, the density is low, $2·5 \times 10^3$ kg m^{-3}, and the strength high (see Appendix

A.) Fibres tested at room temperature in air have *average* strengths of $8 \cdot 5 \times 10^5$ psi (Fig. 2.8(b)). At temperatures above 300°C the strength is time- and temperature-dependent. At room temperature the strength is reduced in the presence of water vapour but even so exposure for an indefinite period does not reduce the strength below 4×10^5 psi. Mechanical damage or local chemical attack reduces the strength drastically. Such fibres must therefore be coated in some way in order to prevent the formation of fissures and notches by chemical and mechanical means.

The behaviour of glass at low temperature is closely paralleled by that of the inherently strong crystals discussed in section 3.2. In all of these the strength at low temperatures is governed by the presence of cracks and notches. Since, as we have seen in section 2.5, the strength of glass closely approaches the theoretical value for a perfect solid at low temperature, provided the surface is perfect, we must see how cracks are likely to be produced. Since glass has been most extensively studied we can draw upon experience with this material to see what agents cause cracks.

Cracks can be produced by chemical or mechanical means. The chemical means are usually highly specific to the substance in question and the only general point to be made is that in materials without grain boundaries chemical attack is only localized where inhomogeneities exist in the structure. In glasses this can be due to certain areas tending to crystallize, to local inhomogeneities in chemical composition, and to the presence of inclusions introduced during the drawing process. In crystals, in addition to these features, dislocations emerging at the surface will promote enhanced chemical reactivity.

Cracks can be very easily introduced by mechanical means, particularly by means of impact and by sliding contact. Hertz first considered the impact of elastic bodies. A sphere of radius R with kinetic energy W, striking a flat surface of the same material, with Poisson's ratio $0 \cdot 25$, produces a maximum pressure, q_0, given by

$$q_0 = 0 \cdot 37 \left(\frac{5}{2} \frac{W}{R^3} \right)^{1/5} E^{4/5} \qquad (2.19)$$

(see Timoshenko and Goodier 1951). The maximum tensile stress is one-sixth of this, for $\nu = 0.25$. To produce a tensile stress of $E/6$ a sphere of density 3 g cm^{-3} requires a velocity of only 91 cm s^{-1}, which is acquired in falling a distance of 4·2 cm. It is clear that great care is necessary to protect pieces of a strong solid from impact by dust particles and from other pieces of the same material.

Despite the ease with which large stresses can be produced by normal impact, there is evidence that sliding contact between glass fibres produces more severe damage than pressure normal to the contact surface. Gurney (1964) reports this evidence and states that when glass rods are lightly pressed together then little damage occurs if the pressure is normal to the plane of contact but when the direction of relative movement is oblique, damage is easily produced. Gurney suggests that the extreme sensitivity to sliding contact may perhaps be accounted for from Mindlin's (1949) calculation of the shear stresses produced parallel to the contact plane of two elastic bodies which are pressed together and subject to a tangential force.

Consider two cylindrical rods, each of radius R, aligned at right angles and pressed together by a force P. The contact surface is a circle of radius b, given by

$$b = 1.12 \, (PR/E)^{1/3}, \qquad (2.20)$$

for a value of Poisson's ratio of 0·25 and $b \ll R$ (Timoshenko and Goodier 1951). If a tangential force, T, is applied, the tangential shear stress, τ, is given as a function of distance (x) from the centre of the circle of contact by

$$\tau = \frac{T}{2\pi b} \, (b^2 - x^2)^{-1/2}, \, x < b, \qquad (2.21)$$

and thus rises to infinity at the edge of the circle of contact (Mindlin 1949). If we put $\rho = (b-x)$, and substitute for b, then for $\rho \ll b$ (2.21) reduces to

$$\tau = 0.095 \, T(E/PR\rho)^{1/2}. \qquad (2.22)$$

To examine the conditions necessary to produce cracking we can suppose that a critical value of the quantity $\tau\rho^{1/2}$ must be produced to introduce a crack. A reasonable value for this quantity will be 100 kg cm$^{-3/2}$ which is in the middle of the range found by Shand in the experiments referred to in section 2.5. For glass fibres of diameter 0·01 cm and taking $E = 10^7$ psi ($= 6·9 \times 10^{10}$ N m^{-2}) we find that to produce a crack the quantity $T/P^{1/2}$ must be greater than about 10^{-1} kg$^{1/2}$. If fibres slide with a coefficient of friction μ, then $T = \mu P$ so

$$\frac{T}{P^{1/2}} = \mu P^{1/2}. \tag{2.23}$$

Thus, if the fibres are pressed together with a force of 0·01 kg a coefficient of friction of greater than unity is required to produce a crack. Thus, as Gurney suggests, local welding must occur if this mechanism is to produce cracks easily, in small fibres.

The above remarks on mechanical damage apply when pieces of two similar materials come into contact. When materials of very different strengths and elastic properties come into contact the only general guidance we can obtain is from Mohs' hardness scale following Tabor's (1954) interpretation. In Mohs' scale materials are placed in an order of ascending hardness from 1 to 10. A difference of Mohs' hardness of one unit corresponds to an increase in Vickers indentation hardness of 60 per cent. Since the yield pressure (Y) of a material is related to the Vickers hardness (P) by the relation $P \approx 3Y$ (section 1.9), we can assume that if two materials of different hardness are pressed together under conditions of slow straining ($\dot{\varepsilon} \lesssim 10^{-2}$ s^{-1}) the softer will not indent the harder provided it has a Mohs' number more than two units below that of the harder material. Silica has a Mohs' number of 7 which is the same as that of strong metals. Metallic particles can therefore damage silica on this criterion. Materials such as alumina have Mohs' numbers of 9, and therefore may be damaged by silica and the strong metals but not by soft metals or other materials with Mohs' numbers of less than 7.

REFERENCES

G. I. BARENBLATT (1962). *Adv. appl. Mech.* **7**, 55; see also L. M. KEER (1964). *J. Mech. Phys. Solids* **12**, 149.

I. M. BERNSTEIN and M. GENSAMER (1968). *Acta metall.* **16**, 987.

A. H. COTTRELL and A. KELLY (1966). *Endeavour* **25**, 27.

H. A. ELLIOTT (1947). *Proc. phys. Soc.* **59**, 208.

J. J. GILMAN (1961). *J. appl. Phys.* **31**, 2208.

A. GREEN (1945). *Proc. R. Soc.* A**184**, 289.

A. A. GRIFFITH (1920). *Phil. Trans. R. Soc.* A**221**, 163.

C. GURNEY (1964). *Proc. R. Soc.* A**282**, 24.

D. K. HALE (1968). *Nature, Lond.* **217**, 1115.

C. E. INGLIS (1913). *Trans. Instn nav. Archit.* **55**, 219.

G. R. IRWIN (1948). *Fracturing of Metals*, p. 147, Am. Soc. Metals, Cleveland, Ohio.

—— (1957). *J. appl. Mech.* **24**, 361.

T. L. JOHNSTON, R. J. STOKES, and C. H. LI (1958). *Acta metall.* **6**, 713.

A. KELLY, W. R. TYSON, and A. H. COTTRELL (1967). *Phil. Mag.* **15**, 567.

G. KOLOSOFF, *Z. Math. Phys.* (1914) **62**, 26.

K. R. LINGER and D. G. HOLLOWAY (1968). *Phil. Mag.* **18**, 1269.

D. M. MARSH (1963). *Fracture of Solids* (Eds. D. C. DRUCKER and J. J. GILMAN), p. 119, Wiley, New York.

—— (1964). *Proc. R. Soc.* A**282**, 33 and references therein.

R. D. MINDLIN (1949). *J. appl. Mech.* **16**, 259.

J. G. MORLEY (1964). *Proc. R. Soc.* A**282**, 43.

—— P. A. ANDREWS, and I. WHITNEY (1954). *Physics Chem. Glasses* **5**, 1.

H. NEUBER (1937, 1958). *Kerbspannungslehre*, 1st and 2nd eds. Springer Verlag, Berlin.

E. OROWAN (1949). *Rep. Prog. Phys.* **12**, 185.

B. A. PROCTOR (1964). *Appl. mater. Res.* **3**, 28.

—— I. WHITNEY, and J. W. JOHNSON (1967). *Proc. R. Soc.* A**297**, 534.

R. A. SACK (1946). *Proc. phys. Soc.* **58**, 729.

G. N. SAVIN (1961). *Stress Concentration around Holes*, Pergamon Press, Oxford.

J. SCHIJVE (1964). *Analysis of the Fatigue Phenomenon in Aluminium Alloys, Technical Report* M2122, N.A.A.R.I., Amsterdam.

E. B. SHAND (1959). *J. Am. ceram. Soc.* **42**, 474.

—— (1961). *J. Am. ceram. Soc.* **44**, 71 and 451.

J. E. SINCLAIR and B. R. LAWN (1972). *Proc. R. Soc.* A**329**, 83.

D. TABOR (1954). *Proc. phys. Soc.* **67** B, 249.

W. F. THOMAS (1960). *Physics Chem. Glasses* **1**, 4.

S. TIMOSHENKO and J. N. GOODIER (1951). *Theory of Elasticity*, 2nd ed., McGraw-Hill, New York.

I. WHITNEY, J. W. JOHNSON, and B. A. PROCTOR (1966). *Nature, Lond.* **210**, 730.

J. R. WILLIS (1967). *J. Mech. Phys. Solids* **15**, 151.

3

DISLOCATIONS

CRYSTALS flow plastically by the motion of dislocations. Those crystals in which dislocation motion occurs at stresses much less than the theoretical shear strength, e.g. metals, can only be made strong by restricting dislocation motion. This is dealt with in Chapter 4. Some crystals do not sustain plastic flow at low temperatures even if they contain dislocations. Theory indicates how we can recognize these and we deal with this in section 3.1. We call such crystals inherently strong because they also have high theoretical shear strengths. Section 3.2 examines some atomic models of the cores of dislocations in inherently strong crystals. This enables some further predictions about the behaviour of dislocations in these materials to be made, and in particular how it is that dislocation motion becomes possible at high temperatures. At high temperatures the strength of such materials is governed by dislocation motion, and they begin to behave like metals.

Single crystals of a material may undergo plastic flow while polycrystals show only very limited ductility. Section 3.3 discusses the conditions for slip in a single crystal to lead to ductility in polycrystalline samples. Section 3.4 extends these conditions so that they may also apply at very high temperatures where dislocations are able to climb. Provided these conditions can be fulfilled a ductile material can be strengthened by plastic flow. If they are not, small amounts of plastic flow lead to stress concentrations where slip is blocked so that a crack is produced and failure will occur at the yield stress. Section 3.5 deals with some forms of stress concentration in polycrystals.

Ductile materials are unstable under uniaxial tensile stresses in excess of the yield stress unless they exhibit work-hardening. Section 3.6 deals with the stability of a ductile material in tension.

3.1. The Peierls–Nabarro stress

When crystals contain dislocations their strength usually falls well below the theoretical value and is governed solely by the properties and interactions of the dislocations. However, in certain crystal structures, the stress to move dislocations at a low temperature can still be very large even if the crystal contains no additional imperfections.

A finite stress should be required to move a straight dislocation in an otherwise perfect crystal. The stress to do this, assuming that the dislocation remains straight as it moves, is called the Peierls–Nabarro stress τ_P. This stress is very difficult to calculate because to a first approximation it vanishes. Only a qualitative discussion is possible at present, because calculations are not sufficiently accurate, for particular crystal structures.

The latest detailed calculation is due to Sanders (1962). His results are in good agreement with earlier treatments for the value of the width of a dislocation. Sanders's calculation applies strictly to a primitive cubic crystal but for this case has the advantage that it involves a model of discrete atoms. The qualitative results will apply to all crystal structures. Sanders's calculation shows that

$$\tau_P \propto \exp(-W) \tag{3.1}$$

where W is the width of the dislocation. Thus τ_P is very sensitive to the value of W. The dislocation width is defined as the width of the region, measured perpendicular to the dislocation line and in the slip plane, within which the relative displacement of the atoms above and below the slip plane is greater than one-half of its maximum value. Equation (3.1) predicts that narrow dislocations are difficult to move and wide ones correspondingly easier. This is in agreement with all theoretical treatments of τ_P. The quantitative differences between Sanders's calculation and those of others are not important for the following qualitative discussion. The width of a dislocation varies inversely as τ_{max}/G, the ratio of the theoretical shear strength to the shear modulus. It also depends on the ratio of central to non-central forces holding the crystal together. Some of Sanders's results are shown in Fig. 3.1. When G/τ_{max} is small and the ratio, R, of central to non-central forces also small then the dislocation is narrow, and difficult to move. When G/τ_{max} is large and R is large, the dislocations are wide and move under a very small stress.

To apply calculations of τ_P to real crystals we note that the magnitude of the Peierls–Nabarro stress depends upon two factors:

(a) the value of the ratio of theoretical shear strength to the shear modulus, τ_{max}/G, and

(b) the type of atomic binding in the crystal.

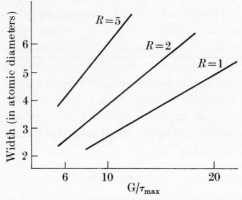

Fig. 3.1. The variation in dislocation width with the value of the ratio of shear modulus to theoretical shear strength (G/τ_{max}). R is the ratio of central to non-central forces. The calculation is due to W. T. Sanders (1962). *Phys. Rev.* **128**, 1540.

This distinction between the two factors is artificial because (a) must depend on (b) but it has value for a qualitative discussion which is all that is possible at present. A detailed and accurate evaluation of τ_P requires a knowledge of the interatomic forces and of the atomic structure in the bad crystal at the core of a dislocation.

Values of τ_{max}/G were derived in Chapter 1 and are shown in Table 1.5. They are very low for face-centred cubic metals and somewhat higher for the body-centred cubic metals. They are greatest for covalently bound solids and for ionic crystals. Body-centred cubic metals occupy a somewhat intermediate position because non-central forces contribute to the binding. Values of τ_{max}/G depend on the plane and direction of shear in a crystal and will vary with the value of b/h (section 1.5), being largest for large values of b/h. Thus τ_P will be larger for non close-packed planes (large value of b/h) than for close-packed planes. Thus, jogs in dislocations will usually show an increased resistance to motion compared with the rest of the dislocation line when the jog lies in a less close-packed plane. Amongst different crystal structures b/h is minimized if b is small and densely packed planes occur in a crystal (f.c.c. metals and graphite slipping parallel to the layer planes).

The reasons for the variation of τ_P with bond type are not far to seek. Because metallic binding is multipolar and characterized by lack of directionality—the binding energy depending rapidly upon the atomic volume but not on the exact position of nearest neighbours—dislocations are wide and the energy of the crystal is not greatly affected by the small changes in the atomic positions at the core of the dislocation as the dislocation moves. These determine τ_P and so τ_P is low. The situation is changed if the binding is ionic in character or of a strongly directional nature. Strongly directional bonds are found in covalently bound crystals, and in crystals with highly polarized ionic bonds. In ionic crystals τ_P arises from ions of the same sign having to pass close to one another during slip (e.g. by slip of $a/2$ [110] on the (001) plane in the NaCl structure). Strongly directed bonding makes dislocations very narrow thus raising τ_P. In addition, the value of b is often greater than the separation of nearest neighbours as it is in the diamond structure (Fig. 3.2). The dislocation core then contains a crack of atomic dimensions. From these qualitative remarks and the Table of Theoretical Shear Strengths (Table 1.5) we see that materials of high Peierls stress are also those of high theoretical shear strength.

Since τ_P has not been calculated with any accuracy for real crystals we have to rely upon experiment to indicate actual values of the stress to move dislocations. Without very detailed and accurate calculations of the cohesion of a crystal it is not possible to say *a priori* whether sufficiently strong directional forces are present to give a large value of τ_P. An indication of a large value of τ_P is however obtained from the value of Poisson's ratio (ν). A low value of this quantity, as we saw in Chapter 1, implies a resistance to shear in the crystal and this implies a large value of τ_{max}/G. All crystals with values of ν less than 0·25 are expected to show significant values of τ_P. Another useful fact is that if dislocations are very difficult to move the ratio of indentation hardness to Young's modulus should be high. Empirically, if this ratio exceeds about 0·01 plastic flow is only observed with extreme difficulty even if the material contains dislocations. A number of materials with values of Poisson's ratio less than 0·25 and with ratios of Vickers hardness number to Young's modulus of greater than 0·01 are shown in Appendix A, Table 3.† The values of the tensile yield stress in this table were calculated according to the method given in Chapter 1, section 1.9. The values approach twice the theoretical shear strength, given in Table 1.5, for those materials for which τ_{max} can be estimated. In the case of aluminium oxide, diamond, tungsten carbide, and aluminium nitride it is very well-established that all the specimens contain dislocations. We see then that these dislocations cannot normally be moved at stresses much below the theoretical shear strength at room temperature. Materials in which dislocations behave like this we will call inherently strong solids. If they can be prepared in a form with smooth surfaces and contain no cracks or fissures they will then show great strength even in large pieces. This has been completely confirmed experimentally both for aluminium oxide and silicon (see the references in Appendix A, Table 1). The chemical compositions producing inherently strong solids are those compositions producing marked directional binding. These include the carbides, borides, silicides, nitrides, and oxides of early polyvalent metals

† A large ratio of indentation hardness to Young's modulus is shown by polymeric materials such as polymethylmethacrylate and polystyrene. These have low values of Young's modulus. This is again because plastic flow is difficult but for quite different reasons than in crystals.

and of the transition metals; ionic compounds of widely differing radius ratio and with an ionic charge of at least two so that a strongly polarized bond is formed; crystals of the elements carbon, boron, silicon, and germanium.

3.2. Dislocations in strong solids

At elevated temperatures dislocations in the inherently strong solids can move.† The temperature at which this occurs depends upon the particular material and of course it is only significant if the dislocation density and mobility is such as to allow plastic deformation to accommodate an imposed *tensile* rate of straining so that a crystal becomes ductile instead of brittle. Tensile tests are usually conducted at strain rates between 1 and 10^{-5} s^{-1}. In crystals with the zinc blende or diamond structure plasticity then becomes evident at a temperature such that T/T_M (where T_M is the melting temperature in degrees K) is close to 0·5. Silicon is a typical member of this class of crystal—its behaviour has been intensively studied (Pearson, Read, and Feldmann 1957) and is followed by many inherently strong solids. We will therefore use it as an example. At room temperature and up to T/T_M equals 0·5 (provided no plastic flow has been induced at a higher temperature) silicon crystals fracture without any appreciable plastic flow. The strength depends upon the size for normally prepared samples when special precautions are not taken. The strength increases with decreasing size and for specimens of diameter about 50 μm or less approaches 10^6 psi which is within a factor of 2 of the value expected from the theoretical shear strength (Table 1.5). If small samples are prepared from larger ones by, for example, cutting and etching, the strength is independent of the method of preparation. This behaviour is similar to that of glass (see section 2.5). The scatter in measured strength increases as the specimen size decreases. The fracture

† Some dislocation motion can be enforced at low temperatures either under conditions of net hydrostatic pressure or else under an indenter as in a hardness test. The hardness of inherently strong solids, which is very important in their use in drills and polishing operations, can be greatly influenced by the environment and the presence of fluids which do not appear to be corrosive, e.g. aliphatic alcohols affect the hardness of alumina—see, for example, Westwood and Macmillan (1972).

strength at room temperature is independent of the density of dislocations (introduced by deformation at a high temperature) and so it does not matter whether dislocations are present or not. Since the scatter in strength increases as size decreases the size effect appears to arise from a random distribution of stress concentrations (e.g. surface irregularities). This is supported by the etching of bulk samples and by the fact that large pieces have been made with strengths of over one-half that of whiskers by careful chemical polishing of the surface. Very similar behaviour is established in detail for titanium carbide (Williams 1964) and sapphire (Wachtmann and Maxwell 1959, Mallinder and Proctor 1966).

At temperatures equal to or greater than about one-half the melting temperature plastic flow occurs in silicon, e.g. at 600°C in a previously undeformed crystal ($T/T_M = 0.50_6$). This temperature is lowered by prior deformation at a higher temperature; after prior deformation at 800°C a specimen will appear to yield before fracture at 450°C. The plastic yield stress depends very strongly on temperature. Since this rapid dependence occurs in the temperature range 600 to 860°C and silicon melts at 1450°C, it cannot be due to thermal generation of dislocations in the perfect crystal under the action of stress (see section 1.6), and so must be due either to the motion of dislocations already present or those introduced via the surface. At high temperatures there is no effect of size on the yield stress, so even small crystals which show large values of the fracture stress at low temperatures, contain dislocations which become mobile as the temperature is increased.

The behaviour of mobile dislocations in inherently strong solids follows qualitatively from the distribution of the atoms in the dislocation core. We will now examine this for the case of silicon. Figure 3.2 illustrates the expected appearance of a 60° dislocation in the silicon structure (Haasen 1957). If drastic alteration of the bond angles is not allowed a crack will appear between the two atoms below the extra half-plane. This arises because of the very strong directional binding and because the Burgers vector (b) of the dislocation is 60 per cent greater than the separation of the nearest neighbours s ($|b| = 1\cdot63\,s$)†. Although there is no extra half plane in the screw dislocation the bonds must still therefore be stretched more than 60 per cent at the core. The motion of a dislocation containing such a crack as in Fig. 3.2 requires diffusion of the crack with it, because we note that to move the dislocation in Fig. 3.2 by a length b to the right requires the atom at X to move a distance

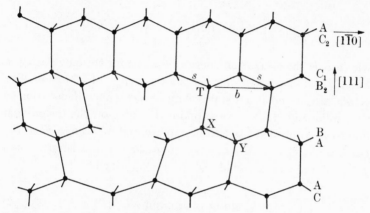

Fig. 3.2. A drawing of a 60° dislocation in the silicon (diamond) structure. b is the Burgers vector of the dislocation, and s the separation of nearest neighbours. The line of the dislocation is at 60° to the plane of the paper, along the direction [$\bar{1}$01]. The atom positions are projected onto (11$\bar{2}$). The letters ABC indicate the projections of the undistorted atomic positions on (111).

greater than s, i.e. to move more than an interatomic distance. In fact, the bond between atoms X and Y must be broken for this to occur. Approximately one bond must be broken as the dislocation centre moves a distance equal to one-half of the Burgers vector. The stress to do this is then about

$$\tau \sim 2E_B/b^3$$

where E_B is the bond energy. The bond energy in silicon (Appendix A, Table 5) is 2·3 eV. This yields a value of $13\cdot4 \times 10^9$ N m^{-2} which is of the same order as the theoretical shear strength of the crystal (Table 1.5).

† We expect a covalent bond to break at an elongation of about 20 per cent (section 1.3).

We have just estimated the stress required to move a dislocation rapidly through the crystal and this stress approaches the theoretical shear stress. A dislocation may be able to move at lower stresses if sufficient time is available for diffusion of the crack at its core (Haasen 1957). Under the action of a force F an isolated singularity of the type in Fig. 3.2 could move by diffusion acquiring a net drift velocity in the direction of the force of

$$v \sim \frac{vb}{6} \, 2 \sinh Fb/kT \times \exp{(-U/kT)},$$

where U is the activation energy required for the singularity in Fig. 3.2 to move a distance b. v is a frequency of vibration. The cracks are spaced at a distance b apart along a 60° dislocation so that following Haasen we suppose the force on the dislocation due to an applied stress τ to be represented by a force F on the crack multiplied by the number of cracks per unit length. Then $F = \tau b^2$ and the expected dislocation velocity is

$$v \sim \frac{vb}{3} \sinh \frac{\tau b^3}{kT} \times \exp{(-U/kT)}. \tag{3.2}$$

If $\tau b^3 \ll kT$ this gives a simple dependence of v on the first power of τ and an exponential temperature dependence since the exponential term will outweigh the dependence on $1/T$. When τb^3 is comparable with kT, v will appear to depend on τ to a higher power.

Measurements of dislocation velocity in real crystals are not simply related to an equation such as (3.2) for a number of reasons. The most important is that (3.2) applies only to a straight dislocation lying accurately along a particular direction in the lattice. If the dislocation is not straight its motion will be governed by the motion of kinks along it.† Nevertheless equation (3.2) indicates certain features of dislocation motion in an

---

† The relationship between the atomic movements required to provide dislocation motion and the resultant velocity of dislocation motion as well as the theory of kinks and the Peierls stress are all treated in the book *Dislocation Dynamics* (Eds. A. R. Rosenfield, G. T. Hahn, A. L. Bement Jr., and T. I. Jaffee) (1968). McGraw-Hill, New York.

inherently strong crystal. The velocity of motion of a dislocation is expected to depend on the applied shear stress raised to a power greater than one and to vary exponentially with temperature.

In very pure silicon and germanium (<0·1 ppm impurity) a dislocation velocity varying with stress and temperature as

$$v = B\tau^m \exp\left(-U/kT\right) \tag{3.3}$$

is found from direct measurements of dislocation motion (Chaudhuri, Patel, and Rubin 1962). In silicon the value of m is between 1·4 and 1·5 and $U \sim 2·2$ eV. The activation energy for self diffusion in silicon is $\sim$4 eV, or about $2U$. Similar behaviour is found for germanium again with $2U$ equal to the activation energy of self-diffusion. In compounds with the α–ZnS structure, the value of $2U$ is less than the activation energy for self-diffusion of either component.

The behaviour of dislocations in other inherently strong solids is qualitatively similar to that in silicon. The dislocations can only move at stresses much less than τ_{max} if diffusive motion of atoms can occur. In the elements this is mainly due to the strongly directional binding and the resulting very narrow dislocations. In compounds and particularly those with complicated crystal structures it is due to the atoms of different kinds having to move together to preserve the structure during motion of the dislocations. This process is called *synchroshear* (Kronberg 1957). It was introduced to explain the behaviour of alumina and probably applies to many intermetallic compounds and the transition metal carbides. Figure 3.3 illustrates the slip plane of sapphire. The distance XY represents one complete unit of slip. The oxygen ion at X is expected to follow the dotted path to Y to avoid riding over the underlying oxygen ions.

Passage of the overriding oxygen ions say from A to B then requires the aluminium ion at B to move in a different direction, along BY, to retain octahedral coordination. Thus a single vector cannot describe the motion of both types of ion. Slip vectors for both kinds of ion must be specified. The dislocations defined by these do not lie upon the same atomic plane in the crystal. The core of the dislocation in sapphire is then extended in a direction normal to the glide plane. Such a dislocation is called a zonal dislocation. As the oxygen ions move the aluminium ions must move in synchronism at the core of the dislocation; hence the name 'synchroshear'. The aluminium ions

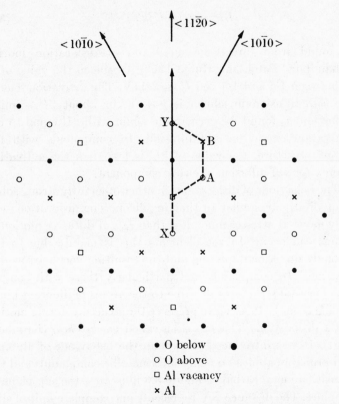

FIG. 3.3. A drawing of the atomic positions projected onto the slip plane of sapphire (Al$_2$O$_3$), after M. L. Kronberg.

make a diffusion-like jump at the core of the dislocation. The motion of the dislocation will then be a thermally activated process as in silicon.

The relation between the velocity of motion of the individual dislocations over small distances in a crystal, and the simultaneous motion of high numbers over large distances which occurs when a crystal yields, is still unsettled. However, the above remarks on the motion of individual dislocations in crystals of inherently strong solids, enable us to deduce the following points about their mechanical behaviour. At low temperatures they are always brittle and will be very strong with strengths governed by the theoretical shear strength *provided* the surfaces are very carefully prepared and they contain no internal flaws or fissures. Small samples yield higher average strengths experimentally because they cannot contain deep flaws. However, they are not inherently stronger than big pieces and there is no theoretical reason why large very strong pieces cannot be made. This has been achieved in the cases of sapphire and silicon. The strength at low temperature is independent of the presence of dislocations.

At high temperatures, dislocation motion will become observably fast and the materials become plastic when the dislocations can move sufficiently rapidly to allow a crystal to deform in response to an applied strain rate, $\dot{\varepsilon}$. We can write

$$\dot{\varepsilon} = \rho b \bar{v} \tag{3.4}$$

where ρ is the dislocation density, b the Burgers vector, and $\bar{v}$ the average dislocation velocity.† Since v will obey an equation of the form of (3.3) we see that the temperature for the onset of plasticity will be influenced by the dislocation density and will be higher if fewer dislocations are present (e.g. in whiskers). The observed flow stress will be extremely strain-rate and temperature dependent and hence the ductile-brittle transition temperature will depend on the mode and rate of stressing. Creep by the motion of dislocations will then be observed as the ductile-brittle temperature is approached. There is consequently an incubation period for large scale plastic flow. Slip may lead to production

† v for an individual dislocation will obey an equation of the form (3.3) but $\bar{v}$ to be inserted in (3.4) will be governed by the number of dislocations which are mobile at any instant and by the interaction between these dislocations. This leads to the strain-rate depending on the shear stress to a different power from that governing the stress dependence of the velocity of an individual dislocation in a perfect crystal.

of cracks in a crystal and consequent fracture. A form of delayed failure due to slip must therefore be expected. Some values of U and m for different materials are collected in Table 3.1. The values for Ge and Si are deduced from measurements of

TABLE 3.1
Parameters controlling dislocation motion in strong solids

Material	Melting temperature (°C)	m (equation (3.3))	U eV/atom	U cation (eV/atom)	U anion (eV/atom)	T/T_M
Ge[a]	958	1·3–1·6	1·5–2·2	2·97		0·53
Si[a]	1450	1·4–1·5	2·2	$\sim$4		0·51
Al_2O_3[b]	2050	3–6[g]	3·7	5$\pm$0·5	6·6	0·65
TiC[c]	3150	2	2·3[f]			>0·4
TiO_2[d]	2640 decomposes	1·9	2·9	1·2	3·1	0·45[e]

U is the activation energy for motion of a dislocation. U_{cation} and U_{anion} are the activation energies for diffusion of the cation and anion respectively. T/T_M is the ratio of T to the melting temperature in absolute units where T is the temperature for the onset of plasticity in a tensile test at normal strain rates, $10^{-5}\,s^{-1} < \dot{\varepsilon} < 10^{-1}\,s^{-1}$.

(a) A. R. CHAUDHURI, J. R. PATEL, and L. G. RUBIN (1962). *J. appl. Phys.* **33**, 2736;
    M. N. KABLER (1963). *Phys. Rev.* **131**, 54.
    S. SCHÄFER (1967). *Phys. Stat. Solidi* **19**, 297. It is possible to distinguish between the values of m for screw and for edge dislocations.
(b) M. L. KRONBERG (1962). *J. Am. ceram. Soc.* **45**, 274.
(c) W. S. WILLIAMS (1964). *J. appl. Phys.* **35**, 1329. There is a marked dependence on stoichiometry. The values of U and of m apply to $TiC_{0\cdot9}$ at $T > 1050°C$ and strain rates of $\sim 4\times10^{-4}\,s^{-1}$.
(d) Values evaluated from creep experiments on material of stoichiometric composition. There is a marked dependence on stoichiometry. W. H. HIRTHE and J. O. BRITTAIN (1963). *J. Am. ceram. Soc.* **46**, 411.
(e) From bend tests: J. B. WACHTMAN, Jr. and L. H. MAXWELL (1954). *J. Am. ceram. Soc.* **37**, 291.
(f) Derived following P. HAASEN (1963). *The Relation between the Structure and Mechanical Properties of Metals*, p. 588, H.M.S.O., London.
(g) H. CONRAD (1965). *J. Am. ceram. Soc.* **48**, 195 and *Trans. Amer. Inst. min. metall. petrol. Engrs.* (1965). **233**, 819.

dislocation velocity. The values of U are about one-half the activation energy of self-diffusion. In these elements the temperature at which they become plastic in tensile tests at normal strain rates ($10^5-10^{-4}\,s^{-1}$) is about $T/T_M = 0.5$. For the other materials in Table 3.1 the values are deduced from measurement of the strain-rate and temperature dependence of the flow stress. In crystals of compounds the behaviour depends markedly upon the stoichiometric ratio. This is not important in sapphire where there is no large departure from stoichiometry. For materials such as rutile (TiO_2) it is very important—here oxygen deficiency raises the yield stress and hence raises the ductile-brittle transition temperature. The material can vary in composition from $TiO_{1.983}$ to TiO_2. In addition, oxygen deficiency alters the activation energy for creep—since the material can be reduced at low oxygen pressures there is clearly an *atmosphere dependence*. In carbides, and, of course, in intermetallic compounds, the solidus temperature depends on composition and this must be allowed for in assessing at what fraction of the melting point a ductile-brittle transition will occur. In addition to departures from stoichiometry, all of the materials discussed in this section have their yield stresses raised by impurities.

Crystals of inherently strong solids offer much promise as the reinforcing material in fibre-reinforced composites (Chapter 5). This is because dislocations do not affect the strength at low temperatures so that there will be no loss of strength if these are introduced, provided the surface perfection of the crystals is maintained. Since all inherently strong solids possess large Mohs' hardness numbers they will be undamaged by the commonest abrasive fortuitously present (silica). Metal whiskers and carefully prepared crystals of ionic solids such as magnesium oxide can be prepared with very few mobile dislocations. They can then be extremely strong but they lose their strength drastically if dislocations are introduced, producing extremely large yield drops and catastrophic failure. They are thus not worth considering as a reinforcement although isolated crystals are very strong.

Polycrystals of the inherently strong solids are always expected to be weaker than monocrystals. If flawless specimens of theoretical density are produced with very smooth surfaces then under stress, concentrated forces will be produced at grain boundaries due to anisotropy of the elastic constants. It is not easy to produce pore-free polycrystals because of the high melting points. This has only recently been attained for magnesium oxide and then only by recrystallizing a single crystal. At temperature above $0 \cdot 5$ T_M where plastic flow is possible in single crystals, there are additional modes of deformation in polycrystals. These are Nabarro–Herring creep by the emission and absorption of vacancies from grain boundaries (Nabarro 1948, Herring 1950), and by grain boundary sliding. The former

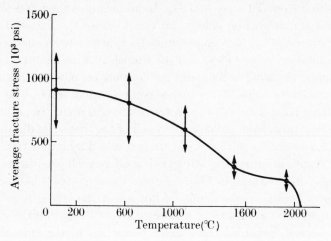

Fig. 3.4. The average dynamic fracture stress of sapphire whiskers as a function of temperature. The arrows show the standard deviation. The data is replotted from S. S. Brenner (1962). *J. appl. Phys.* **33**, 33.

is well understood in principle and the creep rate is inversely proportional to the square of the grain size. The exact mechanism of the latter is not known. It may be due to the presence of an impure glassy phase at grain boundaries (it certainly is in many commercial ceramics) or it may be an inherent property of the material. The plastic properties of polycrystals are, like those of single crystals, very sensitive to impurities. A useful review of the physical effects governing the strength of polycrystalline ceramics is given by Davidge and Evans (1970).

In considering inherently strong solids as reinforcing materials the theoretical strength can be regarded as the ultimate attainable at absolute temperatures below about $0 \cdot 5$ T_M and above this

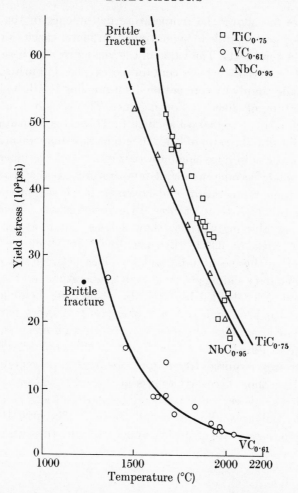

FIG. 3.5. Temperature dependence of the yield stress of some polycrystalline metallic carbides. The data is from A. Kelly and D. J. Rowcliffe (1967). *J. Am. ceram, Soc.* **50**, 253.

temperature the yield stress for plastic flow will be the limiting quantity. The transition between these two regimes is not well understood. Figure 3.4 shows the measured fracture stress of small sapphire crystals as a function of temperature. High strengths ($\sim$200 000 psi or 1·4 GN m^{-2}) are still obtainable in short time tests at 1900°C.

Figure 3.5 shows the temperature dependence of the yield stress for polycrystals of some transition metal carbides determined in bend tests. The value of the yield stress in these commercial materials, which contain pores and impurities and were made simply by conventional hot pressing is still high at a temperature of 2000°C. For instance $TiC_{0.75}$ shows a yield strength of over 20 000 psi at 2000°C. This gives a yield stress to specific gravity ratio of 0.5×10^4 psi at this temperature.

Dislocations in pure single crystals of most of the inherently strong solids become mobile at temperatures greater than half the melting temperature and so creep in these materials is expected at high temperatures. In addition static fatigue can occur; e.g. alumina whiskers show delayed failure at temperatures as little as 630°C (Brenner 1962). In impure ceramic materials or those containing a glassy phase between the grains, grain boundary sliding occurs at high temperature and the creep behaviour is controlled by impurities. The creep behaviour of alumina has been reviewed by Stokes (1964). In very pure and dense polycrystalline alumina Nabarro–Herring creep controls the rate of flow between 1200°C and 1800°C (Folweiler 1961). The stresses required to produce creep in a polycrystal are larger than those necessary to produce creep, at the same strain rate, in a single crystal. There may be an advantage, therefore, in using polycrystalline material. However, Nabarro–Herring creep produces a rate of strain $\dot{\varepsilon}$ under a tensile stress σ given by

$$\dot{\varepsilon} = \frac{k\sigma}{d^2}$$

where k is a constant proportional to the diffusion coefficient and inversely proportional to the temperature and d is the grain diameter. Thus small grain sizes will be expected to show the largest creep rates. It was pointed out above that in order to provide strength at a low temperature, in a polycrystalline specimen of an inherently strong solid there are advantages in decreasing the grain size. This is incompatible with provision of the greatest resistance to Nabarro–Herring creep.

3.3. Independent slip systems and slip flexibility

The presence of mobile dislocations in a crystal reduces the strength much below the ideal strength. At the same time dislocations can relieve stress concentrations by plastic flow and hence reduce the notch sensitivity of a material. In order to reduce an arbitrary stress concentration an arbitrary change of shape must take place. In many crystals the change of shape which can be produced by dislocation motion on the observed glide systems is quite limited and therefore particular applied stresses cannot produce plastic flow. In such crystals an arbitrary applied stress may not produce yield. We may then have a situation in which the individual crystals of a material may undergo plastic flow and show work-hardening so that the yield stress can be raised to give a stronger material, whilst at the same time a polycrystal is rendered more prone to failure by slip in some of the grains within it. This type of behaviour is shown by many ionic solids and by some of the body-centred cubic metals. The observation of slip in single crystals is then not sufficient either to ensure notch insensitivity or polycrystalline ductility. These two properties are then only observed at very much higher temperatures than slip is observed in single crystals. Materials in which such behaviour is found are not ideal structural materials for they are weakened at all temperatures by plastic flow and at the same time this plastic yielding does not ensure notch insensitivity as it does in a typical metal. We will now discuss these statements in detail.

A glide system is characterized by a slip plane (or glide plane) and a slip direction in this plane. The observed glide systems for a number of crystals are listed in Appendix B, Table 1. There is always a multiplicity determined by the point group of the crystal. All those combinations of slip plane and slip direction which must arise from the point group symmetry of the crystal if one slip plane and one slip direction are given, are called the family of slip systems. Thus crystals with the rock-salt structure glide on $\{110\}$ in the direction $\langle 1\bar{1}0 \rangle$. There is one slip direction in each slip plane. (No distinction is drawn between slip in $[1\bar{1}0]$

and in the reverse direction [$\bar{1}$10].) There are six planes of the type {110} and hence six physically different glide systems in the {110} $\langle 1\bar{1}0 \rangle$ family.

The primary slip direction of all crystals is in the direction of the shortest lattice translation vector of the Bravais lattice.† The explanation of the slip planes is less clear; the choice depends on details of the structure of the core of a dislocation. In metals the observed slip plane is the one of densest packing and hence of largest spacing.

A crystal can undergo a general change of shape (without change of volume) solely by slip, provided it possesses five independent glide systems. A glide system is independent of other physically distinct ones if it produces a change of shape which cannot be produced by appropriate combinations of various amounts of shear on the others. The proof that five are necessary is then as follows. A general strain is described by the tensor ε_{ij} with components

$$
\begin{pmatrix}
\varepsilon_{11} & \varepsilon_{12} & \varepsilon_{13} \\
\varepsilon_{21} & \varepsilon_{22} & \varepsilon_{23} \\
\varepsilon_{31} & \varepsilon_{32} & \varepsilon_{33}
\end{pmatrix}
$$

The tensor is symmetric so $\varepsilon_{12} = \varepsilon_{21}$ etc., and there are six independent components. If there is no change in volume $\varepsilon_{11} + \varepsilon_{22} + \varepsilon_{33} = 0$ and hence the number of independent components is reduced to five. Glide on a single system changes just

† This rule is never disobeyed except for a few metal crystals showing an order-disorder transformation when it is not followed in the ordered state. (The ordering energy is low.) Only one slip direction is observed if a general change of shape is possible with the most commonly observed family. If a general change of shape is not possible with this family (e.g. in rutile the direction [001] is unique lying along the tetragonal axis and hence an extension normal to this axis for instance could not be produced with this glide direction) then other slip directions are observed. The other directions, e.g. [10$\bar{1}$] in rutile or $\langle 11\bar{2}3 \rangle$ in hexagonal metals, are always in the direction of larger lattice translation vectors but these directions are such that dislocations with corresponding Burgers vectors cannot certainly reduce their energy by dissociating into dislocations with smaller lattice translation vectors (Frank and Nicholas 1953).

one component of the strain tensor independently of the others.†
So five independent slip systems are needed to produce the five
independent components of the strain tensor. This was first
pointed out by von Mises in 1928.

All the families of slip systems in Table 1 of Appendix B can
be tested for the number of independent systems which they

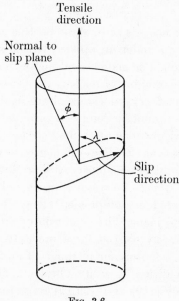

FIG. 3.6.

yield. The results are collected in Table 2 of Appendix B. A
simple way of testing for the number of independent systems
has been given by Groves and Kelly (1963).

If a crystal does not possess five independent systems there
are certain directions in which it cannot be extended or compressed or certain orientations of shear stress which cannot

† For example, if the axes of the tensor are taken so that X_1 is parallel to
the glide plane normal and X_2 parallel to the slip direction then a small glide
strain of amount $\Delta\gamma$ is described by the tensor components

$$\varepsilon_{12} = \varepsilon_{21} = \frac{\Delta\gamma}{2},$$

all other components being zero.

produce glide. These are usually easily recognizable. Figure 3.6 shows a rod-shaped crystal with the slip plane normal making an angle ϕ with the axis of the rod and the slip direction making an angle λ with this axis. An increment of shear strain $\Delta\gamma$ on such a glide system produces an increment of tensile strain along the axis of the rod given by

$$\varepsilon = \Delta\gamma \cos\phi \cos\lambda. \qquad (3.5)$$

If either $\cos\phi$ or $\cos\lambda$ is zero, shear on this glide system produces no extension under an applied tensile stress parallel to the axis of the rod. The geometrical factor in equation (3.5) is identical to the Schmid factor relating tensile stress and resolved shear stress in a single crystal. Hence, the recognition of directions in which crystals cannot be deformed becomes the same as that of recognizing orientations of applied stress which produce no resolved shear stress on the glide system in question. For instance, the $\{110\}\langle1\bar{1}0\rangle$ family in a cubic crystal produces just two independent glide systems. A crystal slipping only on this family cannot be extended or compressed along $\langle111\rangle$ nor sheared parallel to a $\{100\}$ plane. The condition of zero resolved shear stress is only exactly obeyed for a precisely oriented applied stress over an indefinitely small range of angles. However, in practice this condition is easily obtained. Magnesium oxide crystals show only $\{110\}\langle1\bar{1}0\rangle$ slip at room temperature and if compressed parallel to $\langle111\rangle$ shatter without plastic flow. (Hulse, Copley, and Pask 1963.) Similarly, hexagonal crystals such as zinc and graphite can be pulled apart normal to the basal plane without any plastic flow on this plane.

The deformation of a polycrystal can only proceed without the production of voids, provided each grain can undergo a general strain so as to conform to the applied strain and the constraints imposed by its neighbouring grains. Crystals listed in Table 2 of Appendix B which do not possess five independent systems, either with one family or a combination of families, are never ductile in polycrystalline form (small plastic elongations can be obtained if there is a marked preferred orientation or if twinning can occur).

The formal possession of five independent systems does not ensure polycrystalline ductility. It is a necessary but not sufficient condition. The five systems must, of course, be operative at comparable shear stresses. Secondly, they must be available throughout each grain. This second condition involves the idea of *slip flexibility*. This is the ability of a crystal to undergo small arbitrary amounts of slip simultaneously on five independent systems in any small volume of the crystal. For a crystal to do this, dislocations must be able to cross slip easily (so that with a given slip vector a variety of shears on planes parallel to this slip vector can be produced) and slip bands must interpenetrate, so that dislocations moving on one system are not blocked by those on another. Each operative slip direction can at most produce two independent slip systems (Groves and Kelly 1963). The requirement of slip flexibility is that each slip direction be able to do this within any arbitrary small volume of the crystal. The volume in question seems from experience to be a region a few cubic microns in size.

Examples can be found where one or other of the two properties necessary for polycrystalline ductility is lacking. Johnston, Davies, and Stoloff (1965) have produced quite striking proof of the importance of slip flexibility. In FeCo-2 per cent V alloys, with a body-centred cubic lattice, ordering suppresses wavy glide and hence slip flexibility and immediately reduces the ductility by a large amount. Ordering, in fact, reduces the flow stress of the material, but on ordering, polycrystals become much less ductile even though the number of independent slip systems is five, independent of the degree of order. An example of a material with very flexible slip but an insufficient number of independent systems is cesium bromide (Johnson and Pask 1964). Single crystals slip on $\{110\}$ in $\langle 001 \rangle$. There are two slip planes common to each slip direction. This family of slip systems provides only three independent systems. At all temperatures slip is flexible and cross-slip occurs frequently between the two $\{110\}$ planes with a common $\langle 001 \rangle$ direction. Polycrystals are always brittle because even unlimited slip flexibility with only three $\langle 001 \rangle$ slip vectors provides only three independent slip systems.

Many non-metallic materials behave like magnesium oxide, in which the number of independent slip systems and the degree of flexibility change with temperature. At low temperatures, less than 350°C, slip occurs only on {110} planes. The slip direction is $\langle 1\bar{1}0 \rangle$. Only two independent slip systems are available. Above 350°C, slip can occur on {001} planes with slip direction $\langle 1\bar{1}0 \rangle$ and this is produced by dislocations cross slipping from {110} planes. There are then five independent systems. However, the shear stress required to produce slip on {001} planes is much larger than that to produce it on {110}. Polycrystals show only very limited extensions of 1 per cent or so before failure. The intersection of {110} slip bands in single crystals is not possible. Cracks are produced where {110} slip bands are impeded either by other slip bands or at grain boundaries. The ratio of the shear stress required for slip on {001} to that required for slip on {110} falls as the temperature is raised. It is about ten at 350°C and three at 1200°C (Hulse *et al.* 1963). At 1500°C the two resolved shear stresses are equal. Slip lines are very wavy and five independent systems are available. There is still not sufficient interpenetrability of slip. Only at 1700°C can slip bands interpenetrate so that the five independent systems are available in any arbitrary volume of the crystal. Polycrystals are then fully ductile and behave like specimens of pure face-centred cubic metals (Day and Stokes 1966). Inherently strong solids are all expected to behave qualitatively like magnesium oxide.

3.4. Change of shape due to dislocation climb

At temperatures above that at which diffusion of atoms either through the lattice or along dislocations becomes possible, a change of shape may occur in a crystal due to dislocation climb. Dislocation climb is necessarily accompanied by a local dilatation, but a change of shape of a crystal without change in volume could occur provided sets of dislocations with different Burgers vectors are able to climb together.

During climb the change of shape produced is an extension (or contraction) of the crystal in a direction parallel to the Burgers vector b. The principal strains produced by climb over an area A

per unit volume of a crystal by dislocations with Burgers vector b parallel to the X_1 axis is $\varepsilon_{11} = Ab$, all other components being zero. The dilatation is hence also Ab. Climb parallel to one Burgers vector changes just one component of the strain tensor independently of the others. If n climb systems, each characterized by a different Burgers vector, operate together the condition that there be no change of volume is

$$A_1b_1 + A_2b_2 + A_3b_3 + \ldots A_nb_n = 0 \qquad (3.6)$$

If the volume of the crystal can change, the infinitesimal strain tensor has six independent components, so under this condition six independent climb systems are needed to produce a general strain. To produce a general change of shape without change of volume by climb alone, six independent climb systems are still needed, because of the condition (3.6).

The reason why six independent climb systems are needed to produce a general strain with zero dilatation while only five independent glide systems would be necessary to produce the same type of deformation is that in the case of glide, operation of each glide system automatically produces a non-dilatational strain so that the condition of zero dilatation is automatically satisfied. In the case of climb the prescription of zero dilatation imposes six conditions and so requires the presence of six independent climb systems (Groves and Kelly 1969).

Crystals of many inherently strong solids such as β-quartz, sapphire, beryllia, and graphite possess such limited numbers of glide systems that even at high temperature a general change of shape cannot occur by glide alone. For instance, the total number of independent glide systems in quartz at temperatures above one-half the melting temperature is only two, and in alumina at eight-tenths of the melting temperature, four only are available. Extensive plastic deformation does occur in such materials at high temperature, and climb of dislocations makes an essential contribution to this in many cases, by permitting a general change of shape to occur. The intermetallic NiAl, which has the structure of CsBr, is another important example of a material in which this occurs. In the case of β-quartz, climb by dislocations with three different Burgers vectors is needed to allow a general change in shape.

3.5. Stress concentrations in polycrystals

We have considered the ability of a crystal to undergo plastic flow to relieve constraints due to applied stresses. There are many obvious ways in which stresses can be concentrated in polycrystals. Thermal expansion in non-cubic crystals is anisotropic. Grains must accommodate the different thermal expansion of their neighbours. Changes in temperature induce strains proportional to the differences in thermal expansion coefficient in a given direction. Such differences can be as large as $55 \times 10^{-6}/°C$, so that a change of temperature of $100°C$ produces a strain of 0·5 per cent over certain temperature ranges. If such stresses cannot be relieved by plastic flow brittle fracture may occur. If they are relieved by plastic flow thermal fatigue on repeated cycling must be expected.

The inherently strong solids often have high melting temperatures and complicated crystal structures containing a variety of atomic species. These properties lead to the presence of voids and to a slow approach to chemical equilibrium so that concentration gradients are present. Voids act as stress concentrators and concentration gradients lead to elastic inhomogeneities.

Localized stresses can arise in polycrystals even of cubic materials due to a difference, (ΔE) in the elastic stiffness (E) of neighbouring crystals in different directions. The exact magnitude of these in a particular case depends on the shape of the crystal boundary. For a grain size d, and radius of curvature ρ the concentrated stress when a stress σ_a is applied will be

$$\sigma \approx \sigma_a (\Delta E / E) \, (d/\rho)^{1/2}. \qquad (3.7)$$

Values of $\Delta E / E$ can be appreciable, e.g. a value of two is not uncommon.

For illustrative purposes we may note from (3.7) that if failure occurs when the concentrated stress reaches some fixed fraction

α of the Young's modulus, then the observed failure strain ε_f which is equal to (σ_a/E) will be given from (3.7) by

$$\varepsilon_f = \frac{\alpha}{\Delta E/E} \sqrt{(\rho/d)}. \tag{3.8}$$

This equation predicts that the failure strain will be independent of the magnitude of the elastic constants but sensitive inversely to the anisotropy of elastic constants. If ρ does not depend on d, ε_f will vary inversely with the square root of the grain size—such is often found in practice for polycrystals of inherently strong solids but may arise from a number of other causes.

The stress concentration due to the above effects cannot be eliminated without sufficient slip flexibility. It must be emphasized that when slip is not flexible, a small amount of slip in a few grains within a polycrystal, rather than relieving stress, actually enhances stress concentrations because a shear crack is produced. The stress concentrating effect of such a crack is similar to that of the crack under tension (discussed in sections 2.2 to 2.4) and so is reduced if the grain size is small because the crack length is limited to one grain diameter. Stresses due to difference in thermal expansion and to difference in elastic constants also decrease in magnitude with decrease in grain size (see equation (3.8)). Polycrystals of an inherently strong solid will therefore always be less strong than single crystals, but at low temperatures the strength will be increased by decreasing the grain size and producing a preferred orientation.

This is well illustrated by the properties of fibres of boron produced by decomposition of boron chloride by hydrogen on to a tungsten wire (Talley 1959) see section 6.2.3. There has been some controversy over the crystalline texture of boron filaments but the presence of the β-rhombohedral structure appears certain, with an extremely small crystallite size, which may be as small as 20 Å. This does not constitute the whole of the filament and the rest is composed of an 'amorphous' or 'glassy' arrangement so that the properties are homogeneous on a scale of size large compared to 20 Å. The structure prevents plastic flow at low stresses. The strength of boron filaments depends on the length tested, as in all brittle materials, but average strengths of as much as 4·5 GN m^{-2} (650 000 psi) are obtained with a standard deviation of ∼1 GN m^{-2}.

Similarly, high strength graphite fibres—see for example Watt (1970)—show a very small crystal size and a very marked preferred orientation. Speaking roughly there are two types: high modulus fibres of strength ∼2 GN m^{-2} and with Young's modulus 420 GN m^{-2} and strong fibres of strength 3·5 GN m^{-2} and modulus 220 GN m^{-2}. In high modulus fibres, small crystallites are present, of dimensions in the basal plane (L_a) ∼ 80 Å and normal to this ∼60 Å (see Fig. 6.3). The preferred orientation is very marked with ⟨0001⟩ normal to the axis of the fibre in nearly 100 per cent of the volume—see section 6.2.5.

3.6. Ductile failure

Normal metal crystals contain many dislocations and are ductile over a very wide temperature range. Other crystals become ductile at high temperature. Above a fairly well-defined stress, the yield stress, which depends on the material, the elastic constants, the grain size, temperature, and dislocation arrangement, dislocations in these materials can move and multiply. Under uniaxial tension this will immediately lead to failure unless the material shows some work-hardening, i.e. an increase in the stress required to produce further plastic flow.

Consider a rod of cross-sectional area A, which is being extended plastically. Let the instantaneous load supported be F. Then for stability in the tensile test we must have $dF/dl > 0$ where l is the length. This sets a condition on the rate of work-hardening necessary for stability. $F = \sigma A$ where σ is the tensile flow stress, and the condition for stability is

$$\sigma \, dA + A \, d\sigma > 0.$$

In terms of true tensile strain, ε, this can be written

$$\frac{d\sigma}{d\varepsilon} > \sigma, \qquad (3.9)$$

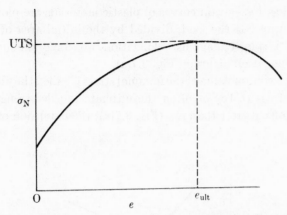

FIG. 3.7(a). A plot of the nominal tensile stress (σ_N) against elongation for a typical ductile metal plastically deformed in uniaxial tension. After an elongation greater than e_{ult} the elongation is no longer uniform throughout the specimen. The maximum nominal stress is called the ultimate tensile stress (UTS).

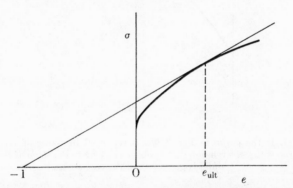

FIG. 3.7(b). If the curve in Fig. 3.7(a) is replotted in terms of true tensile stress (σ) against elongation, the true stress corresponding to the UTS is found as the point where the tangent to the curve passes through the point -1 on the elongation axis. This is the graphical interpretation of the relation (3.10).

since $d\varepsilon = -dA/A$. In terms of elongation $e, = (l-l_0)/l_0$, we have

$$\frac{d\sigma}{de} > \frac{\sigma}{1+e} \tag{3.10}$$

where l_0 is the original length. The condition (3.10) is called Considère's relation.

Tensile stress–strain curves of plastic materials are plotted in various ways. If the load, divided by the initial area of cross-section, is plotted against elongation we have the nominal stress-elongation diagram, Fig. 3.7(a).

The maximum value of the nominal stress is called the ultimate tensile stress (UTS) or often the ultimate tensile strength. At elongations greater than e_{ult} (Fig. 3.7(a)) the extension of a rod

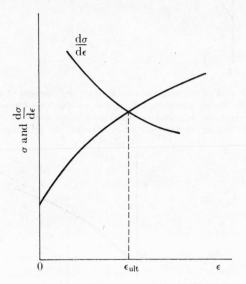

FIG. 3.7(c). If the curve in Fig. 3.7(a) is replotted in terms of true stress against true strain the relation (3.9) is obeyed so long as the slope of the curve ($d\sigma/d\varepsilon$) is greater than the true stress.

is no longer uniform along its length and necking occurs. Necking will continue until the material is drawn down to a point in fully ductile material. Most materials will not neck to a point unless extremely pure. Fracture occurs in the neck. Equations (3.10) and (3.9) are interpreted graphically in Figs. 3.7(b) and (c), respectively.

Although the nominal stress passes through a maximum during a tensile test, the true stress, i.e. load divided by actual area, does not necessarily do so and usually does not do so in fact.

The capacity for work-hardening of a material depends on temperature. For most metals the largest flow stress produced by extensive plastic flow is about $E/100$, where E is Young's modulus.

Ductile materials such as the common face-centred cubic metals and iron can have their yield strength increased by two orders of magnitude by large plastic deformation at low temperatures ($T \leqslant 0.35\ T_{\mathrm{M}}$; this temperature depends markedly on purity in the range up to 100 ppm). The greatest values of yield stress are produced by wire drawing. The nature of work-hardening and of the cold work state has been extensively studied, but the details are still obscure. The greatest contribution to work-hardening undoubtedly comes from the elastic interaction between dislocations. Without making detailed assumptions we can assume that in a face-centred cubic metal crystal the yield stress in shear is given by

$$\tau = \alpha G b \sqrt{(\rho)}, \qquad (3.11)$$

where $\alpha \approx 0.2$, and $\rho =$ dislocation density (see Nabarro, Basinski, and Holt 1964). It is then interesting to speculate what dislocation densities would be needed to produce a yield stress equal to the theoretical shear stress for a perfect crystal. Putting $\tau = G/20$ in the last equation, we obtain $\rho \sim 10^{18}$ m^{-2} for a typical metal. This is a very large dislocation density; it requires every tenth atom to be at the centre of a dislocation. Such large densities have not been observed. A dislocation line in a metal has an energy of about 5eV per atom plane threaded; this will be reduced by about 50 per cent when so many dislocations are present. A dislocation density of 10^{18} m^{-2} then implies a stored energy of at least 1.55×10^{9} J m^{-3} or 2×10^{5} J kg^{-1} for a metal of density 7.5×10^{3} kg m^{-3}. This value is very large compared to the elastic strain energy of a crystal stressed to the theoretical value of $G/20$ ($\sim 6 \times 10^{3}$ J kg^{-1} for $G \sim 4.5 \times 10^{10}$ N m^{-2}). It is about a tenth of the heat of sublimation. It seems unlikely that such values of the yield stress can be achieved by work-hardening alone.

The efficacy of ductile materials in engineering structure

derives from their ability to deform plastically when highly stressed so that accidental overload does not weaken a structure. Equations (3.9) and (3.10) show that if the flow stress of a ductile material is increased this capacity will not be maintained unless the rate of work-hardening is increased accordingly. If the flow stress is increased to $E/100$ then the rate of work-hardening must be at least 1 per cent of E to maintain stability according to (3.9). In high strength aluminium alloys this condition is not easy to attain at room temperature, and it is one of the factors affecting the properties of very high strength steels (section 4.5).

At temperatures above $0.5\,T_M$, where T_M is the melting temperature, the flow stress of a metal depends markedly upon the strain rate as well as upon the strain. Conditions of stability then affect the elongation which is possible under conditions when the metal creeps (section 4.7). To deal with materials in which the flow stress depends on both strain and strain rate is complicated (see for instance Campbell (1967)). One can see the principle by supposing flow stress to depend only on strain rate so that $\sigma = \sigma(\dot{\varepsilon})$. If a rod of such a material of cross-sectional area A is flowing under constant load F

$$F = \sigma A = \sigma(\dot{\varepsilon})A = \sigma(-\dot{A}/A)A. \qquad (3.12)$$

If stress depends on strain rate, i.e. on $-(\dot{A}/A)$ to a power less than 1†, the deformation is unstable since $-\dot{A}$, the rate of decrease of area, is larger for smaller areas of cross-section and any chance diminution in area will be accentuated with increasing strain.

---

† So then $\sigma = K\,\dot{\varepsilon}^n$ say. The rate-dependence of the flow stress of most metals at temperatures above $0.5\,T_M$ is such that $n \ll 1$, e.g. for copper at 900°C, $n \sim 1/12$. Such materials are unstable in creep in the absence of static work-hardening effects. Campbell also considers the rate of necking, i.e. the rate of accentuation of the differences in cross-section of the specimen. The interesting paradox emerges that the more unstable the material (small values of n) the longer the strain before the differences in cross-section attain a certain chosen value.

REFERENCES

S. S. BRENNER (1962). *J. appl. Phys.* **33**, 33.

J. D. CAMPBELL (1967), *J. Mech. Phys. Solids* **15**, 359.

A. R. CHAUDHURI, J. R. PATEL, and L. G. RUBIN (1962). *J. appl. Phys.* **33**, 2736.

R. W. DAVIDGE and A. G. EVANS (1970). *Mater. Sci. and Eng.* **6**, 281.

R. B. DAY and R. J. STOKES (1966). *J. Am. ceram. Soc.* **49**, 345.

R. C. FOLWEILER (1961). *J. appl. Phys.* **32**, 773.

F. C. FRANK and J. F. NICHOLAS (1953). *Phil. Mag.* **44**, 1213.

G. W. GROVES and A. KELLY (1963). *Phil. Mag.* **8**, 877.

—— and A. KELLY (1969). *Phil. Mag.* **19**, 977.

P. HAASEN (1957). *Acta metall.* **5**, 588.

C. HERRING (1950). *J. appl. Phys.* **21**, 437.

C. O. HULSE, S. M. COPLEY, and J. A. PASK (1963). *J. Am. ceram. Soc.* **46**, 317.

L. D. JOHNSON and J. A. PASK (1964). *J. Am. ceram. Soc.* **47**, 437.

T. L. JOHNSTON, R. G. DAVIES, and N. S. STOLOFF (1965). *Phil. Mag.* **12**, 305.

M. L. KRONBERG (1957). *Acta metall.* **5**, 507.

F. P. MALLINDER and B. A. PROCTOR (1966). *Phil. Mag.* **13**, 917.

F. R. N. NABARRO (1948). *Rep. Conf. Strength of Solids*, p. 75, Physical Society, London.

—— Z. S. BASINSKI, and D. B. HOLT (1964). *Adv. Phys.* **13**, 193.

G. L. PEARSON, W. T. READ, Jr., and W. L. FELDMANN (1957). *Acta metall.* **5**, 181.

W. T. SANDERS (1962). *Phys. Rev.* **128**, 1540.

R. J. STOKES (1964). *Microstructure of Ceramic Materials*, p. 41, U.S. Dept. of Commerce, National Bureau of Standards, Washington D.C.

C. P. TALLEY (1959). *J. appl. Phys.* **30**, 1114.

R. VON MISES (1928). *Z. angew. Math. Mech.* **8**, 161.

J. B. WACHTMANN, Jr. and L. H. MAXWELL (1954). *J. Am. ceram. Soc.* **37**, 2911; and ibid. (1959) **42**, 433.

W. WATT (1970). *Proc. R. Soc.* A**319**, 5.

A. R. C. WESTWOOD and N. H. MACMILLAN (1972). Environment-sensitive Hardness of Non-metals. In *Science of Hardness Testing.* (Ed. A. R. C. WESTWOOD), Chapman and Hall, London.

W. S. WILLIAMS (1964). *J. appl. Phys.* **35**, 1329.

4

STRONG METALS

METALS and their alloys are the principal strong materials used in engineering today. They can be produced easily in both high and low strength forms and in all of these the strengths are highly reproducible. Austenitic (face-centred cubic) stainless steel can be used to contain liquid helium at temperatures close to absolute zero and a similar material can be used in tension to support a stress of 140 MN m^{-2} (20 000 psi) for more than 100 hours at over 500°C.

Face-centred cubic metals and alloys are distinguished by low values of τ_{max}/G. This means that the theoretical strains are not high compared with those of other materials (Chapter 1) but dislocations are always freely mobile. The high value of σ_{max}/τ_{max} makes cleavage very difficult or impossible except under corrosive conditions. Face-centred cubic metals and alloys exhibit typical metallic mechanical properties at all temperatures. The commonly used body-centred cubic metals do also at higher temperatures, but at absolute temperatures below about $0 \cdot 2 \, T_M$ (T_M = melting temperature) dislocations become much more difficult to move (see for example Conrad 1963). Whilst this effect is undoubtedly enhanced by the presence of interstitial elements, such as carbon and nitrogen, in solution, it is principally due to the Peierls stress becoming of importance at low temperatures.

Because of the non-directional nature of the interatomic binding forces in metals the energies of large-angle grain boundaries are smaller than the surface energy. (The value of the surface energy is typically about three times the energy of a large-angle boundary; see Inman and Tipler 1963.) The common crystals structures (f.c.c. and b.c.c.) show slip on five independent slip systems. These two properties of metals lead to their being useful and readily fabricable in polycrystalline form, and in this state they can be subjected to almost unlimited plastic deformation in compression.

With the exception of aluminium, the common metals are produced in their strongest usable form as cold-drawn wires. Only whisker crystals exceed these in strength. The strongest aluminium alloy known to the author has a strength of 760 MN m^{-2} (110 000 psi) (Nock and Hunsicker 1963). The strengths of strong metal wires are listed in Appendix A, Table 4. These are strengths developed in uniaxial tension. They should be compared with values of $2\tau_{max}$ from Table 1.5. $2\tau_{max}$ represents a lower limit to present-day theoretical estimates of the greatest strength expected in uniaxial tension. The strength of 0·9 per cent C steel wire approaches one-third of the theoretical value. that of β-titanium alloy wire one-quarter (taking G' for β-titanium as 42 GN m^{-2} (6×10^6 psi) and $\tau_{max}/G = 0·11$). For aluminium a strength of 760 MN m^{-2} (110 000 psi) is between 0·13 and 0·4 of the theoretical. The uncertainty arises because of the different possible estimates of the theoretical strength in this case. Tungsten wires attain a strength of one-tenth of the theoretical. All of these values are measured at room temperature. This temperature represents a significant fraction of the melting temperature for aluminium and it should be noted for aluminium that the lower estimate of τ_{max} is reduced at room temperature because of the effect of temperature on the theoretical strength (section 1.6).

The theoretical maximum strength of iron in tension ($2\tau_{max}$) is 14 GN m^{-2} (2×10^6 psi). This is equal to $E/15$ where E is Young's modulus of polycrystalline material. Strong wires show strengths of $E/50$. Large steel forgings can be produced today with values of the tensile strength of about $E/80$. Copper–beryllium alloys are available with strengths of $E/100$ and nimonic alloys at room temperature have strengths of $E/150$. For copper the theoretical maximum strength is about $E/50$ (this low value arises because of the small value of G' with respect to E for the noble metals (see Table 1.5). Such strong metal specimens can be produced in large pieces and are approximately isotropic as regards their strength showing these large values of the strength in all directions. At the present time strong metals are used at larger fractions of their theoretical strengths than any other engineering materials. (At room temperature glass-reinforced plastics are used at stresses up to $\frac{1}{100}$ of the value of Young's modulus of the glass and nylon fibres are used at a fraction of about $\frac{1}{24}$ of the theoretical breaking strength.)

Metals are amazingly versatile in the range of properties which can be produced. Nickel-base alloys can be designed so as to prevent more than 2 per cent creep elongation in 1000 hr under a stress of 61 MN m^{-2} (8800 psi) at a temperature of 980°C, i.e. bright red heat. This corresponds to a viscosity of greater than 3.7×10^{16} poise at a temperature corresponding to a fraction of 0.73 of the melting point. This is comparable with the viscosity of soda-lime glass at about 350°C (0.37 of the melting temperature).

The great versatility of metals is due to the large number of elements which are metallic. These dissolve at least small quantities of one another so that a rich variety of solid solutions may be made. The microstructure of metals is well understood and can be controlled by the use of phase changes to obtain the desired properties.

Since dislocations are freely mobile in the pure metals there is no question of an applied stress being concentrated at the tip of a crack so that the stress locally attains the theoretical fracture strength. Instead, plastic flow occurs and failure takes place by shear. High strength must therefore be obtained by preventing dislocation motion. The restriction of dislocation motion, however, may then lead to failure by brittle cracking. This is because the process of plastic flow itself can produce cracks in metals (e.g. Hahn, Averbach, Owen, and Cohen 1959) and because these, or those produced by other means, may spread catastrophically.

4.1. Fracture mechanics

A necessary condition for the rapid propagation of a long and sharp crack in an elastic body is that the energy–balance relation of section 2.3 be obeyed. This states that the elastic strain energy released as the crack advances (due to the body containing the crack becoming more deformable) must be at least equal to the energy required to carry out the processes occurring at the tip of the crack so that physical separation of new surfaces occurs. Following Irwin and Orowan we apply the same equation to a situation where some plastic flow occurs close to the crack tip by writing all of this latter energy as γ_p and letting γ_p replace 2γ in the equations of the type of (2.11) to (2.13). γ_p is the work which must be done in order to extend the area of the crack by unit amount and includes plastic work. We then obtain from equation (2.12), for a condition of plane stress

$$\sigma = \sqrt{(E\gamma_p/\pi c)}. \tag{4.1}$$

If rewritten as

$$\gamma_p = \pi c \sigma^2/E = G_c \tag{4.2}$$

this equation sets a limit to γ_p which must be exceeded to prevent unstable propagation of a crack of length $2c$ in a sheet under a working stress σ. The quantity G_c is taken as a criterion for the application of very strong metals and indicates what depth of notch can be tolerated in a material subject to a given stress. Acceptable values of γ_p for strong steels (strengths $\gtrsim 200\ 000$ psi) are between 100 and 1000 psi in (i.e. between $0 \cdot 17 \times 10^8$ and $1 \cdot 7 \times 10^8$ mJ m^{-2}). The higher value is about 10^5 times as large as the surface energy.

Values of γ_p are not easily measured and so the resistance to crack propagation of a material is often found by rewriting (4.2) as

$$\sigma\sqrt{(\pi c)} = K_c, \tag{4.3}$$

where K_c is called the critical stress intensity factor. It can be measured by introducing a thin sharp crack of length $2c$ into a material (say via a saw-cut) and then measuring the applied stress necessary to cause propagation of that crack. As the applied stress in such an experiment is increased from zero one sees by comparing equation (4.3) with (2.4), (2.6) or (2.15) that the stress at the tip of the crack increases with the applied stress σ. When a critical value is reached, which is a property of the material and of the state of stress, the crack propagates. K, the stress intensity factor has therefore an upper limit, K_c which is an important property of an engineering material.

From (4.2) we have

$$K_c = \sqrt{(EG_c)} \qquad (4.4)$$

and hence from measured values of K_c, values of G_c can be found. Values of K_c and of G_c for various materials are collected in Appendix A, Table 7.

To apply equations (4.1) to (4.4) the crack length $2c$ must be very small with respect to the dimensions of the specimen and the state of stress must be one of plane stress. For other conditions of stress, e.g. plane strain, torsion, etc., various numerical factors and Poisson ratios will be introduced into the relationship between K_c and G_c; in addition the formulae will be modified if the length $2c$ becomes comparable with any dimension of the specimen. Plastic flow occurs around the tip of the crack before and during propagation. The distance from the tip of the crack over which this occurs R_p, will of course depend upon the yield stress of the material σ_y. Provided the dimensions of the specimen are much larger than R_p then for conditions of plane stress, we shall have

$$R_p = \frac{K_c^2}{\pi \sigma_y^2} = \left(\frac{\sigma}{\sigma_y}\right)^2 \times c \qquad (4.5)$$

where σ is the applied stress. This equation follows from, for instance, (2.15) since K_c determines the upper limit to the stress at the tip of a crack. Equation (4.5) can be used to determine whether or not R_p, the radius of the plastic zone, is small with respect to the crack length and relevant specimen dimensions.†

† A clear and readable account of the mechanics of crack propagation is given by Irwin and Wells (1965); Wells (1967) gives an interesting personal account of the difficulties of establishing the concepts of fracture mechanics. Useful formulae and an account of experimental methods are given in *Fracture Toughness and its Applications*, American Society for Testing Materials, Philadelphia, (1965).

The above treatment applies to the opening of a crack by a tensile stress applied normal to its plane. Cracks may be opened in other ways, e.g. by a shear stress. Three modes are usually distinguished which are illustrated in Fig. 5.20. For each of these modes formulae of the form of equations (4.1) and (4.3) can be devised to give the conditions for rapid propagation.

The value of γ_p is controlled by the value of the maximum stress reached at the tip of a crack and by the value of the displacement necessary to produce fracture there (Cottrell 1963). In a strong metal the value of γ_p, and hence of G_c, can be much larger than the value of the surface energy because plastic flow occurs at the tip of a crack. The requirement of a large value of γ_p and the requirement of a large value of the yield stress for plastic flow are mutually contradictory. Thus, the conventional design of a very strong metal involves a compromise between large values of the strength and large values of the work of fracture. In the remainder of this chapter we describe what success has been obtained in producing strong metals with values of the work of fracture which are acceptable to the engineer.

It is first necessary to make a remark about the grain size, since metals are usually used in polycrystalline form. We do this in section 4.2. Section 4.3 deals with ways of restricting dislocation motion in metals, by means of atoms in solution and by precipitation-hardening. Section 4.4 deals with the work-hardening of metals strengthened by dispersions and the relation of this to fibre-reinforcement which is discussed in Chapter 5. Section 4.5 deals with strong steels, since these are the most widely used strong engineering materials, and section 4.6 deals with strong metal wires. Some remarks on metals used at high temperatures are made in section 4.7.

4.2. Grain size

Metals are used in polycrystalline form. The strength can be increased by decreasing the grain size. Many metals and alloys show a dependence of the tensile flow stress, σ_t, at a constant plastic strain, on the grain diameter (d) of the following form

$$\sigma_t = \sigma_0 + k\, d^{-1/2} \tag{4.6}$$

(Armstrong, Codd, Douthwaite, and Petch 1962). σ_0 depends upon temperature much more strongly than does k and increases with strain. k is largest at very small strains when the material shows a sharp yield point. After strains greater than a few per cent k is a constant for a given metal at a given temperature. The form of equation (4.6) arises from the condition necessary for propagation of slip from grain to grain in a polycrystalline metal and hence k is found to be larger, the smaller the number of slip systems observed in a material. When applied to initial yield, values of k range up to 19×10^4 Nm$^{-3/2}$ (6 kg mm$^{-3/2}$ or 1689 psi in$^{1/2}$); when used to describe the flow stress values of k up to 6×10^4 Nm$^{-3/2}$ (2 kg mm$^{-3/2}$ or 563·0 psi in$^{1/2}$) are found. The values are largest in materials which show dislocation locking by impurities and smallest in pure face-centred cubic metals.

An equation similar to (4.6) describes the variation of flow stress of lamellar structures with spacing of the two component lamellae (Cline and Lee (1970)) and also applies to distorted crystals containing low-angle boundaries and to subgrains; the value of k for subgrains is usually about one-half the appropriate value for the grains (Embury 1971). A number of theoretical explanations for equation (4.6) have been given, starting from the original one due to Petch (1953)—see also Hall (1951). These depend essentially on the idea of free slip in a single grain producing a pile-up of dislocations which can be viewed essentially as a type of shear crack, near the tip of which the concentrated stress depends upon the square root of the length of the crack (grain diameter) and falls off inversely as the square root of the distance from the tip of the crack (c.f. equations (2.6)). Modification of the formulae to take account of the small length of the slipped region have been given (Armstrong, Chou, Fisher, and Louat 1966).

We can take equation (4.6) as an empirical description of the effect of grain size on the strength of a polycrystalline specimen. Taking $k = 2$ kg mm$^{-3/2}$ (6×10^4 Nm$^{-3/2}$) an increase in σ_t of 100 kg mm^{-2} (1 GN m^{-2} or 142 000 psi) then requires a value of the grain diameter of $\sim$4000 Å, at most. Such small grain sizes are not usually obtained. The increase in free energy of a metal specimen with such a grain size is less than 2 cal cm^{-3} greater than the corresponding single crystal, so that a significant increase in strength by very marked grain refinement is possible.

In materials showing a ductile to brittle transition, such as ferritic steels, there are advantages in increasing the yield stress by decreasing the grain size because at the same time the tendency to brittle fracture is reduced (Petch 1958, Cottrell 1958).

4.3. Solution and precipitation strengthening

The detailed understanding of the yield stress of an alloy containing dispersed obstacles to dislocation motion which are located within the grains requires particular consideration of each alloy system. Since the highest strengths obtainable today in various alloy systems will be mentioned later we will confine ourselves here to generalities. All detailed treatments of solution- and precipitation-hardening (e.g. Fleischer and Hibbard 1963, Kelly and Nicholson, 1963, Brown and Ham 1971) stem from the ideas of Mott and Nabarro (1948).

Under the action of an applied shear stress an initially straight dislocation—the dotted line XX′ in Fig. 4.1(a)—is forced against the obstacles in its path. The dislocation is flexible with line tension T approximately equal to $Gb^2/2$, where b is the Burgers vector, and bends between the obstacles in such a way that the segments on either side of the obstacle meet at angle ϕ ($< \pi$). If τ is the shear stress, and the variation of line tension with orientation of the dislocation is ignored, the dislocation will lie on a set of circular arcs of radius

$$\rho = T/\tau b. \tag{4.7}$$

The total force exerted by the dislocation on one obstacle is seen from Fig. 4.1(a) to be

$$F = 2T \sin (\phi/2). \tag{4.8}$$

There will be a critical force at which the obstacle will break. If the critical breaking angle is ϕ_c then, since the force per unit length on the dislocation due to the applied stress is τb, the stress required to force the dislocation through the obstacle is, from (4.8)

$$\tau_c = \frac{T}{bl_o} 2 \sin (\phi_c/2) \approx \frac{Gb}{l_o} \sin (\phi_c/2) \qquad (4.9)$$

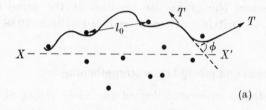

(a)

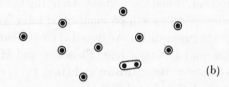

(b)

FIG. 4.1(a). An initially straight dislocation XX', is forced by an applied shear stress against a set of obstacles of spacing l_0. ϕ is the angle turned through at an obstacle. (b) The appearance of a slip plane after a dislocation has passed across it leaving Orowan loops about the particles.

where l_o is the spacing of the obstacles. The maximum value of τ_c is then

$$\tau_0 = Gb/l_o \qquad (4.10)$$

which corresponds to a critical breaking angle of π, and to the dislocation being bent into an unstable semicircular shape and passing between the obstacles leaving a loop of dislocation around each (Orowan 1948)—Fig. 4.1(b). The maximum strength is independent of the strength of the obstacle. Yield of polycrystalline pure metals occurs under a stress of less than 10^{-3} G, so, in order to produce an order of magnitude increase in yield strength, obstacles to dislocation motion must be spaced so that $l_o \leqslant 100$ b. This is a stringent requirement and is most easily accomplished by use of a solid solution which may be decomposed, if supersaturated, to form precipitates.

Quantitative evaluation of the flow stress of an alloy strengthened by discrete obstacles requires evaluation of equation (4.9). Except when $\phi_c \approx \pi$, the spacing of the obstacles along the dislocation line depends upon ϕ_c, i.e. upon the strength of the obstacle. For instance, for weak obstacles ($\sin \phi_c \sim \phi_c$)

$$\tau_c \approx (Gb/L)(\phi_c/2)^{3/2} \qquad (4.11)$$

and the effective obstacle spacing is $L(\phi_c/2)^{-1/2}$. The strength of the various obstacles usually varies in a given population, due to differences in size or position with respect to the dislocation slip plane. The latest treatment of dislocation–particle interaction takes these effects into account (Brown and Ham 1971).

The origin of the strength of the obstacle lies in the various ways in which the properties of such a particle differ from those of the solvent crystal, and in the existence of an interface between the particle and the solvent crystal which possesses a specific energy per unit area.

There is an interaction energy between a dislocation and the various obstacles which it meets. If the dislocation is stationary the interaction energy, U, is just the change in energy of the system of crystal plus dislocation if the inhomogeneity is removed and replaced by an undistorted array of solvent atoms. When U is known the force required to move a dislocation a distance dX normal to its length is dU/dX. We can distinguish then two types of barrier which produce long- or short-range interactions with a dislocation. Long-range interactions are those for which U varies when the dislocation line lies wholly outside the precipitate. For example, if a precipitate has a different atomic volume from the matrix then the change of energy due to introducing the precipitate into the crystal, due solely to the dilatation produced, falls off as $1/r$, where r is the separation of dislocation and precipitate (U clearly also depends on angular factors) (Cottrell and Bilby 1949). An example of short-range interaction would be an interaction between the precipitate and the dislocation core, e.g. in face-centred cubic metals the dislocation is split at its core into partial dislocations and the energy of the dislocation depends on the stacking fault energy of the material at the core. If the dislocation passes through a precipitate its energy is changed and U has a finite value. If the dislocation does not pass through the precipitate U is zero.

4.3.1. *Solution-hardening*

An increase in yield stress is produced by elements in solid solution. This is most marked when the individual solute elements produce elastic distortions in the host lattice which are markedly asymmetric, e.g. the strain field in a cubic host lattice may show tetragonal symmetry (Fleischer and Hibbard 1963). Substitutional atoms in cubic crystals produce spherically symmetric distortions and hence weak solution-hardening, and interstitial atoms in body-centred cubic metals produce a tetragonal distortion and hence very strong effects, e.g. carbon in martensite. The distinction, however, is not simply between interstitial and substitutional solutes.

When the solute atoms are atomically dispersed in solid solution the separation of the individual barriers is small and the interaction energy with an individual barrier is also small. The largest interaction energies will be between the dislocation and those solute atoms lying on the same or adjacent atomic planes. If N is the number of inhomogeneities per unit volume, and f the volume fraction, then for atomic obstacles, the number of these per unit area of slip plane, N_s, is equal to f/b^2 (b equals the atomic separation in a metal) and so even for values of f as small as 1 per cent the average separation of obstacles in the slip plane is only $10b$, and the breaking angle per obstacle governs the flow stress via equations (4.8) and (4.9).

Solution-hardening can be strong if U is large. Interstitial atoms in body-centred cubic crystals produce large values. The maximum value of the interaction energy for an interstitial carbon atom in iron is about 0.75 eV (Cochardt, Schoek, and Wiedersich 1955). Substitutional solutes in face-centred cubic metals produce much smaller values of about 0.1 eV (Saxl 1964). Under these conditions strong solid solution-hardening is only observed at low temperature. This is because the rate of flow, $\dot{\varepsilon}$, under a stress τ, will be proportional to

$$\exp\left\{-(U-\tau bA)/kT\right\},$$

where A is the area of slip plane described by a dislocation when it is released from an obstacle. Thus if $U \gg kT$ we just have

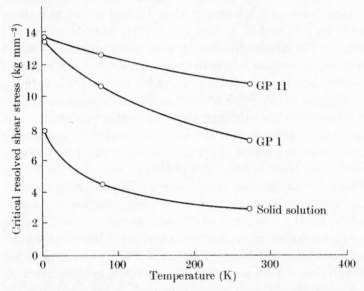

FIG. 4.2. The variation of critical resolved shear stress with temperature of single crystals of an aluminium alloy containing 1·7 atomic per cent copper. The three curves indicate the results when the copper is in solid solution, when it is clustered into very thin discs of thickness 3 Å and diameter 100 Å (GP I) and when it is clustered into larger precipitates which are also discs of thickness about 50 Å and diameter 500 Å (GP II). Data from G. J. Byrne, M. E. Fine, and A. Kelly (1961). *Phil. Mag.* **6**, 1119.

τbA closely equal to U to produce flow. However, if $U \sim kT$ thermal fluctuations assist the dislocations to overcome obstacles and the solid solution strengthening is much reduced above a certain critical temperature. An example is shown in Fig. 4.2.

Interstitial atoms in body-centred cubic lattices produce very strong solution-hardening, e.g. 2 at. % C in iron produces a yield stress of 1·5 GN m^{-2} (220 000 psi) at 0°C (Winchell and

Cohen 1962). The dislocations are so strongly pinned that the material is liable to brittle failure.

4.3.2. *Precipitation-hardening*

In precipitation-hardening a supersaturated solid solution, produced by quenching from the homogenization temperature, is annealed to produce precipitates containing 100–1000 atoms. U then becomes much greater than kT and so the flow stress is not very dependent on temperature. An example is shown in Fig. 4.2. The stresses required to move dislocations are $\sim G/200$ so that a dislocation is bent to values of $\rho \sim 100b$. For values of $f \sim 0\cdot10$ and precipitates containing 1000 atoms the separation of precipitates $(N_\mathrm{s}^{-1/2})$ is about $25b$. The dislocations are therefore forced to pass through the precipitates produced in the early stages of annealing. The alloy is annealed for a period to promote the formation of precipitates with properties different from the solvent crystal. The different properties are accompanied by an increase in the spacing of the precipitates. A distinction can be made between 'cutting' and 'looping' mechanisms for the flow stress (Kelly and Nicholson 1963). Cutting occurs when $\phi_\mathrm{c} < \pi$, so no Orowan loop is left behind as the dislocations advance. Looping occurs if an Orowan loop is left behind (Fig. 4.1(b)) and then the flow stress is independent of the character of the obstacle. If the particle has a radius in the slip plane of r_s associated with a stress τ' in its neighbourhood then the force F preventing the dislocation moving forward is $\sim\tau' b 2 r_\mathrm{s}$ and the Orowan loop will collapse unless

$$\tau' \gtrsim Gb/2r_\mathrm{s}. \tag{4.12}$$

Usually τ' does not depend on r_s and so in general larger particles give rise to looping and smaller ones to cutting. This means that, in very general terms, during the earlier stage of precipitation-hardening the flow stress is governed by the properties of the precipitate but in the later stages the flow stress is independent of the properties of the precipitate and is governed only by the spacing, decreasing with increased spacing according to equation (4.10). Precipitation-hardened alloys are at their strongest when dislocations are forced to cut the precipitates, i.e. before the obstacle spacing and strength attain the values necessary for (4.10) to govern the flow stress.

During cutting, the resistance to dislocation motion arises from a number of causes. The dislocations may encounter adverse stress fields due to the atomic volume of the precipitate being different from that of the matrix (Mott and Nabarro 1948). The passage of the dislocation through the precipitate may disorder the slip plane at the precipitate–matrix interface or within the precipitate (Kelly and Fine 1957). There can be large interactions between a precipitate and the dislocation core. In many face-centred cubic matrices this will be important when the stacking fault energy of the matrix and of the precipitate differ (Hirsch and Kelly 1965).

The latest review of all the various possibilities is due to Brown and Ham (1971) who are comprehensive and original. They conclude that effects due to the differing elastic modulus of precipitate and matrix have a negligible effect on the flow stress and that the effects of the strain fields around precipitates are extremely difficult to estimate quantitatively, although the beautiful experiments of Phillips (1965) prove these to be dominant in some cases. A particularly significant recent advance is the understanding of the flow stress of nickel alloys strengthened by the so-called γ' precipitate (Ni_3Al in a distorted form) which has been investigated experimentally by Gleiter and Hornbogen (1968) and others. The precipitates are completely coherent with a shear modulus close to that of the matrix. Stress fields around the precipitates are not an important source of strength. The precipitates contain an ordered superlattice and the resistance to flow is caused by disruption of this order by the first dislocation to enter the precipitate. The energy of the disordered surface is $\sim$150 mJ m^{-2}. Because the Burgers vector for slip in the solvent crystal is precisely one-half that for slip within the γ' precipitates a second dislocation restores the order disrupted by the first and under certain ageing conditions the dislocations are observed to move in coupled pairs; theory accounts excellently for the spacing of the dislocations. Due to the force exerted by the applied stress upon the second dislocation of the pair, the second dislocation drives the first through the precipitates. At large spacings ~ 300 Å the strength decreases with increasing spacing without ever attaining the Orowan stress (equation (4.10)).

The theory of all these ideas predicts a yield strength of the alloy proportional to f^n where n lies between $\frac{1}{2}$ and 1. Thus to obtain high strength f must be as large as possible. There will be an optimum size of precipitate for maximum strength which depends on the value of T for the dislocation line and the value of U. Since the obstacles to dislocation motion are discrete there is usually the possibility that dislocations will be forced between obstacles and bypass them; the initial yield stress can never be made greater than that given by equation (4.10).

Resistance to dislocation motion depends on the difference in physical properties of the matrix and precipitate, e.g. it will depend on the differences in atomic volume, if elastic strain fields hinder dislocation motion, or on differences in stacking fault energy. For a large yield stress the difference in physical properties must be large. The two requirements of large difference in properties and large volume fraction tend to be mutually exclusive since a large difference in physical properties between solvent and solute implies large departures from ideality or regularity of a solution and hence a small solid solubility follows from the Hume-Rothery rules for metallic systems. The largest strengths in precipitation-hardened systems are then found when metallurgical ingenuity is employed to obtain the largest volume fraction consistent with solubility at a high temperature. Addition of third elements to alter the solubility of a particular solute in a given solvent is one ruse and the use of an allotropic change in the solvent crystal when a particular element has widely differing solubilities in the two allotropes, is another. Various additional tricks have been developed in recent years designed to avoid the restrictions of the equilibrium phase diagram, such as very rapid cooling from the liquid phase where solubilities are generally greater (Duwez 1967), and high energy grinding (Benjamin 1970). A review of some of these is given by Nicholson (1971).

The great practical advantage of precipitation-hardening is that materials can be formed to shape with the solute in solution and then strengthened by a simple heat treatment. In a ductile matrix dislocation motion is not eliminated, and dislocations can still move at points of high stress concentration and reduce the effects of these by plastic flow. The conditions, as we have seen, are stringent. The spacing of precipitates must be less than about 1000 Å. Since the precipitates are produced by diffusion the strength is only maintained at low temperatures, because at temperatures at which diffusion can occur readily the precipitates will grow in size and increase their spacing (see section 4.7). The strength can also be lost under conditions of oscillating stress (i.e. under conditions leading to fatigue). This is because point defects produced during deformation lead to enhanced diffusion (see e.g. Kennedy 1962).

Another disadvantage of the production of obstacles to dislocation motion by precipitation is that the microstructure may be different at places which are efficient sources or sinks of vacant lattice sites. This is particularly marked in aluminium-base alloys where low temperature diffusion, necessary to produce a fine dispersion, is enhanced by quenched-in vacancies. The properties of grain boundary regions then become very different from those of the interior of the grains. The precipitate is usually coarser at the grain boundaries and each boundary may be flanked by a region denuded of precipitates (see Plate 1.). Alternatively, grain boundaries may be associated with the formation of a continuous brittle phase, rendering the alloy fragile. Denudation of precipitates at grain boundaries limits the use of some strong aluminium alloys (e.g. Al plus Mg and Zn) and renders them brittle and liable to cracking under stress in a corrosive environment.

The highest yield strengths obtained at room temperature by precipitation-hardening alone, without subsequent cold work, are about 700 MN m^{-2} (100 000 psi) in aluminium alloys (containing Mg, Zn, and Cu), about 1·1 GN m^{-2} (160 000 psi) in copper alloys (containing Be) and approximately 1·4 GN m^{-2} (200 000 psi) in nickel-base alloys (the nimonics). Taking half these figures as the maximum shear stress they correspond to $G/78$, $G/88$, and $G/108$ respectively. At these large fractions of the theoretical strength inadequate fracture toughness limits the usable strengths, particularly in the aluminium alloys (Nock and Hunsicker 1963). Such materials have strengths which it appears pointless to exceed very much whilst still relying on the ductility of the material to provide adequate notch-insensitivity.

Most failures of metallic parts in service, however, are not due to static overloading but due to fatigue, i.e. failure at less than the UTS produced by cyclic reversal of stress. In metals fatigue is due to small amounts of plastic flow at stresses which may be below the yield stress (see Kennedy 1962, for a review) and the failure is atmosphere-dependent (Wadsworth 1959). Fatigue is not understood well theoretically and there is still much to be gained by raising the possible operating stress level under fatigue conditions without necessarily raising the static strength of the material.

4.4. Work-hardening

The stress–strain curve of an alloy containing fully coherent particles, which are cut by the dislocations, is very different from one containing particles of an inherently strong solid which do not, in the early stages of deformation, deform with the matrix (Kelly and Nicholson 1963). In the former case, as the material is deformed plastically the rate of work-hardening (the slope, $d\sigma/d\varepsilon$, of the stress–strain curve) is similar to that of the pure metal; there may be small effects due to elements in solid solution altering the stacking fault energy and small effects due to the passage of the dislocations through the precipitates due to the resulting change in the precipitate shape and the nature of the precipitate–matrix interface.

When non-deforming particles are present in sufficient volume fraction, the initial yield stress is controlled by the interparticle spacing and conforms to equation (4.10) very closely when proper attention is paid to the variation of the line tension of the dislocation with orientation, and to measurement of particle spacing (Jones and Kelly 1968, Hirsch and Humphreys 1970, Brown and Ham 1971). The rate of work-hardening can then be very much greater than that shown by the matrix alone. The dislocation density increases very rapidly with strain. Examples of the behaviour of an alloy containing deforming and non-deforming particles is shown in Fig. 4.3. When non-deforming particles are

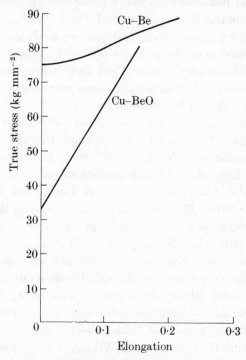

FIG. 4.3. The stress–elongation curves at 77 K for a precipitation-hardened Cu-Be single crystal containing a volume fraction of 20 per cent of precipitates which are sheared by dislocations and the curve for a crystal containing 2·8 per cent of BeO which does not deform plastically. (From A. Kelly (1964). *Proc. R. Soc.* A282, 63.)

present with a spacing much less than one micron, slip lines are not easily observed on the surface and slip on a number of glide systems occurs very early in the deformation, for particles of diameter $\geqslant 5000$ Å.

When this type of work-hardening occurs there is evidence of the following effects: (1) the particles are subject to large elastic strains (Wilson 1955, 1965); (2) a dense array of dislocations is built up at the particles and subsequently a cell structure is formed with the particles predominantly in the cell walls (Plate 4), and the scale of the cell structure is related to the spacing of the particles; (3) the rate of work-hardening appears greater for plate-shaped particles than for spheres; and (4) increases with increasing volume fraction of particles and with decreasing size of particle for a given volume fraction (see Kelly and Nicholson 1963). Extraction of the particles present in alloys of this type shows them to be very strong (Webb and Forgeng 1958). This is expected because they have dimensions comparable with those of whiskers and are often dislocation-free.

Careful measurements on face-centred cubic alloys show that the additional rate of work-hardening due to the (approximately) spherical particles varies as $(f/\bar{r})^{1/2}$ when the temperature is sufficiently low, where f is the fraction of particles and $\bar{r}$ their average radius (Jones and Kelly 1968, Jones 1969, Hirsch and Humphreys 1970). The glissile dislocation loops on the primary glide system, shown schematically in Fig. 4.1(b), are usually converted into prismatic loops at small strains and as strain proceeds prismatic loops are punched out on secondary slip systems. The structures formed depend upon strain and the size of the obstacles (Humphreys and Stewart 1971). The work-hardening is due to the interference which the various dislocation loops offer to the passage of further dislocations.

Observation (1) above, due to Wilson, is very important and indicates that the particles are subject to large elastic strains which increase rapidly at very small strains. However, these elastic strains do not lead to failure of the particle when the particles are equiaxed. Stresses in the matrix are relieved by various dislocation manoeuvres and annihilation of dislocations due to thermally activated processes occur (Jones 1969) at room temperature in copper alloys. The particle–matrix interface breaks before the fracture strength of the particle is attained and voids are formed at the particles leading to a ductile fracture of the alloy (Palmer and Smith 1968, Humphreys and Stewart 1972).

The only way to achieve fracture of the strong particles, and hence ensure that they contribute their maximum load bearing capacity to the material, is to arrange that they are either of a fibrous or of a plate-like shape. Then, flow of the matrix parallel to the fibres must result in fracture of the fibres provided that these are sufficiently long. This is because, even though the shear stress of the matrix is limited, flow of the matrix produces a frictional force on the particle and if the particle is long enough these forces must eventually lead to its failure. This is observed to occur (Herzberg and Kraft 1963). This is the principle of fibre reinforcement (first pointed out, for metallic matrices, so far as the author is aware, by Cottrell (1960)). The aim of making this type of microstructure is not to prevent flow of the matrix altogether, but to arrange that flow can only take place easily, parallel to the fibres so that it leads to the loading of the strong particles and hence they make their full contribution to the strength. The principle of fibre reinforcement is explored in Chapter 5. There, no mention is made of the spacing of the fibres and the plastic properties of the matrix are considered to be those of the bulk matrix containing no dispersion. This section connects fibre reinforcement and dispersion strengthening. In Chapter 5 the spacing of the fibres is regarded as of no importance— it is controlled by the volume fraction of fibres and the fibre diameter.

This discussion shows that only when the fibres are closely spaced—say with less than between 1 and 10 μm separating their surfaces—so that the yield stress of the matrix between them is controlled by the Orowan stress, will dispersion-hardening of the matrix result and its properties become different from those of the bulk matrix; such is seen in the experiments of Kelly and Lilholt (1969) and of Garmong and Shepard (1971). When closely spaced small fibres are present, the matrix can only be regarded as behaving as it is assumed to do in Chapter 5, provided it possesses five independent slip systems and sufficient slip flexibility (section 3.3) on a scale of distance small compared with the fibre separation. If these conditions are fulfilled it may then be considered as flowing essentially parallel to the fibres, whatever the detailed crystallographic nature of the slip movements.

4.5. Strong steels

Conventional strong steels are produced, in other than wire form, by simply quenching austenite containing carbon in solid solution to produce martensite, a metastable tetragonal structure (c/a increasing with increasing carbon content). On quenching steels with more than 0·4 per cent carbon a high yield strength may be developed ($> 1\cdot7$ GN m^{-2} or 250 000 psi) but the steel is so brittle that it cannot be used without first tempering to a more ductile but less strong product. The yield stress of martensite increases rapidly with increasing carbon content up to about 0·4 per cent carbon but at higher contents the effect is less pronounced. The predominant strengthening effect is hardening by atomically dispersed carbon (Winchell and Cohen 1962). Other effects such as the fine structure of the martensite, precipitation-hardening at low temperature, and solution-hardening due to the other alloying elements are smaller. The primary function of alloying elements in conventional martensitic steels is to allow slower quenching rates to produce a fully martensitic structure in larger specimens than is possible in steel containing essentially only carbon. Since increase in the carbon content above 0·4 per cent carbon leads to little increase in strength, while the fracture toughness and weldability is reduced, most high strength conventional steels contain up to 0·4 per cent C. The alloying elements are manganese, silicon, nickel, chromium, and molybdenum, the total amount of the last three elements being between 2 and 4 per cent. Ultimate tensile strengths up to 1·7 GN m^{-2} (250 000 psi) are obtained.

All of these alloy steels show a decrease in fracture toughness when tempered in the temperature range 250–450°C. This appears principally due to impurity in the steel (Capus and Mayer 1960) but prevents tempering in this range. Tempering above 450°C leads to a rapid decrease in yield stress, and tempering below 250°C does not lead to sufficient relief of the stresses introduced by quenching. Modification of the composition allows tempering up to 300°C, which whilst allowing further decrease in internal stresses, also assists the elimination of hydrogen and reduces the risk of hydrogen embrittlement. This has been attained notably by increasing the silicon content and the molybdenum content and adding vanadium and sometimes boron. Cobalt has also been added to allow higher tempering temperatures.

Secondary-hardening steels are used when complete removal of quenching stresses is required by tempering in the region 500–600°C. The possible operating temperature is then raised also. These steels contain increased Cr-Mo-V contents in which the Cr content is at least 5 per cent. Carbides of these elements are precipitated on tempering and lead to an increase in yield stress due to precipitation-hardening—hence the name. Strengths up to 320 000 psi can be obtained. Thus far we have indicated the conventional development of strong steels (following Ineson 1965).

Modern very high strength steels have been developed since the recognition of the concepts of fracture toughness. High strength must be accompanied by acceptable values of the critical stress intensity factor. It is realised that ahead of a notch high biaxial stresses exist. The elimination of *large* brittle carbide particles without significant change in the volume fraction of the phase increases the value of K_c. In the region ahead of a notch the strain rate which is imposed upon the material is much larger than elsewhere. It is the behaviour of the metal at the increased rate of strain under biaxial stress which is then recognized as being of importance. In metals this material must retain the ability to deform plastically without cracking and so the 'ideal' material at the head of a notch possesses a high strength with either a very long elongation to failure or else with a rate of work-hardening sufficiently high to prevent plastic instability of the type described in section 3.6. Finely dispersed and hard precipitate particles of small size, increase the rate of work-hardening and these are present in all modern high strength steels.

The prominent feature of modern strong steels is the use of

precipitation-hardening in association with structures containing a very high density of dislocations. The first of these processes, developed by Zackay and his associates, we shall call austforming, following Owen (1964). Here the yield strength of a quenched steel is increased by interrupting the quench to subject the steel to extensive plastic deformation whilst it is still austenitic. There is little decrease in strength on tempering below 400°C and after this treatment the steel has appreciable ductility.

Plastic deformation of the austenite must be carried out without decomposition to pearlite or bainite and therefore steels showing a range of temperature in which austenite is stable, between the pearlite and bainite range, are required. In the early alloys chromium was thought to be most effective in producing this, and a steel of composition (by weight per cent) 0·35 per cent C, 5·0 per cent Cr, 1·5 per cent Mo, 0·4 per cent V, used. However, nickel and manganese now appear to be better (Christian 1971). In addition, carbide-forming elements of high diffusivity are important, provided the carbides formed from these can be taken into solution prior to austforming.

Austformed steels, after about 80 per cent deformation at temperatures between 400 and 600°C (depending on the composition) followed by tempering in the same range after the quench, show UTS values up to 450 000 psi for a 3 per cent Cr-Ni-Si steel. Strengths up to 2·3 GN m^{-2} (330 000 psi) with K_c values of 40 MN m$^{-3/2}$ (40 000 psi in$^{1/2}$) are obtained and strengths of 1·4 GN m^{-2} with a K_c value of 120 MN m$^{-3/2}$ (120 000 psi in$^{1/2}$) in a steel containing 9·0 per cent Ni, 4 per cent Co and 0·25 per cent C. The high strength is derived from the hardening due to carbon in solution in the martensite, which seems to be essential, coupled with a very high dislocation density and with precipitation of carbides. Increasing the deformation increases the resulting strength and the strength is greatest when the deformation is carried out at the lowest possible temperature. The dislocation density is very high and is very uniform. Carbides are formed during deformation and their presence contributes to the dislocation density produced by the deformation. The plastic deformation itself enhances the diffusion and allows the carbides to form. The increase in strength of austformed steels over conventional ones is primarily due to the large dislocation density (Thomas, Schmatz, and Gerberich 1965)†. The large plastic deformation necessary to produce this is one of the disadvantages of austforming but it is suitable for things which are to be shaped by a deformation process. There is evidence, referred to by Ineson, that austforming removes some of the embrittling effects found in tempered low-alloy steels. The idea of combining plastic deformation at other stages of the γ- to α-transformation in steels with a thermal treatment is being actively explored at present.

All of the steels described so far, suffer from the practical disadvantage that they are difficult to machine in their very hard condition and difficult to join by welding. To produce a very strong steel with acceptable toughness in the presence of notches, but without applying a deformation process, it appears necessary to remove the principle interstitial solute elements, carbon and nitrogen, and to produce hardening by the precipitation of inter-metallic compounds. Fully austenitic stainless steels in which precipitation-hardening is produced by the addition of titanium, aluminium, and molybdenum have been in use for some time but a new principle has been introduced in the last decade (see for example Decker 1963), by producing precipitation in a carbon-free (and hence cubic) martensite. This process is known as marageing. The base alloy is iron with 18–25 per cent of nickel, containing less than 0·03 per cent carbon, and various additions are made of cobalt, molybdenum, titanium, aluminium, and niobium. Figure 4.4 illustrates the thermal hysteresis en-countered in the γ–α transformation in these alloys; also included is the calculated temperature at which the free energy of austenite and of ferrite are equal. For 18 per cent Ni this temperature is less than 400°C, so that on cooling in air from the γ range no extensive phase separation occurs before the diffusionless trans-formation takes place at between 150 and 220°C, depending on

† These authors measure a value of 10^{13} cm^{-2} and use of this figure for ρ in equation (3.11) with $\alpha = 0·4$ (appropriate for body-centred cubic metals) gives a flow stress of $G/50$ or about $1·2$ GN m^{-2} due to the increased dislocation density.

the composition. Thus, no quenching is required, and these alloys can be produced in a fully martensitic condition throughout thick sections. On reheating, the martensite decomposition to γ may occur by diffusion at between about 400 and 550°C but the precipitation processes occur more quickly and so it is possible to age to maximum strength before appreciable amounts of

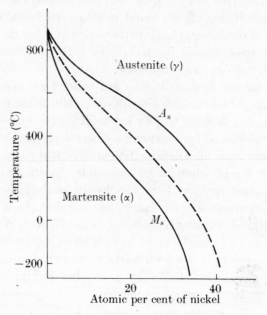

Fig. 4.4. The austenite to martensite transformation starts at M_s on cooling and at A_s on heating, for rates of change of temperature of 5°C min^{-1}. The dotted curve represents the calculated temperature at which the free energies of austenite and ferrite are equal. (From Owen 1964.)

austenite are formed. On ageing, dimensional changes are negligibly small, so that in practice finished dimensions may be machined before the final ageing treatment.

The form of martensite produced depends upon the rate of cooling and on the composition of the alloy. It always possesses a high dislocation density and is usually what is called massive (as distinct from, for example, a circular) martensite. This arises from the absence of carbon, in which feature maraging steels differ from all other high strength steels. A major strengthening mechanism is precipitation-hardening of A_3B type structures, e.g. when the titanium content is high ($\sim$6 per cent) Ni_3Ti is precipitated, and in alloys with 5 per cent molybdenum Ni_3Mo is precipitated. The volume fraction of precipitate possible is clearly large and the high dislocation density and the boundaries within the martensite ensure a uniform distribution of small precipitates with spacings between 200 and 500 Å. Long-range ordering of the alloy may contribute to the strength. Floreen (1968) reviews the possibilities.

The highest strength so far attained in unworked 18 per cent Ni maraged steels is about 270 000 psi[†]. Specimens showing this strength also show a reduction in area of 50 per cent in a tensile test so that very large values of G_c are obtained. Although maraged steels are not particularly soft after air cooling they exhibit very little work-hardening and can be extensively cold-worked without annealing. This facilitates the production of sheet, strip, and wire and allows other forming operations to be carried out easily. Such cold-work also produces a marked increase in the yield stress on subsequent marageing so that values of up to 2·3 GN m^{-2} (330 000 psi) can be obtained with K_c values of more than 70 MN m$^{-3/2}$ and recently 4·6 GN m^{-2} (660 000 psi) has been achieved in tension. Due to the low carbon content the material possesses excellent welding properties. Maraged steels can be used at temperatures well above room temperature since the ageing temperature is greater than 480°C. There is little work-hardening in these alloys, although the fracture toughness is high. The normal engineer's design criterion which requires a large UTS to yield stress ratio, is thus seen to be an inadequate one in this case (Ineson 1965). It is the value of G_c which is important. In these alloys the yield stress and UTS are very close.

The variation of yield strength with plane-strain fracture toughness is shown in Fig. 4.5 for a number of steels. The highest

[†] A modern composition would be (by weight per cent) 18 per cent Ni, 8 per cent Co, 3·5 per cent Mo, 0·2 per cent Ti, 0·1 per cent Al, with the major precipitate being Ni_3Mo. This combination of cobalt and molybdenum is found to be most effective.

toughness is attained with austformed steels HP or H–11 but the maraged steel maintains its toughness at much higher values of the strength.

The disadvantages of strong maraging steels are that they are not corrosion resistant and still appear to suffer from hydrogen embrittlement as do low alloy steels. Young's modulus is less than that of conventional steels, and the density a little higher,

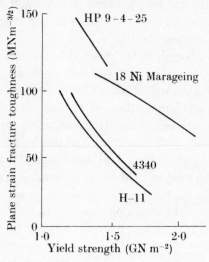

FIG. 4.5. The plane strain-fracture toughness and yield strength of some high strength steels at room temperature. HP 9–4–25 contains 9 per cent Ni, 4 per cent Co, and 0·25 per cent C. 4340 contains 0·42 per cent C, 0·78 per cent Mn, 1·7 per cent Ni, 0·8 per cent Cr, and 0·33 per cent Mo. H–11 contains 0·35 per cent C, 5 per cent Cr, 1·5 per cent Mo, and 0·4 per cent V. (Data from C. M. Pierce, J. A. Hall and T. M. Ronald, *Astronautics and Aeronautics*, July 1970.)

so that the specific modulus is reduced. Maraging steels are regarded as expensive in the steel world since the cost of vacuum-melted maraging steels is now about five times that of conventional strong steels. A search for cheaper materials has therefore been made and recently a new steel containing 10 per cent Al, 25 per cent Mn, and 1 per cent C (British Patent No. 841,366) has been made with a strength of 260 000 psi, adequate ductility, and a density only 0·85 times that of conventional steel.

4.6. Strong wires

Strong metal wires available today are listed in Appendix A, Table 4. The strongest are produced by cold drawing†. Only in the case of steel wire has the microstructure been thoroughly investigated (Embury and Fisher 1966). The strongest steel wire is made from 0·9 per cent carbon steel (approximately eutectoid) containing about 0·4 per cent manganese and 0·2 per cent silicon. The material is austenitized (converted to an f.c.c. solid solution) for a few minutes at 1000°C and then transformed at 500°C to a fine pearlite (a lamellar mixture of ferrite and cementite, Fe_3C). At this stage the interlamellar spacing in the pearlite is about 700 Å and the pearlite colonies are unaligned.‡ After drawing to a true strain of about 0·7 the cementite plates are aligned in the drawing direction. This alignment occurs by slip in those Fe_3C lamellae, originally parallel to the drawing direction, and by fracture of others, together with slip. After drawing to a true strain of 3 the wire consists of 'cells' relatively free of dislocations with a high dislocation density in the 'cell' walls. These cells are very much elongated in the direction of the wire axis and the cell dimension transverse to the wire axis is 100–200 Å and decreases with increasing drawing strain. During drawing the proof stress (stress to produce 0·2 per cent plastic strain) is inversely proportional to the square root of the wire diameter. The salient feature of Embury and Fisher's observations is that the cell dimensions normal to the wire axis, of the structure formed in drawing, is reduced during continued drawing in proportion to the reduction in diameter of the wire. Embury and Fisher suggest that new barriers to dislocation motion are not produced during drawing but that the spacing of cell walls (d) normal to the wire axis is continuously reduced so that one can write

$$\frac{d_0}{d_s} = \frac{D_0}{D_s} \tag{4.13}$$

† Recently, wires of marageing steel with strengths of 5 $GN\ m^{-2}$ have been made by drawing from the melt in a glass sheath—section 6.2—(Nixdorf 1970). Such a method is likely to be much cheaper than methods based on cold drawing.

‡ This process is known as patenting. The subsequent drawing is carried out at room temperature.

where D is the wire diameter and the subscripts refer to the dimensions before drawing and after a true strain of ε. Since $\varepsilon = 2 \ln(D_0/D_\varepsilon)$ we have

$$\frac{d_0}{d_\varepsilon} = \exp(\varepsilon/2). \tag{4.14}$$

The cell walls of spacing d are found to be related to the proof stress (σ_y) of the drawn wire by a relationship of the type of (4.6), i.e.

$$\sigma_y = \sigma_i + k\, d^{-1/2}.$$

So using (4.14), the proof stress as a function of strain is

$$\sigma_y = \sigma_i + \frac{k}{d_0^{1/2}} \exp(\varepsilon/4). \tag{4.15}$$

σ_i is a constant and the value of k is $3 \cdot 1$ kg mm$^{-3/2}$ (876 psi in$^{1/2}$), taking d_0 as the initial pearlite spacing, ~ 700 Å.†

Figure 4·6 shows a plot of the proof stress against $\exp(\varepsilon/4)$ for a number of drawn and swaged ferritic materials. Equation (4.15) appears well obeyed. For materials such as pure iron this relationship is only obeyed for strains greater than that at which a stable cell structure has been developed. This can be ascertained from electron microscope observations, and d_0 must be taken as the cell dimension normal to the wire when it is the case.

It is apparent from equation (4.15) and Fig. 4.6 that much greater strengths can be obtained with fine pearlite than with the other ferritic materials because d_0 is much smaller for the fine pearlite, being controlled by the initial spacing of cementite lamellae. Thus to obtain the greatest strengths with a given deformation, d_0 should be as small as possible. When d_0 is controlled by a second phase, Embury and Fisher point out that this phase must be capable of sustaining plastic deformation so

† This derivation of equation (4.15) has been criticised by Longford (1970) who finds that the fragmentation of the cementite is extensive, and that the deformation of the ferrite is in plane strain due to the $\langle 110 \rangle$ texture produced by drawing, instead of being axially symmetric as assumed by Embury and Fisher. However, Longford's results confirm the validity of (4.15).

that the material as a whole can be subject to large deformations without failure. How important this is has not been determined experimentally. Introduction of 2 per cent BeO into beryllium has been reported to increase the attainable strength by 10–15 per cent and dispersions of ThO_2 in tungsten increase the strength

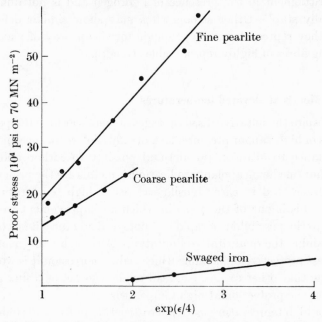

FIG. 4.6. The variation of proof stress (stress at 0·2 per cent plastic strain) with the quantity exp $(\varepsilon/4)$, for drawn pearlite and for swaged iron. ε = true strain. (From Embury and Fisher 1966.)

a little. The strength of β-Ti wire in Appendix A, Table 4, corresponds to a tensile stress of $E/53$ which closely approaches the fraction of Young's modulus attained by patented steel wire ($E/48$). Other strong wires have not attained these strengths yet. Introduction of a dispersion with the correct properties to yield a small value of d_0 could assist in this. This is particularly important when it is appreciated that to obtain strengths of 4 GN m^{-2} (600 000 psi), the patented steel wire is subject to a reduction in area of 98 per cent corresponding to a true strain of 4·2.

The strong metal wires listed in Appendix A, Table 4, show plastic deformation before failure; in the case of the steel wire this amounts to a 20 per cent reduction in area in a tensile test and the material also work-hardens. The strengths are thus highly reproducible. Strong steel wire has a marked tendency to embrittlement in the presence of hydrogen and is not dimensionally stable. Other strong wires may show similar defects but they represent an easy, though not cheap, way of making strong fibres of highly reproducible strength.

4.7. Metals at elevated temperatures

Despite the putative disadvantages of metals at high temperatures of high vapour pressure, lack of oxidation resistance and of resistance to nitrogen (in air) and possibly to carbon and to sulphur (in chemical plant applications), metals are the principal materials used to carry tensile stresses at high temperatures. Since this is one of the areas in which an improvement would lead to the possibility of rapid technological advance, it is worth examining the quantitative limitations. Although many metals possess protective oxide films which reduce corrosion it is worth noting that other oxides, e.g. lead oxide, can act as a flux and reduce the protection at high temperatures.

For high temperature use a microstructure must be extremely stable. Small dispersed particles which act as barriers to dislocation motion are therefore required to maintain their small size and spacing at high temperatures. This is usually considered in terms of the Thomson–Freundlich relation which relates the equilibrium vapour pressure (π) about a spherical drop of radius r and the equilibrium vapour pressure (π_0) above a flat surface. From elementary thermodynamics we have

$$\ln \left(\frac{\pi}{\pi_0} \right) = \frac{2V\gamma}{rRT}, \tag{4.16}$$

for a liquid of molar volume V, at absolute temperature T. R is the gas constant and γ the liquid-vapour interfacial energy. For a solute which obeys Henry's law, π is proportional to the equilibrium concentration of solute and therefore the last equation can be written

$$\ln \frac{c_r}{c_0} = \frac{2V\gamma}{rRT}, \tag{4.17}$$

showing that the equilibrium solubility close to a particle of radius r is greater than that close to a particle of infinite radius. The higher concentration close to small particles gives rise to diffusion currents which lead to the disappearance of small particles and the growth of large ones. From equation (4.17), for a solute of molecular weight 50, and density 7×10^3 kg m^{-3}, an interfacial free energy of 500 mJ m^{-2} at 1000 K, produces an increase in solubility of 42 per cent close to a particle of radius 25 Å. The rate of diffusion of solute between small and large particles is controlled by the diffusion coefficient and the separation of the particles, and clearly the initial rate of coarsening will depend on the difference in size of neighbouring particles. Particular expressions for the rate of increase of the average particle size with time have been given, and their applicability to metallic systems experimentally checked (Speich and Oriani 1965).

To provide strength at an elevated temperature the aim is therefore to reduce γ, principally by arranging for completely coherent† precipitates to be present; to reduce the diffusion coefficient; and to ensure that c_0 is as low as possible. In addition, the volume fraction of the dispersion must be such that the interparticle spacing is 1000 Å or less, if possible, to provide high strength. This will normally imply that r is small ($\sim$100 Å). There are clearly advantages in having a very small range of particle sizes. Since the solubility at high temperature is usually decreased, if the solubility at low temperature is small, the simultaneous requirements of small c_0 and of a large volume fraction in order to provide sufficient strength, imply that means other than precipitation will be required to provide a stable dispersion.

† A completely coherent precipitate is one in which all Burgers circuits passing through both matrix and precipitate close, when chemical species of the atoms is neglected.

The rate of steady-state creep can be described as the result of approximate equilibrium between the competing processes of work-hardening, which reduces the rate of creep as strain proceeds, and of recovery of the flow stress which increases it as time proceeds (McLean 1968). The rate of work-hardening is increased by an increase in volume fraction of stable barriers and by decrease in their size (see section 4.4); the same factors limit recovery. It follows that the rate of creep at elevated temperature is decreased by a large volume fraction of small stable particles. Rupture under conditions of creep is controlled by other factors. Under uniaxial tension most materials possess flow laws which lead to unstable deformation. Cavities are also produced at grain boundaries during creep and there is evidence that these form very soon after the imposition of stress at elevated temperature (Greenwood 1969). Under unstable conditions of plastic deformation these cavities must grow. Cavities are formed most easily at grain boundaries under stress and so the grain size *and shape* are important factors.

The strength of all the steels referred to in section 4.5 decreases rapidly at temperatures between 500 and 600°C. In addition, the Young's modulus of iron falls rapidly at higher temperatures and is only 18×10^6 psi at 830°C. Highly alloyed forms of iron and particularly alloys based on nickel, cobalt, and chromium are used or are under active exploration. An empirical criterion for high temperature use is often employed. This criterion is the maximum temperature at which a material can withstand a tensile stress of, usually, 20 000 psi for 100 hr without failure (see for example Decker and DeWitt 1965).

Iron-base alloys for high temperature use usually contain about 15 per cent Cr, to provide corrosion resistance, and up to 25 per cent Ni to develop an austenitic structure. Most contain Al and Ti to provide precipitation-hardening by the precipitation of $Ni_3(Al, Ti)$. Temperatures of about 800°C can be obtained under a stress of 500 00 psi. Cobalt-base alloys contain Mo, W, Ta, and Nb which provide solid solution strengthening and there is some carbide precipitation. The highest temperatures attained are $\sim$930°C at 20 000 psi. Chromium-base alloys suffer from a tendency to form nitrides and there is a tendency to vaporize readily at temperatures above 1000°C. In addition, chromium-base alloys have very high ductile-brittle transition temperatures, e.g. 150 to 200°C.

Nickel-base alloys are used at temperatures representing a higher fraction of the melting temperature of the base than any others. The nickel, often with cobalt and sometimes iron (in the cheaper alloys), forms the face-centred cubic matrix—the gamma phase. The cobalt (up to 30 per cent) restricts precipitation of unwanted phases. The chief commercial alloys contain 15–20 per cent Cr to ensure oxidation resistance, and resistance to sulphur. The most effective strengthening is achieved by the addition of Al and Ti to form the $Ni_3(Ti, Al)$ precipitate, i.e. the gamma prime phase. Further strengthening is achieved by Mo, Nb, Ta, and W which form carbides (the alloys contain up to 0·20 per cent C) and these elements increase the temperature at which the γ' dissolves. The strengths attained are up to 200 000 psi at room temperature and the alloys can be used for 100 hr under 20 000 psi at up to 1000°C. In these nickel-base alloys a very large volume fraction of precipitate is achieved, about 40 per cent. The precipitates possess atomic volumes within 1–3 per cent of that of the matrix so that they are usually coherent with the matrix, and γ in equation (4.17) is small. The precipitates are ordered and the strength is probably connected with this.

The alloys for use at the highest temperatures must be cast to shape, because of the extreme difficulty in plastically deforming these materials at high temperatures. Cast alloys, used in air-craft turbine blades, invariably break at grain boundaries running normal to the largest principal stress, and so such grain boundaries have been eliminated by solidifying in a temperature gradient so that grains grow in the shape of columns with the $\langle 001 \rangle$ axis parallel to the principal stress. By control of the growth of these crystals a monocrystal blade may be produced. Directional solidification gives an improved resistance to the effects produced by cyclic changes in temperature.

In all the alloys described above the strengthening agent is a precipitate which dissolves at high temperature. The ideally stable barrier to dislocation motion is one of the inherently strong solids (Chapter 3). A dispersion of such a material with a much higher melting point than the metal and which also has a low solubility (low c_0 in equation (4.17)) should provide the ideal barrier to dislocation movement at high temperatures. Many oxides satisfy these criteria and if dispersed finely can effectively hinder dislocation motion at temperatures close to the melting point of the metal, e.g. Al_2O_3 in aluminium (see Bloch 1961) and dispersions of Al_2O_3 and SiO_2 in copper (Preston and Grant 1961). Recently a very effective dispersion of thoria (ThO_2) in nickel has been produced by making a uniform mixture of colloidal oxides of nickel and thorium and subsequently reducing the nickel to metal (Alexander and Pasfield 1961, Worn and Marton 1961). The volume fraction of thoria is about 2 per cent and the particle diameter varies between 100 Å and 1000 Å. The majority of the particles are of diameter close to the smaller figure but the large particles occupy the major part of the volume fraction. The mean planar inter-particle spacing is 2800 Å, and so the yield stress in shear at room temperature according to equation (4.10) is 10^8 N m^{-2} which is within a factor of 2 of that observed (von Heimendahl and Thomas 1964). This yield strength is small at room temperature but at high temperature ($\sim$1100°C) the material is superior to the nickel-base alloys (Fig. 4.7), and shows a strength of $E/1000$ at a temperature equal to 0·8 of the melting temperature.

Although thoria particles may be introduced into an alloy of Ni containing 20 per cent Cr, attempts to introduce thoria in a sufficiently finely-divided form into a creep-resistant alloy of nickel by chemical techniques have so far failed. Benjamin (1970) has shown that this may be achieved by high-energy grinding of nickel powder and a Ni–Al–Ti vacuum-melted master alloy powder, together with thorium oxide and or/yttrium oxide powders containing particles of between 100 Å and 500 Å in size. The oxide powder is produced by the thermal decomposition of a less stable compound. The high energy grinding breaks up the metallic powders and also welds them, together with the oxide, into larger particles of the required average composition, together with 1–2 per cent of oxide. Finally the powder is hot-extruded. The method successfully introduces particles of a strong solid into an alloy which can be precipitation-hardened by appropriate thermal treatment. Figure 4.7 shows the behaviour of one of these alloys. The material is a little stronger than nickel

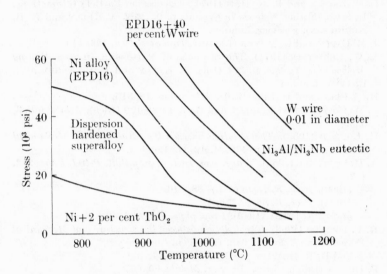

FIG. 4.7. Variation with temperature of the tensile stress which produces rupture in 100 hours of various materials. EPD 16 is a nickel-base alloy containing 11 per cent W, 6 per cent of Al and of Cr, 2 per cent Mo and 1·5 per cent Nb.

containing thoria at temperatures above about 1000°C. Below this temperature it is greatly superior in strength and its resistance to stress at high temperatures is very close to that of the commercial alloy Nimonic 80A which has a composition very similar to that of the matrix of the dispersion-strengthened material. This in a typical case might be 0·06 per cent C, 0·92 per cent Al, 2·46 per cent Ti, 20·4 per cent Cr, 0·029 per cent Zr, 0·005 per cent B (composition in per cent by weight).

REFERENCES

G. B. ALEXANDER and W. M. PASFIELD (1961). U.S. Patent 3,019,013.

R. W. ARMSTRONG, Y. T. CHOU, R. M. FISHER, and N. LOUAT (1966). *Phil. Mag.* **14**, 943.

R. ARMSTRONG, I. CODD, R. M. DOUTHWAITE, and N. J. PETCH (1962). *Phil. Mag.* **7**, 45.

J. S. BENJAMIN (1970). *Trans. Metall. Soc. A.I.M.E.* **1**, 2943.

E. A. BLOCH (1961). *Metall. Rev.* **6**, 193.

L. M. BROWN and R. K. HAM (1971). Dislocation-Particle Interactions. In *Strengthening Methods in Crystals* p. 9. (Eds. A. KELLY and R. B. NICHOLSON), Elsevier, London.

J. M. CAPUS and G. MAYER (1960). *J. Iron Steel Inst.* **196**, 149.

J. W. CHRISTIAN (1971). The Strength of Martensite. In *Strengthening Methods in Crystals*, p. 261 (Eds. A. KELLY and R. B. NICHOLSON), Elsevier, London.

H. E. CLINE and D. LEE (1970). *Acta metall.* **18**, 315.

A. W. COCHARDT, G. SCHOEK, and H. WIEDERSICH (1955). *Acta metall.* **3**, 533.

H. CONRAD (1963). *The Relation between the Structure and Mechanical Properties of Metals*, p. 476, H.M.S.O., London.

A. H. COTTRELL (1958). *Trans. Am. Inst. Min. metall. Petrol. Engrs* **212**, 142.

—— (1960). *Proc. R. Instn Gt Br.* **38**, 346.

—— (1963). *Proc. R. Soc.* A**276**, 1.

—— and B. A. BILBY (1949). *Proc. phys. Soc.* A**62**, 49.

R. F. DECKER (1963). *The Relation between the Structure and Mechanical Properties of Metals*, p. 648, H.M.S.O., London.

—— and R. R. DeWITT (1965). *J. Metals* **17**, 139.

P. DUWEZ (1967). *Trans. Am. Soc. Metals.* **60**, 607.

J. D. EMBURY (1971). Strengthening by Dislocation Substructures. In *Strengthening Methods in Crystals*, p. 331 (Eds. A. KELLY and R. B. NICHOLSON), Elsevier, London.

—— and R. M. FISHER (1966). *Acta metall.* **14**, 147.

R. L. FLEISCHER and W. L. HIBBARD, Jr. (1963). *The Relation between the Structure and Mechanical Properties of Metals*, p. 262, H.M.S.O., London.

S. FLOREEN (1968). *Metall. Rev.* **13**, 115.

G. GARMONG and L. A. SHEPARD (1971). *Met. Trans.* **2**, 175.

H. GLEITER and E. HORNBOGEN (1968). *Materials Science and Engineering*, **2**, 285.

G. W. GREENWOOD (1969). *Phil. Mag.* **19**, 423.

G. T. HAHN, B. L. AVERBACH, W. S. OWEN, and M. COHEN (1959). *Fracture* (Eds. B. L. AVERBACH *et al.*), p. 91, Wiley, New York.

E. O. HALL (1951). *Proc. R. Soc.* A**64**, 747.

R. W. HERZBERG and R. W. KRAFT (1963). *Trans. Am. Inst. Min. metall. Petrol. Engrs* **227**, 580.

P. B. HIRSCH and F. J. HUMPHREYS (1970). *Proc. R. Soc.* A**318**, 45.

—— and A. KELLY (1965). *Phil. Mag.* **12**, 881.

F. J. HUMPHREYS and A. T. STEWART (1972). *Surface Science* **31**, 389.

E. INESON (1965). *The Development and Application of Very Strong Steels.* Ministry of Defence Inter-Service Metallurgical Research Council Publication, ISMET 3452, H.M.S.O., London.

M. C. INMAN and H. R. TIPLER (1963). *Metall. Rev.* **8**, 105.

G. R. IRWIN and A. A. WELLS (1965). *Metall. Rev.* **10**, 223.

R. L. JONES (1969). *Acta metall.* **17**, 229.

—— and A. KELLY (1968). *Proceedings Second Bolton Landing Conference on Oxide Dispersion Strengthening*, p. 229, Gordon and Breach, New York.

A. KELLY and M. E. FINE (1957). *Acta metall.* **5**, 365.

—— and H. LILHOLT (1969). *Phil. Mag.* **20**, 311.

—— and R. B. NICHOLSON (1963). *Prog. mater. Sci.* **10**, 149.

A. J. KENNEDY (1962). *Processes of Creep and Fatigue in Metals*, p. 306, Oliver and Boyd, Edinburgh.

G. LONGFORD (1970). *Met. Trans.* **1**, 465.

D. McLEAN (1968). *Trans. Am. Inst. Min. metall. Petrol. Engrs* **242**, 1193.

N. F. MOTT and F. R. N. NABARRO (1948). *Rep. Conf. Strength of Solids*, p. 1, Physical Society, London.

R. B. NICHOLSON (1971). *Strong Microstructures from the Solid State.* In *Strengthening Methods in Crystals*, p. 535 (Eds. A. KELLY and R. B. NICHOLSON), Elsevier, London.

J. NIXDORF (1970). *Proc. R. Soc.* A**319**, 17.

J. A. NOCK, Jr. and H. Y. HUNSICKER (1963). *J. Metals* **15**, 216.

E. OROWAN (1948). *Symposium on Internal Stresses in Metals and Alloys*, p. 451, Institute of Metals, London.

W. S. OWEN (1964). *Proc. R. Soc.* A**282**, 79.

I. G. PALMER and G. C. SMITH (1968). *Proceedings Second Bolton Landing Conference on Oxide Dispersion Strengthening*, p. 253, Gordon and Breach, New York.

N. J. PETCH (1953). *J. Iron Steel Inst.* **174**, 25.

—— (1958). *Phil. Mag.* **3**, 1089.

V. A. PHILLIPS (1965). *Phil. Mag.* **11**, 775.

O. PRESTON and N. J. GRANT (1961). *Trans. Am. Inst. Min. metall. Petrol. Engrs* **221**, 164.

I. SAXL (1964). *Czech. J. Phys.* B**14**, 381.

G. R. SPEICH and R. A. ORIANI (1965). *Trans. Am. Inst. Min. metall. Petrol. Engrs* **233**, 623.

G. THOMAS, D. SCHMATZ, and W. GERBERICH (1965). *High Strength Materials* (Ed. V. ZACKAY), p. 251, Wiley, New York.

M. VON HEIMENDAHL and G. THOMAS (1964). *Trans. Am. Inst. Min. metall. Petrol. Engrs* **230**, 1520.

N. J. WADSWORTH (1959). *Internal Stresses and Fatigue in Metals* (Eds. RASSWEILER and GRUBE), p. 382, Elsevier, Amsterdam.

W. W. WEBB and W. D. FORGENG (1958). *Acta metall.* **6**, 462.

A. A. WELLS (1967). *Contemp. Phys.* **8**, 75.

D. V. WILSON (1955). *Trans. Am. Soc. Metals* **47**, 321.

—— (1965). *Acta metall.* **13**, 801.

P. G. WINCHELL and M. COHEN (1962). *Trans. Am. Soc. Metals* **55**, 347.

D. K. WORN and S. F. MARTON (1961). *Powder Metallurgy.* (Ed. LESZYNSKI), p. 309, Interscience, New York.

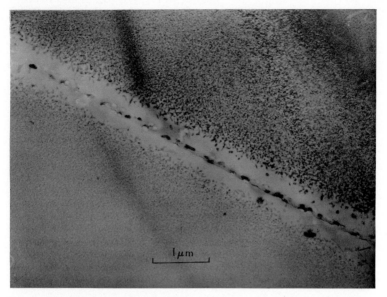

1. An electron micrograph of a grain boundary region in an aluminium alloy containing 6 per cent zinc and 3 per cent magnesium. Ageing 3 hours at 180°C produces a region denuded of precipitate at the grain boundaries.

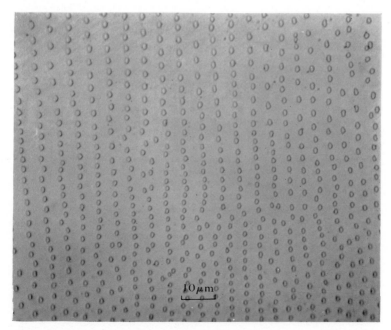

2. A section normal to the direction of solidification of a copper–chromium alloy of eutectic composition which has been frozen so as to produce aligned rods of chromium in a copper matrix.

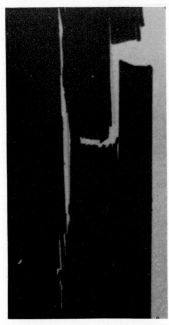

3. Fracture at the end of a notch in copper containing aligned silica fibres. Instead of the notch advancing from the side of the specimen the composite material has split parallel to the fibres.

5. The appearance, in transmitted light, of an epoxy resin containing silica fibres which has been deformed at 77 K. The matrix is traversed by a set of parallel cracks running normal to the fibres.

4. Tangles of dislocations forming a cell structure. The cell walls contain particles of silica. The specimen is of polycrystalline copper and contains a volume fraction of 2·6 per cent of silica. It has been deformed 34 per cent in tension at 77 K.

5

FIBRE REINFORCEMENT

BECAUSE the breaking strength of a glass or of an inherently strong solid is sensitive to the presence of cracks, a useful article with a reproducible and reliable strength can only be produced by forming fibres of the strong solid into a fibrous bundle. A parallel bundle of fibres of these materials will have a breaking strength much less sensitive to cracking than a monolithic piece of the same shape. This is clearly because the geometry ensures that cracks must either be very short, across a fibre, or be parallel to the fibres and hence harmless. A strong solid with a high and very reproducible strength can then be made, in principle, by arranging strong strands of the material in the form of a parallel bundle. Ropes of flax and hemp fibres are made this way. The strength in a direction normal to the fibre axis is not large and ropes are only used in tension parallel to the fibre direction.

The individual fibres must be joined together, somehow. With natural fibres such as flax or synthetic polyester fibres this is easily done by coiling the individual fibres into a rope. Stress can then be transmitted between the individual fibres by sliding friction when the rope is stretched, since due to the helical shape of the individual fibres they are pressed against one another strongly and the normal pressure between fibres is increased as they are strained parallel to the axis of the helix. This helical form is easily attained when spinning together polyester and natural fibres for a number of reasons. These are, firstly that the breaking strain of the individual fibres is large and their moduli quite small ($\lesssim 5 \times 10^6$ psi) and so they can sustain sharp bends in the making of the helix. Secondly, the individual fibres fail by drawing apart of the individual long chain molecules; they are therefore not so notch-sensitive as crystalline material and stress cannot be highly localized in them.† A third point, clearly connected with the other two, is that rubbing of the individual fibres against one another does not lead to a drastic reduction in the strength of the individual fibres. None of these conditions is fulfilled by the inherently strong solids.

Strong glass fibres, with a strength very sensitive to surface damage, cannot be formed into a rope of useful strength without some medium to protect the surface and bind the individual fibres together. A suitable medium is a resin or plastic. Using this the strength of glass can be exploited. This is the principle of glass-reinforced plastics. A composite material analogous to glass-reinforced plastics may also be made using other strong solids with much greater elastic stiffness than glass. Such are carbon fibres and boron filaments (section 3.5). Some strong solids are available in the form of whiskers. Carbon and boron fibres of strengths up to 3.5 GN m^{-2} (500 000 psi) are much less sensitive to surface condition than filaments of the mineral glasses. The high strengths are only obtainable in these materials when they are in fibrous form and so a matrix or binder must be found to produce a useful article.

The matrix carries out the following functions: (1) it provides a means by which load is applied to the strong phase. This function is carried out by interfibre friction in a conventional rope; (2) it separates the individual fibres and prevents a brittle crack passing completely across a section of the compact entirely in the strong and usually brittle phase; and (3) in the case of glass, it protects the surface of the individual fibres so that the strength is not lost by abrasion of the surface either by extraneous matter or by other fibres. In carbon, boron, or glass-reinforced plastics the composite material is put together in order to exploit a property of the strong phase and a plastic is used because it is a suitable binder. The word 'reinforced' is a misnomer but has historical sanction because the technologist has aimed to exploit the easy fabricability of plastics, using methods already to-hand

† At least not until they have been highly drawn to produce a very well-oriented arrangement.

in order to form the composite material. To him the plastic appears 'reinforced'.

The simplest case of a fibrous solid is the one with straight, parallel, isotropic, and homogeneous fibres in a similar matrix. The composite is heterogeneous on a scale of size comparable with the fibre diameter and anisotropic. The science of fibrous composite materials attempts to explain the mechanical properties of the composite in terms of those of the (usually) two components and of their interaction. The engineer, and particularly the engineer concerned with design, wishes to predict the properties of the fibrous composite body from those of the two constituents without reference to the heterogeneity. He is concerned with the 'effective' properties of the composite.

In this chapter we deal first with the elastic moduli of an aligned composite. We then deal with some aspects of the stress–strain curve. In a fibrous composite the two components fail at different strains and some consideration of this is necessary in order to introduce a number of the concepts governing the strength of the composite. Following this we discuss in a semi-intuitive fashion the transfer of stress between fibre and matrix. This discussion emphasizes that any fibrous composite containing a fibre-end or discontinuous fibres cannot be fully elastic if once extended to a strain close to that necessary to break a fibre. In section 5·4 we are then able to deal with the strength of composites containing fibres of variable strength, with local stress concentrations in section 5.5, and with the strength of arrays of discontinuous fibres in 5.6. Section 5.7 suggests how to measure the critical aspect ratio of fibres in a given matrix, 5.8 with the behaviour of cracks in composites and 5.9 with orientation effects. Section 5.10 deals very briefly with some questions of engineering design.

5.1. Elastic moduli of an aligned composite

Classical elasticity theory shows that for a multiphase material the average of the stress components over the volume may be expressed as functions of the tractions at the boundary only; the volume average of the strain components can be expressed as functions of the surface displacements only (Hill 1963). Relations between the average stresses and average strains in the unidirectional fibrous composite may then be studied and used to derive the elastic moduli by considering surface tractions (or displacements) which when applied to a homogeneous body give rise to uniform stresses (or strains).

An aligned composite will have nine independent elastic constants if it is orthotropic—possessing three mutually perpendicular planes of symmetry—and five independent constants if it is, in addition, isotropic in a plane normal to the fibre axis. Isotropy normal to the fibre axis permits variation of fibre cross-section and of fibre arrangement. Rigorous bounds for the independent moduli can be obtained (Hill 1964, Hashin 1965).

It is possible to select five independent moduli such that, for specified states of stress and of strain, only one of these moduli appears in the strain energy function. Such moduli are

$$E = C_{33} - \left(\frac{2C_{13}^2}{C_{11} + C_{12}} \right)$$

$$G = G_{xz} = G_{yz} = C_{44}$$

$$K_{xy} = \tfrac{1}{2}(C_{11} + C_{12})$$

$$G_{xy} = \frac{E_x}{2(1 + \nu_{xy})} = \tfrac{1}{2}(C_{11} - C_{12})$$

and C_{33}. The subscript z or 3 indicates the direction of the fibre axis, with x and y two perpendicular directions in the cross-section. E is the Young's modulus, parallel to the fibres and E_x that normal to them. G the shear modulus for shear on a plane parallel to the fibres in the direction of the fibres; K_{xy} the plane strain bulk modulus for loading in the (x, y) plane, without contraction along z. Other important moduli may be derived from these five (see Appendix C, Table 4).

By using a variational principle to determine bounds for the strain energy, Hashin (1965) obtained bounds for K_{xy}, G_{xy} and G. Bounds for K_{xy}, the axial Young's modulus E, and Poisson's ratio ν had previously been obtained by Hill (1964) using a different method. ν is the Poisson contraction relating transverse contraction to strain parallel to the fibres.

These bounds for *arbitrary cross-sectional geometry* can be represented by the following expressions which show the deviation from elementary bounds which correspond to the phases being deformed in parallel (Voigt average) or in series (Reuss average). V_1 and V_2 are the component volume fractions.

$$E = E_1 V_1 + E_2 V_2 + 4 V_1 V_2 (\nu_2 - \nu_1)^2 \bigg/ \left(\frac{V_2}{K_{p_1}} + \frac{V_1}{K_{p_2}} + \frac{1}{G_2} \right), \quad (5.1)$$

$$\nu = \nu_1 V_1 + \nu_2 V_2 + V_1 V_2 (\nu_1 - \nu_2) \left(\frac{1}{K_{p_2}} - \frac{1}{K_{p_1}} \right) \bigg/$$
$$\left(\frac{V_2}{K_{p_1}} + \frac{V_1}{K_{p_2}} + \frac{1}{G_2} \right), \quad (5.2)$$

$$\frac{1}{K_{xy}} = \frac{V_1}{K_{p_1}} + \frac{V_2}{K_{p_2}} - V_1 V_2 \left(\frac{1}{K_{p_1}} - \frac{1}{K_{p_2}} \right)^2 \bigg/ \left(\frac{V_2}{K_{p_1}} + \frac{V_1}{K_{p_2}} + \frac{1}{G_2} \right), \quad (5.3)$$

$$\frac{1}{G} = \frac{V_1}{G_1} + \frac{V_2}{G_2} - V_1 V_2 (G_1 - G_2)^2 / [G_1 G_2 \{G_1(1 + V_1) + G_2 V_2\}], \quad (5.4)$$

$$\frac{1}{G_{xy}} = \frac{V_1}{G_1} + \frac{V_2}{G_2} - V_1 V_2 (G_1 - G_2)^2 \bigg/ \left\{ G_1^2 G_2^2 \left(\frac{V_2}{G_1} + \frac{V_1}{G_2} + \frac{1}{G_2} + \frac{2}{K_{p_2}} \right) \right\},$$
$$(5.5)$$

where K_{p_1} and K_{p_2} are the plane strain bulk moduli of the two components. The plane strain bulk modulus of an isotropic solid is equal to $3K/2(1+\nu)$ where K is the bulk modulus. If $G_2 > G_1$ and $K_{p_2} > K_{p_1}$ then these expressions represent the upper bounds on the five moduli. The lower bounds are obtained by interchanging the suffixes 1 and 2. If $G_1 > G_2$ and $K_{p_1} > K_{p_2}$, then the expressions give the lower bounds, and upper bounds are obtained by transposing suffixes. In the special case where $G_1 = G_2$ the bounds coincide and we have exact expressions for all five moduli. It may be noted from equation (5.1) that the

Young's modulus of a undirectional composite cannot be less than the 'law of mixtures' estimate.†

Hill (1964) shows that the bounds on E, v, and K_{xy} for a composite with arbitrary cross-sectional geometry correspond to the exact results for the rudimentary composite represented in Fig. 5.1 when the sleeve has the rigidity modulus appearing in

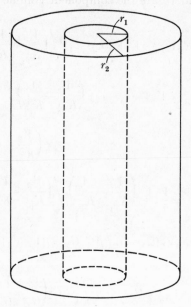

FIG. 5.1. Composite cylinder model. The relative volume fractions are determined by the radii from

$$V_1 = r_2^2/r_1^2, \ V_2 = (r_2^2 - r_1^2)/r_2^2.$$

the denominator of expressions (5.1), (5.2), and (5.3) and $V_1 = r_1^2/r_2^2$. The expressions given for E, v, K_{xy}, and G (but not for G_{xy}) are also exact results for a composite cylinder assemblage when fibres of material 1 are embedded in material 2. The composite cylinder assemblage is one in which the composite is modelled

---

† This is easily seen, since for a possible extension ε under uniaxial load the actual energy of deformation of a unit volume (containing many fibres) $\frac{1}{2}E\varepsilon^2$ *exceeds* that of the fibres and matrix, imagined free of any mutual constraint, viz. $\frac{1}{2}(E_f V_f + E_m V_m)\varepsilon^2$ (Hill 1964).

as a set of cylinders as in Fig. 5.1 with the triangular voids between contiguous outer cylinders filled with smaller composite cylinders containing the same volume ratio of components 1 and 2, and so on until all voids are filled. This model was introduced by Hashin and Rosen (1964). It follows that the bounds on E, ν, K_{xy} and G for the arbitrary phase geometry are the 'best possible' bounds in terms of the information available (Hill 1964, Hashin 1970).

In practically important fibrous composites, the fibre is more rigid than the matrix, i.e. $G_1 > G_2$, and the result for the composite cylinder assemblage then coincides exactly with the lower bound for E, ν, K_{xy}, and G. An exact result for the transverse shear modulus of the composite cylinder assemblage has not so far been obtained. A lower bound is given by equation (5.5) (Hashin 1970); this supersedes that given by Hashin and Rosen (1964). The upper bound derived by Hashin and Rosen is given by Rosen (1970) as

$$G_{xy} = G_2 \frac{(\alpha + \beta_2 V_1)(1 + \rho V_1^3) - 3 V_1 V_2^2 \beta_2^2}{(\alpha - V_1)(1 + \rho V_1^3) - 3 V_1 V_2^2 \beta_2^2}, \qquad (5.6)$$

where

$$\alpha = \frac{\gamma + \beta_2}{\gamma - 1}; \quad \beta = \frac{1}{3 - 4\nu}; \quad \rho = \frac{\beta_2 - \gamma \beta_1}{1 + \gamma \beta_1}; \quad \gamma = \frac{G_1}{G_2}.$$

The expressions (5.1) and (5.2) for the axial Young's modulus and Poisson ratio show that the upper and lower bounds are not far apart and hence can be used to estimate moduli of the composite if those of the (usually) two components are given. In the other cases the bounds vary widely and many attempts have been made to give closer estimates for particular geometries of cross-section. These are reviewed by Chamis and Sendeckyj (1968).

The composite cylinder assemblage represents an extreme case which would not, at first sight, be expected to serve as a satisfactory model for a real composite since it is built up from fibres of varying diameter each surrounded by an appropriate thickness of matrix. However, as Rosen (1970) points out the model incorporates randomness of structure and permits the derivation of simple closed-form expressions for four of the five elastic moduli. For the transverse shear modulus, Rosen recommends the upper bound given by equation (5.6). He uses the expressions for E, ν, K_{xy}, and G given in equations (5.1) to (5.4) which are rigorous lower bounds (when $G_1 > G_2$) but can also provide upper bounds.

Equation (5.1) shows that for E, the Young's modulus parallel to the fibres, the departure of the actual value from that given simply by

$$E = E_1 V_1 + E_2 V_2 \tag{5.7}$$

is very small since it depends on $(\nu_2 - \nu_1)^2$. As an example, if we take $\nu_1 = 0.25$, $\nu_2 = 0.4$, which could apply to carbon or to boron fibres in an epoxy resin, then at $V_1 = 0.5$ the departure of the elastic modulus of the composite from that given by the simple law of mixtures is at most 2 per cent.

From equation (5.2) we see that

$$\nu \gtrless (\nu_1 V_1 + \nu_2 V_2) \tag{5.8}$$

according to whether

$$(\nu_1 - \nu_2) \left(\frac{1}{K_{p_2}} - \frac{1}{K_{p_1}} \right) \gtrless 0. \tag{5.9}$$

Since ν_1 is usually less than ν_2 and $K_{p_1} > K_{p_2}$, the value of ν is less than that given by the law of mixtures in practical cases.

The form of equations (5.3) and (5.4) illustrates that the value of the plane strain bulk modulus of the composite and the value of the shear modulus parallel to the fibres are both dominated by properties of the matrix, since $1/K_{p_2} \gg 1/K_{p_1}$ and $1/G_2 \gg 1/G_1$.

The dominance by the shear modulus of a compliant matrix in controlling the axial shear modulus of the composite can be appreciated by noting that if G_1/G_2 is as large as 100, then at a volume fraction of 0.5 of fibres, G/G_2 is only about 3. Equation (5.6) shows that the transverse shear modulus is also dominated by the shear modulus of the matrix when this is much less than that of the fibres, though here the values of the Poisson ratio of both fibre and matrix are involved. If in equation (5.6) we take $G_1/G_2 = 100$ with $\nu_1 = 0.25$, $\nu_2 = 0.40$ we obtain $G_{xy} = 5.3$ G_2, at $V_1 = V_2 = 0.5$.

The transverse Young's modulus E_t of the transversely isotropic composite can be written in terms of the quantities already defined as

$$E_t = \frac{4K_{xy}\, G_{xy}}{K_{xy} + G_{xy}\left(1 + \dfrac{4K_{xy}\, \nu^2}{E}\right)}. \tag{5.10}$$

Its variation with volume fraction according to this equation is shown in Fig. 5.2 for the case $E_1/E_2 = 100$ and $\nu_2/\nu_1 = 1.75$;

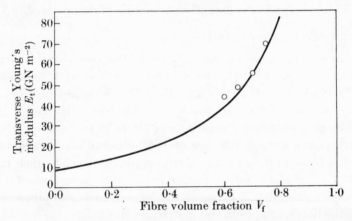

Fig. 5.2. Plot of transverse Young's modulus versus volume fraction for boron fibres of Young's modulus $420\ \mathrm{GN\ m^{-2}}$ and Poisson ratio 0.2 in an epoxy resin matrix of Young's modulus $4.2\ \mathrm{GN\ m^{-2}}$ and Poisson ratio 0.35. The full line is the theoretical curve for $(E_t/E_m) = 100$. Circles are the experimental points of Whitney and Riley (1966).

the figures correspond to boron fibres in epoxy resin. At a volume fraction of 0.5 the ratio of E_t to the Young's modulus of the matrix is only 3.5. Figure 5.2 also shows the comparison between the predictions of equation (5.10) and experimental results of Whitney and Riley (1966). The theoretical predictions are well borne out by experiment.

5.2. Stress–strain curves

The prediction of the breaking stress of a fibre composite when strained in tension parallel to the fibres involves a knowledge of the breaking stresses and strains of all the individual fibres. The problem becomes a statistical one. This is deferred until section 5.4, because some general and important points can be made, which are well supported by experiment, for the case of fibres of identical breaking stress and strain. Furthermore, the influence of the matrix and the conditions under which fibres will in fact reinforce the matrix are most easily seen for the case of fibres of uniform properties. We assume then that all fibres have an identical breaking stress and strain and we define the strength of the composite σ_c as the maximum load divided by the initial area of cross-section of the specimen.

5.2.1. *Plastically deformable matrix*

In general there are four stages in the stress–strain curve shown see—Fig. 5.3 (McDanels, Jech, and Weeton, 1960, 1965). These are; (1) the matrix and fibres both elongate elastically; (2) the matrix flows plastically and the fibres elastically; (3) both components are plastic; and (4) failure of one or other component occurs. Whether or not failure of one component leads to immediate failure of the composite depends upon the relative volume fractions. In this and subsequent sections of this chapter subscripts f, c, and m will be used to denote properties of the fibres, composite and matrix, respectively.

In stage (1) the elastic modulus is given by equation (5.1). Small transverse stresses arise due to the differences in Poisson's ratio. These are never large—see for example Bloom and Wilson (1967) for an exact analysis. Limits may be placed upon these stresses very simply (Kelly 1971). Transition to stage (2) occurs when the matrix yields. Due to the internal stresses plasticity theory predicts that yield will start at a strain ε_{yc} a little less than the yield strain of the matrix ε_{ym} and be complete at a slightly larger strain (Mulhern, Rogers, and Spencer 1967). Experiment confirms that $\varepsilon_{yc} \approx \varepsilon_{ym}$ if the fibre spacing (and hence radius for other than very small V_f) exceeds 10 μm or so.

In stage (2) a lower limit to the slope of the stress–strain curve must be $E_f V_f$ (see, for instance, Hill 1964). For fibre spacings less than 10 μm or so the matrix shows an increased rate of work-hardening over that of the matrix at similar strains without fibres

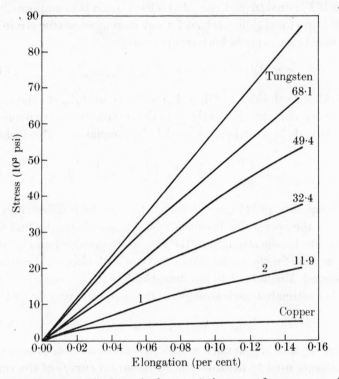

FIG. 5.3. Experimentally determined stress–strain curves of copper composites containing tungsten fibres. The numbers give the volume fractions of tungsten in per cent. The fibres were continuous except for the curve for 32·4 per cent. Regions 1 and 2 of the stress–strain curve are indicated. The data is taken from D. L. McDanels, R. W. Jech, and J. W. Weeton (1963). *N.A.S.A. Technical Note* D-1881. See also *Trans. Am. Inst. Min. metall. Petrol. Engrs* **233**, 636 (1965).

(see section 4.4). At larger spacings one may neglect the contribution of the matrix to the slope of the stress–strain curve in stage (2).

If fibres show plastic deformation, theory predicts a yield at a strain less than that of the fibres tested alone due to the *compressive* effect of the plastically deforming matrix. However, the effect is not large enough to have been reported (see McDanels *et al.* 1965). When both components are deforming plastically, failure of the composite is governed by stability conditions (Kelly and Tyson 1965*b*). Following the treatment in section 3.6, if F_c equal to $(\sigma_f A_f + \sigma_m A_m)$ is the load on the composite, the condition for stability is that for any increment of true strain $d\varepsilon$ (which is the same in both components),

$$dF_c = \sigma_f \, dA_f + A_f \, d\sigma_f + \sigma_m \, dA_m + A_m \, d\sigma_m > 0. \tag{5.10}$$

Dividing both sides by $(A_f + A_m)$ where A_f and A_m are the areas of fibre and matrix respectively in the composite, and remembering that $d\varepsilon = - \, dA_f/A_f = - \, dA_m/A_m$, equation (5.10) yields

$$V_f \left(\frac{d\sigma_f}{d\varepsilon} - \sigma_f \right) + V_m \left(\frac{d\sigma_m}{d\varepsilon} - \sigma_m \right) \geqslant 0. \tag{5.11}$$

The equality (5.11) may be solved to find the tensile strain at which the composite becomes unstable and hence to find the ultimate tensile strength of the composite provided an analytic expression for the stress–strain curve of both fibre and matrix is assumed. Mileiko (1969) has done this.†

The ultimate tensile strength of the composite may be written

$$\sigma_{uc} = \sigma_{uf} V_f \lambda_f + \sigma_{um} V_m \lambda_m. \tag{5.12}$$

λ_f and λ_m are, in general, complicated expressions containing the constants used to describe the stress–strain curves of the components. If the ultimate tensile *strains* of both components are the same, λ_f and λ_m both equal unity and we have,

$$\sigma_{uc} = \sigma_{uf} V_f + \sigma_{um} V_m. \tag{5.13}$$

This equation provides an upper limit to the tensile strength of the composite. If the ultimate tensile strain of the fibre is much

---

† Mileiko assumed for both matrix and fibre a true stress–true strain relation of the form

$$\varepsilon = (\sigma/\sigma^*)^n;$$

other forms for the stress–strain relation lead to the same result.

less than that of the matrix and $\sigma_{uf} V_f \gg \sigma_{um} V_m$, equation (5.12) reduces to

$$\sigma_{uc} = \sigma_{uf} V_f + \sigma'_m (1 - V_f) \qquad (5.14)$$

where σ'_m is the stress on the matrix at the ultimate tensile *strain* of the fibres. The envelope of possible strengths for the composite is shown in Fig. 5.4. Strength must lie within the triangle A O B.

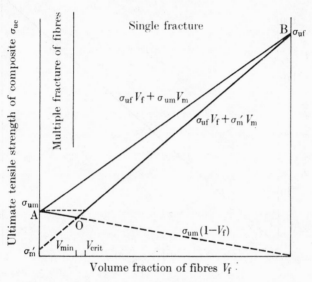

FIG. 5.4. The predicted variation of composite strength, σ_c, with volume fraction, V_f, for reinforcement with ductile and with brittle continuous fibres.

Equation (5.14) is the essential one for considering the strengths expected of fibre-reinforced materials. Since very strong fibres will strain elastically to their UTS, the ultimate tensile strains of the composites are always and σ'_m is very small with respect to σ_{uf}. If the matrix is such as to produce a small critical length (see below) and if the fibres are brittle, then failure of one fibre leads to fracture of the others at the cross-section where the first one fails. This will lead to imme-diate failure of the composite unless the volume fraction of fibres is small. If such is the case, then strain-hardening of the matrix, as it undergoes plastic flow, may enable the cross-section where the fibres have failed to increase its load-bearing capacity. Provided the matrix can work-harden then at small values of V_f the strength is not given by (5.14). It will only be given by (5.14) provided

$$\sigma_{uc} \geqslant \sigma_{um}(1-V_f), \qquad (5.14a)$$

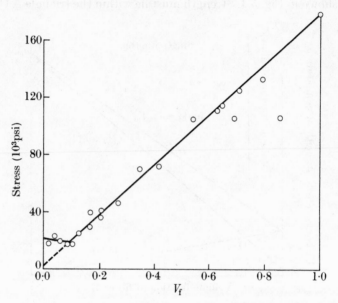

FIG. 5.5(a). Measured ultimate tensile strength of copper reinforced with continuous brittle tungsten wires of 0·5 mm diameter, as a function of volume fraction of tungsten.

where σ_{um} is the ultimate tensile stress of the matrix. Equation (5.14) will only apply provided $V_f > V_{min}$ where V_{min} is given by,

$$V_{min} = \frac{\sigma_{um}-\sigma'_m}{\sigma_{uf}+(\sigma_{um}-\sigma'_m)} = \frac{\sigma_w}{\sigma_{uf}+\sigma_w} \qquad (5.14b)$$

where $\sigma_w = \sigma_{um}-\sigma'_m$ is the total increment in nominal stress which can be obtained in a tensile test on the matrix. For $V_f < V_{min}$ the strength is given by $\sigma_c = \sigma_{um}(1-V_f)$ (Fig. 5.4) for a very brittle fibre; an example is shown in Fig. 5.5(a).

If the matrix has a larger failure strain than the (brittle) fibres and can also work-harden then a composite with a UTS greater than that of the matrix alone will only be obtained by the

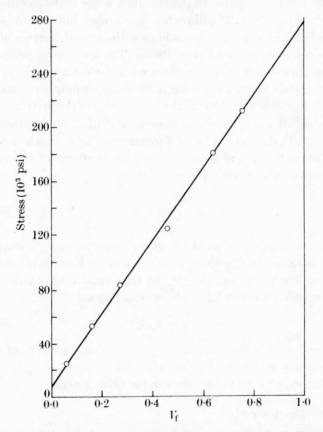

FIG 5.5(b). Failure stress in compression for the same material as in Fig. 5.5(a). (Data from Kelly and Tyson 1965.)

addition of the fibres provided that $\sigma_c \geqslant \sigma_{um}$. From (5.14) this defines a critical volume fraction of fibres given by

$$V_{crit} = \frac{\sigma_{um} - \sigma'_m}{\sigma_{uf} - \sigma'_m} \approx \frac{\sigma_w}{\sigma_{uf}}. \tag{5.14c}$$

V_{crit} must be exceeded if the addition of strong fibres with a small breaking strain is to provide a composite with a breaking strength greater than that of the work-hardened matrix alone.

In the range of volume fractions to the left of $V_{\min}$ the composite can be elongated to strains much larger than the ultimate strain of the fibres. The fibres are then broken into a set of short lengths which tend to a lower limit with increasing strain of the composite (Kelly and Tyson 1965a). The lower limit arises because plastic flow of the matrix produces a shear stress τ at the fibre–matrix interface. τ must have an upper limit governed by the failure stress in shear of the interface or of the matrix. For a fibre of radius r the maximum increment of stress $d\sigma$ produced in a length dx is equal to the force exerted by τ, which is equal to τ times the area of interface, i.e. $2\pi r\tau\, dx$, divided by the area of cross-section of the fibre πr^2, yielding

$$\frac{d\sigma}{dx} = \frac{2\tau}{r}. \tag{5.15}$$

Integration of equation (5.15) shows that a stress σ_{uf} is reached in a distance $r\sigma_{uf}/2\tau$ which provides a lower limit to the size of pieces. The pieces will vary in size from $r\sigma_{uf}/2\tau$ up to twice this value which is called l_{crit}—the *critical length*.

$$l_{crit} = \sigma_{uf}d/2\tau, \tag{5.16}$$

where $d = 2r$ is the diameter. l_{crit} is the shortest length of fibre which may be broken by flow of a given matrix. (l_{crit}/d) is the *critical aspect ratio* of the fibres in the given matrix.

5.2.2. *Brittle matrix*

If the matrix is brittle then $\varepsilon_{ym} \approx \varepsilon_{um}$. If in addition, $\varepsilon_{uf} \gg \varepsilon_{um}$, the matrix fails first. We again have a critical volume fraction to consider. Either the fibres can sustain the load thrown upon them when the matrix breaks or they cannot. The transition between these two occurs at a volume fraction

$$V_f = \sigma_{um}/\{\sigma_{um}+(\sigma_{uf}-\sigma_f')\} \tag{5.17}$$

where σ_f' is the stress on the fibres at the failure strain of the matrix. At smaller volume fractions than defined by equation

(5.17) failure of the matrix results in failure of the composite. For larger volume fractions the matrix becomes split into a series of thin discs. An actual example is shown in Plate 5. The thickness of these discs, i.e. the spacing of the cracks in the matrix, must vary between x' and $2x'$. x' is determined by the distance over which the stretching of the fibres passing through the matrix can transfer a load into the matrix, by means of a shear force at the interface sufficient to break the matrix. If $d\sigma$ is the *stress* transferred to the matrix in distance dx, we have

$$V_m\, d\sigma = (2V_f/r)\tau\, dx, \qquad (5.18)$$

since $(2V_f/r)\, dx$ is the area of interface per unit length of composite and so the shearing force is $(2V_f/r)\tau\, dx$. So, to transfer a stress equal to σ_{um} we require a length of at least

$$x' = \left(\frac{V_m}{V_f}\right)\frac{\sigma_{um}r}{2\tau}. \qquad (5.19)$$

Consideration of the process of cracking leads to the conclusion that cracking will occur over a very small range of strain (Aveston, Cooper, and Kelly 1971) and that the elongation on cracking varies between $\varepsilon_{um}(1+\alpha/2)$ and $\varepsilon_{um}(1+3\alpha/4)$ where $\alpha = (E_m V_m/E_f V_f)$. After cracking is complete the slope of the stress–strain curve is equal to $E_f V_f$ until failure of the composite occurs at a stress

$$\sigma_{uc} = \sigma_{uf} V_f. \qquad (5.20)$$

An example of a stress–strain curve is shown in Fig. 5.6 and the variation of behaviour with variation of volume fraction in Fig. 5.7. This type of stress–strain curve is found in fibre-reinforced cement and plasters. The critical volume fraction given by (5.17) can be very small for such feeble matrices and so small volume fractions of strong fibres lead to marked increases in strength.

A very interesting discovery has been made recently which follows from the form of equation (5.19). The work done by the applied stress during the cracking process is independent of the fibre diameter and depends on the elastic modulus of the composite and cracking strain of the matrix. When multiple cracking occurs the area of crack surface produced per unit volume of composite is proportional to $(1/x')$ times V_m and hence

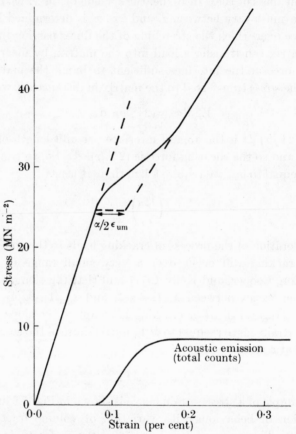

FIG. 5.6. Stress–strain curve parallel to the fibres of a composite of Portland cement containing 8·4 per cent of aligned steel wires of 0·132 mm diameter. $E_m V_m / E_f V_f = \alpha = 0.82$. The final crack spacing is 0·6 mm. The curve labelled 'acoustic emission' shows that cracking started at a strain of 0·08 per cent and is complete at a strain of 0·14 per cent. Data from J. Aveston and J. Sillwood.

to $2(V_f/r)$. If the production of unit area of crack surface requires an energy γ_m then the work necessary to produce the cracks— proportional to $\gamma_m (2V_f/r)$—increases without limit as r decreases. Since the work available from the applied stress remains constant, it follows that $(2V_f/r)$ may be made so large that cracking will not occur at the normal cracking strain of the matrix. The matrix is prevented from cracking and shows larger failure strains in the composite than it does if tested alone. The effect has been observed in a number of systems (Aveston, Cooper, and Kelly 1971, Cooper and Sillwood 1972).

We have assumed in section 5.2.1 and 5.2.2 that brittle fibres or a brittle matrix show a well-defined breaking strength, so that

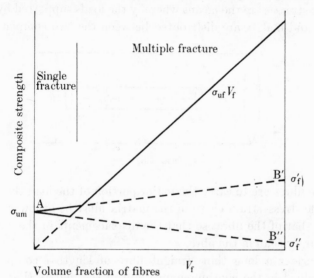

FIG. 5.7. The predicted variation in composite strength with volume fraction for a composite with strong fibres of larger breaking strain than that of the matrix. σ_f' applies for $E_f > E_m$; σ_f'' for $E_f < E_m$.

for instance, σ_{uf} is well-defined even for fibres which show no plastic flow before fracture. In general this is a poor assumption and the value of σ_{uf} to be used in equation (5.14) will depend on how failure of the individual fibre occurs and on possible dependence of σ_{uf} on fibre length and other factors. This is considered in section 5.4.

5.3. Transfer of stress to a fibre

To consider the stiffness and strength of discontinuous fibre composites and the effects that accompany breaking of a fibre within a continuous composite, we need to take account of how stress is transferred to or from a fibre. If a composite body containing uniaxially aligned fibres is stressed in a direction parallel to the fibres the axial elastic displacements in the fibre and in the matrix will be different because of the difference in elastic moduli of the two components. This means that shear strains are produced on all planes parallel to the axis of the fibres in the direction of this axis. The strains and the resulting shear stresses are the means whereby the loads supported by the fibre and matrix are distributed between the two components.

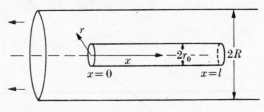

FIG. 5.8.

If the fibres are to carry the major portion of the load then the tensile stress–strain curve of the matrix must be of lower slope than that of the fibres so that the displacements in the matrix are larger than in the fibre.

Consider a long thin straight fibre of length l completely embedded in the continuous medium of the matrix (Fig. 5.8). This will represent sufficiently well for our purpose, the state of affairs around a single fibre. We assume that the matrix as a whole is strained homogeneously, but locally the state of uniform stress and strain is perturbed by transfer of load to the fibres. This will be a good approximation for a dilute concentration of fibres.

The following treatment is due to Cox (1952). We suppose the composite as a whole is subject to a strain e in the direction of the fibre. If P is the load in the fibre at a distance x from the end then we assume

$$\frac{\mathrm{d}P}{\mathrm{d}x} = H(u-v), \qquad (5.21)$$

where u is the longitudinal displacement in the fibre and v is the corresponding displacement the matrix would undergo at the same point if the fibre were absent. H is a constant, the value of which depends on the geometrical arrangement of the fibres and matrix and on their respective elastic moduli.

We have

$$P = E_f A_f (\mathrm{d}u/\mathrm{d}x) \tag{5.22}$$

and $\mathrm{d}v/\mathrm{d}x = e = \text{constant}$. E_f is Young's modulus, and A_f is the area of cross-section of the fibre.

Differentiating (5.21) and substituting (5.22) we have

$$\frac{\mathrm{d}^2 P}{\mathrm{d}x^2} = H\left(\frac{P}{E_f A_f} - e\right). \tag{5.23}$$

To solve this differential equation we take

$$P = E_f A_f e + R \sinh \beta x + S \cosh \beta x \tag{5.24}$$

where R and S are constants. The end conditions are $P = 0$, at $x = 0$ and at $x = l$. We then obtain for the distribution of tensile stress in the fibre, $\sigma (= P/A_f)$

$$\sigma = E_f e\left\{1 - \frac{\cosh \beta(l/2 - x)}{\cosh \beta l/2}\right\} \tag{5.25}$$

where $\beta = \sqrt{(H/E_f A_f)}$.

Since no load is transferred across the end faces of a fibre the tensile stress in a fibre builds up from the ends and this equation shows that only infinitely long fibres can be strained to the strain of the composite. The average tensile stress in a fibre is

$$\bar{\sigma} = E_f e\left(1 - \frac{\tanh \beta l/2}{\beta l/2}\right). \tag{5.26}$$

On this simple model Young's modulus of the composite will be

$$E_c = E_f V_f\left(1 - \frac{\tanh \beta l/2}{\beta l/2}\right) + E_m(1 - V_f) \tag{5.27}$$

where V_f is the fractional area of the cross-section occupied by the fibres and E_m is Young's modulus of the matrix.

We can find an approximate value for H for a particular geometry. Suppose that a composite consists of a set of many parallel fibres each of constant length l, and of circular cross-section of radius r_0. We take the mean centre to centre separation of the fibres, normal to their length, to be $2R$. If $\tau(r)$ is the shear stress, in the direction of the fibre axis, on planes parallel to this axis (Fig. 5.8) then, at the surface of the fibre $r = r_0$, and

$$\frac{dP}{dx} = -2\pi r_0 \tau(r_0) \tag{5.28}$$

$$= H(u-v).$$

Therefore
$$H = -\frac{2\pi r_0 \tau(r_0)}{(u-v)}. \tag{5.29}$$

Now let w be the actual displacement in the matrix close to the fibre. Then at the fibre–matrix interface, assuming that there is no slippage between the fibre and the matrix, $w = u$. At a distance from the central fibre axis equal to R we have $w = v$. If we consider the equilibrium of the matrix between r_0 and R we have

$$2\pi r \tau(r) = \text{constant} = 2\pi r_0\, \tau(r_0)$$

and so the shear strain in the matrix is given by

$$\frac{dw}{dr} = \frac{\tau(r)}{G_m} = \frac{\tau(r_0) r_0}{G_m r} \tag{5.30}$$

where G_m is the shear modulus of the matrix.
Integrating from r_0 to R,

$$\Delta w = \frac{\tau(r_0) r_0}{G_m} \ln (R/r_0). \tag{5.31}$$

But $\Delta w = (v-u)$, so using (5.29),

$$H = 2\pi G_m / \ln (R/r_0). \tag{5.32}$$

Since,

$$\beta = \sqrt{(H/E_f A_f)}, \tag{5.33}$$

we have

$$\beta = \sqrt{\left\{ \left(\frac{G_m}{E_f}\right)\left(\frac{2\pi}{A_f \ln (R/r_0)}\right) \right\}}. \qquad (5.34)$$

The larger the value of G_m/E_f the more rapidly the stress in the fibre increases with distance from the fibre end.

From equations (5.25) and (5.28) we can find the shear stress, τ, in the matrix at the fibre–matrix interface. If the fibres are of circular cross-section

$$P = \pi r_0^2 \sigma,$$

and so

$$\tau = E_f e \sqrt{\left(\frac{G_m}{E_f 2 \ln (R/r_0)}\right)} \frac{\sinh \beta \, (l/2 - x)}{\cosh \beta \, l/2}. \qquad (5.35)$$

This shear stress has a maximum at the fibre ends and a minimum at the centre of the fibre. The variation of σ and of τ from

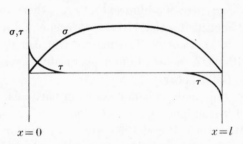

$x = 0$ $x = l$

FIG. 5.9. The variation along a fibre of the tensile stress σ and of the shear stress at the interface τ, according to equations (5.25) and (5.35) respectively.

equations (5.25) and (5.35) is shown schematically in Fig. 5.9. The largest stress in the fibre occurs at the centre and for a very long fibre equals $E_f e$ from equation (5.25). The largest value of τ occurs at the fibre ends, i.e. at $x = 0$ and at $x = l$, and it is zero at the middle of the fibre. The ratio of the maximum value of τ to the maximum tensile stress in the fibre is,

$$\frac{\tau_{max}}{\sigma_{fmax}} = \sqrt{\left(\frac{G_m}{2E_f \ln R/r_0}\right)} \times \coth \beta l/4. \qquad (5.36)$$

This ratio is of great importance. For a very long fibre

$$\frac{\tau_{max}}{\sigma_{fmax}} = \sqrt{\left(\frac{G_m}{2E_f \ln R/r_0}\right)}. \qquad (5.37)$$

The values of τ_{max}/σ_{fmax} for a volume fraction of fibres of 0·5 and various ratios of G_m to E_f are given in Table 5.1, calculated from equation (5.37). The increasing values of G_m/E_f are appropriate to sapphire fibres in a resin, glass fibres in a resin, and sapphire fibres in a metal, respectively.

TABLE 5.1

G_m/E_f	4×10^{-3}	$2{\cdot}5 \times 10^{-2}$	10^{-1}
$\dfrac{\tau_{max}}{\sigma_{fmax}}$	0·08	0·19	0·37

Even for the lowest ratio of G_m/E_f it is seen that τ_{max}/σ_{fmax} approaches one-tenth. To utilize the strength of the fibres to the full a stress equal to the breaking stress of the fibres σ_{uf} must be reached at the centre of a fibre so that σ_{fmax} then equals σ_{uf} and Table 5.1 demonstrates that stresses at least equal to 0·1 σ_{uf} will be reached in the *matrix*. The matrix will usually fail under these conditions. A metal will flow plastically; a resin matrix is expected to fail in shear.

The preceding analysis is not exact; in particular the matrix is assumed to support no tensile load. Other approximate analyses (Dow 1963, Rosen 1965) give very similar results and differ only in the value of β. In all analyses β is proportional to $\sqrt{(G_m/E_f)}$ and differences occur only in the term involving the volume fraction of fibres; ($\ln (R/r_0)$ in the above expression). Despite the shortcomings the expression found for the shear stress at the interface—equation (5.35)—is a very good approximation indeed to that obtained by much more sophisticated analyses of the behaviour of a single fibre (e.g. Smith and Spencer 1970) at distances more than a fibre radius from an end; the exact analysis is in doubt, close to a fibre-end.

Measured shear stresses in the matrix at the ends of a fibre will be much larger than those given by equation (5.36) because of stress concentrating effects at fibre ends. Stress will be concentrated in proportion to the difference in elastic moduli of the fibre and matrix and inversely to the square root of the minimum radius of curvature at the fibre end. Figure 5.10 shows an example where the values are appropriate to aluminium fibres in a resin. The observed shear stresses in the matrix close to the fibre-end are at least three times those calculated from equation (5.36).

If attempts are made to build large stresses into a fibre the accompanying large shear stresses at the interface will lead to failure at the interface or in the matrix. Continuity of elastic displacement at the interface is destroyed and the fibre becomes

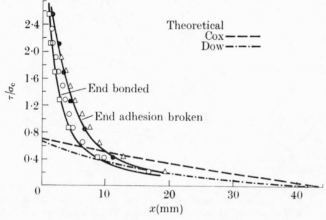

FIG. 5.10. Experimentally determined variation of the shear stress at the interface (τ) between an aluminium fibre and an araldite matrix, when the composite material is stressed. The ordinates represent values of τ/σ_c, i.e. the shear stress divided by the tensile stress on the composite. The dotted lines are the theoretically predicted shear stresses close to the end of a fibre from the present analysis and from that due to Dow (1963). The present theory predicts the larger values of the shear stress. Data from W. R. Tyson (1964).

'debonded' from the matrix. This will occur in a composite containing discontinuous fibres, or in one with continuous fibres containing a broken fibre, as well as in one in which the matrix has cracked but the fibres remain highly stressed. Once debonding has occurred the shear stress at the interface no longer continues to rise with increase in the stress in the fibre, but it is limited to some characteristic value τ. This very simple assumption of a limiting shear stress τ governing stress transfer at the interface is capable of explaining many results in composite theory (as for example those in section 5.2) provided τ is regarded in a particular case as a parameter to be determined experimentally.

If attempts are made to build large stresses into a fibre, failure of the matrix is expected to occur. The results of this will be different for matrices of different types. The case of the metallic

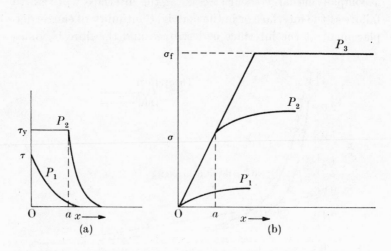

FIG. 5.11(a). Variation of shear stress at the fibre–matrix interface with distance, x, from the end of the fibre: (b). Variation of tensile stress in a fibre with distance, x, from the fibre end.

matrix containing discontinuous fibres or broken fibres is considered in section 5.3.1 and the resin matrix will then be dealt with in 5.3.2.

5.3.1. *The metallic matrix*

The metallic matrix can undergo plastic flow. We take the yield strain for plastic flow (i.e. σ_y/E_m, where σ_y is the tensile yield stress and E_m Young's modulus of the matrix) to be much less than the failure strain of the fibres. As load is first applied to the composite the different displacements in matrix and fibre produce shear stresses in the matrix close to the fibre ends in excess of the shear stresses due to the applied stress alone. The variation of $\tau(r_0)$ with load P on the composite is expected to be as shown in Fig. 5.11(a). At small loads, P_1, $\tau(r_0)$ is governed by the elastic behaviour of the matrix. Above a certain load on the composite, plastic flow is produced in the matrix. This occurs first at the fibre ends and its effect is to limit the maximum value of $\tau(r_0)$ to τ_y ($\approx \sigma_y/2$) the shear yield stress of the matrix; and so to limit the maximum value of the *elastic* strains in the matrix to σ_y/E_m (case P_2 in Fig. 5.11(a)). Since the failure strain of the fibres is greater than σ_y/E_m the matrix will have yielded plastically everywhere before the fibres are broken, i.e. before the tensile stress in the fibre reaches its maximum value σ_{uf}. After the matrix has all yielded and before the fibres fail, the stress in a fibre will be as shown in Fig. 5.11(b)—curve marked P_2. Within the region $0 < x < a$ the matrix has flowed plastically along the fibre so that the longitudinal strains in the matrix just outside the fibre and in the fibre are quite different. Little, exact, can be said about the magnitude of the strain in the matrix. The shear stress exerted at the interface is τ_y which is constant. The stress in the fibre therefore increases linearly, from equation (5.15). In the region $x > a$ the matrix adjacent to the fibre has also yielded plastically but the difference in the longitudinal displacements in matrix and fibre are small and such as to produce a shear stress at the interface less than τ_y. The tensile strains in fibre and matrix *differ* at most by σ_y/E_m. The strain in the fibre is elastic, in the matrix principally plastic. Within a distance $x < a$ from the fibre end (Fig. 5.11) the tensile stress in the fibre is

$$\sigma = 2\tau_y x/r, \quad 0 < x < a, \tag{5.38}$$

and the stress distribution will be as in Fig. 5.13.

5.3.2. *Polymer matrix*

The stress–strain curve in uniaxial tension parallel to the fibre direction will differ for a composite containing a polymer matrix from that expected of a composite with a metallic matrix. The stress–strain curve of the polymer itself is non-linear and there is no sharp division into elastic and plastic behaviour as in the metal case.

For continuous fibres both materials initially deform elastically and the extension of both fibres and resin is equal. The elastic modulus of the fibres is usually greater than 10^7 psi and that of a strong resin is less than 5×10^5 psi. The elastic modulus of the composite is thus expected to be close to $E_f V_f$. Measured moduli are sometimes less than this even for continuous fibres. Some contribution to this reduction may be caused by breaking of the weaker fibres at very small strains when the fibres are brittle and show a large coefficient of variation of their strength. Another effect is that shrinkage of the resin during curing can lead to buckling of the fibres. Failure of continuous filament composites will occur by failure of the fibres and the strength of such composites is discussed in sections 5.2 and 5.4.

For discontinuous fibres we see from equations (5.26) and (5.27) that the contribution of the fibres to the elastic modulus of the composite is limited to a maximum value of $E_f V_f$ and that this will only be approached when l is very long and β as large as possible. The value of β increases with increase of the shear modulus of the matrix and increase in the volume fraction of fibres (decrease in R/r_0).

The stress–strain curve of a composite consisting of discontinuous sapphire fibres in an epoxy resin is shown in Fig. 5.12. The volume fraction is small (~ 0.14) so that the theory of section 5.3 will apply as a first approximation. We have $E_f = 60 \times 10^6$ psi, $V_f = 0.14$, $E_m = 3.5 \times 10^5$ psi. The value of l/d for the sapphire whiskers varies from about 120 to about 1000. The smallest value of l/d applies to the largest whiskers which carry the major portion of the load. Taking $l/d = 120$, $\ln(R/r_0) = 1$, $G_m/E_m = \frac{1}{3}$ we obtain a value of $\beta l/2$ of 15. The predicted modulus at small strains from equation (5.27) is then 8.1×10^6 psi. This is about 30 per cent greater than the measured value of 6×10^6 psi; the measured value is a lower limit because of uncertainty in the measured strain.

At very small strains of the composite the shear stress in the matrix will be less than the yield stress of the resin. However, the stress in the fibres approaches 750 000 psi for the case shown in Fig. 5.12 at an elongation of 3 per cent. From Table 5.1 taking $G_m/E_f = 4 \times 10^{-3}$ the shear stresses in the matrix are then expected to be at least 60 000 psi, neglecting stress concentrations due to the shape of the ends of the fibres. This greatly exceeds the yield stress in shear of the resin (< 5000 psi) and failure of the resin near to the fibre end must therefore have

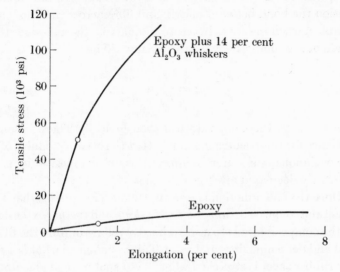

FIG. 5.12. Stress–strain curves of unreinforced and reinforced epoxy resin composites. The point on the curves marks the proportional limit. (Redrawn from Sutton, Rosen, and Flom 1964.)

occurred at quite small elongations. Further straining of the composite will lead to an increase in the size of the region over which failure of the resin occurs and hence to a continuous decrease in the modulus as the strain on the composite is increased; this is what is observed in Fig. 5.12.

The case of a large volume fraction of discontinuous brittle fibres in a polymer matrix has been discussed by Outwater (1956). Outwater emphasizes that the resin shrinks on curing, although the overall change in dimensions may be slight if the volume fraction of resin is small. This shrinkage subjects the fibres to a radial pressure (n) which would be that exerted by a thin walled tube of thickness $t/2$, internal diameter d and hoop stress F, i.e.

$$n = Ft/d, \qquad (5.39)$$

where t is the surface to surface separation of the fibres, d their diameter, and F the yield point of the resin in tension. When discontinuous fibres are present Outwater supposes that under tension the bond between matrix and fibre across the fibre end is broken when the stress in the fibre equals σ_A, the adhesion; the strain of the composite when this occurs will be

$$\frac{\sigma_A}{E_f} = e = \frac{\sigma_c}{E_c} \approx \frac{\sigma_c}{E_f V_f}. \qquad (5.40)$$

The stress on the composite will then be $\sigma_A V_f$. There is some evidence for this occurring, namely that the elastic modulus of a discontinuous glass fibre-reinforced resin composite is permanently decreased after small strains.

Once the end adhesion is broken, Outwater supposes that t is small and so the resin *cannot deflect in shear* and further extension of the composite leads to a shear line travelling in from the fibre end and detaching fibre and resin. This is similar to what is seen if a rubber sheet is stretched which has a spot of rigid glue upon it. The glue is detached from the rubber without effectively altering the strain pattern on the rubber sheet. The resin must then slide over the surface of the fibre and the frictional force between resin and fibre enables further load to be transferred to the fibre as the strain of the composite is increased. We then have a situation very similar to that described in section 5.3.1, for the metallic matrix and equation (5.38) will apply with τ_y replaced by μn. The stress in the fibre will then build up to a value

$$\sigma = 2\mu n x / r. \qquad (5.41)$$

μ is the coefficient of sliding friction between fibre and matrix. Neglecting any shear of the resin the stress-distribution in the fibre will be as in Fig. 5.13 where e is the strain of the composite material.

The strain in the fibre will be the same as that in the composite at a distance a from the end of about

$$a = E_f er/2\mu n. \qquad (5.42)$$

The modulus of the composite will be reduced because parts of the fibres near to their ends will not be loaded. The ratio of the

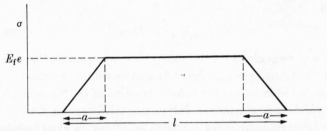

FIG. 5.13. Expected variation of stress along a fibre of length l.

modulus of a discontinuous composite E_{cd} to that of a continuous one E_{cc} will be

$$\frac{E_{cd}}{E_{cc}} = \frac{1}{E_f el} \int_0^l a \, dx. \qquad (5.43)$$

Here we neglect the contribution of the matrix and the integral is evaluated for a discontinuous composite subject to the same strain e as the continuous one. From Fig. 5.13, using (5.42)

$$E_{cd} = E_{cc} \left(1 - \frac{r}{2\mu nl} E_f e \right) \qquad (5.44)$$

and therefore the modulus of a discontinuous composite falls continuously with respect to that of a continuous one as the strain is increased.

This theory predicts that the properties of a composite will not be greatly affected by alteration in values of the adhesion between fibre and resin but much more critically by changes in the value of the coefficient of sliding friction between fibre and matrix. This implies a sensitivity to chemical environment and particularly to moisture, just as is observed (Chapter 6).

It should be noted that according to Outwater's theory the resin matrix transfers load to the fibres by frictional forces at the interface exactly as a metal matrix does. The method of load transfer is formally similar in the two cases; the difference is that voids are expected to be formed at the ends of the fibres in the resin case. There is again a critical length of fibre which must be exceeded if it is to be broken in a given matrix. Replacing τ_y in equation (5.16) by μn, we obtain for the critical aspect ratio

$$l_{\text{crit}}/d = \sigma_{\text{uf}}/2\mu n. \tag{5.45}$$

If n were evaluated from (5.39) then equation (5.45) predicts that the transfer length depends on the volume fraction of the fibres and increases as the volume fraction of the fibres increases (i.e. t/d becomes smaller). Experimental determination of the interfacial pressure gives values of $\sim$700 psi for glass inclusions in a polyester (e.g. Daniel and Durelli 1961). Taking $\mu = 0.4$, μn is then 280 psi.[†] This is much less than the value of the limiting shear strength of a work-hardened metal at room temperature ($\sim$20 000 psi). Critical aspect ratios are then predicted to be between one and two orders of magnitude greater for polymer matrices than for metals.

5.4. Variation of fibre strength

The breaking strengths of the individual fibres in a composite will often cover a range of values. To consider what average of the individual strengths is appropriate for deriving the failure stress of a composite, is inseparable from deducing how the composite fails.

Coleman (1958) shows that for fibres with a strength independent of the rate of loading, the tensile strength is expected to obey the Weibull distribution, i.e.

$$f(\sigma) = L\alpha\beta\sigma^{\beta-1} \exp\left(-L\alpha\sigma^\beta\right), \tag{5.46}$$

[†] The value of n depends on the time after curing of the polyester and the value of μ depends on the finish applied to the glass. The figure of 280 psi is therefore only an estimate of the order of magnitude.

where $f(\sigma)$ is the probability density function, i.e. the probability of the failure stress lying between σ and $(\sigma+d\sigma)$. L is the fibre length and α and β are two parameters describing the distribution. He further shows that α and β are related to the mean fibre strength and the standard deviation by the following expressions:

$$\bar{\sigma} = (\alpha L)^{-1/\beta} \Gamma(1+1/\beta), \tag{5.47}$$

$$s = (\alpha L)^{-1/\beta} \{\Gamma(1+2/\beta)-\Gamma^2(1+1/\beta)\}^{\frac{1}{2}}. \tag{5.48}$$

The coefficient of variation or the standard deviation divided by the mean strength is given by

$$\mu = \frac{s}{\bar{\sigma}} = \frac{\{\Gamma(1+2/\beta)-\Gamma^2(1+1/\beta)\}^{\frac{1}{2}}}{\Gamma(1+1/\beta)} \tag{5.49}$$

and μ is therefore a function of β only. Rosen points out that if $0\cdot05 \leqslant \mu \leqslant 0\cdot5$ then $\mu \approx \beta^{-0\cdot92}$ so that β is an inverse measure of the coefficient of variation and for practical fibres will be greater than unity. For glass fibres, the coefficient of variation may be about $0\cdot1$ corresponding to a value of about 11 for β. For boron filaments, μ is between $0\cdot2$ and $0\cdot4$, corresponding to a value for β of between $2\cdot7$ and $5\cdot8$. It follows from equation (5.47) that for a value for β of 10, an order of magnitude change in the fibre length leads to a 25 per cent drop in the mean fibre strength. If β is about 4, the corresponding fall in fibre strength is about 50 per cent. By differentiating equation (5.46) and setting equal to zero we find that the statistical mode $\sigma^\star$ (i.e. the most probable failure stress) is given by

$$\sigma^\star \cong \{(\beta-1)/\beta\}^{1/\beta}(\alpha L)^{-1/\beta}, \tag{5.50}$$

or, if β is large,

$$\sigma^\star \cong (L\alpha)^{-1/\beta}. \tag{5.51}$$

$(\alpha L)^{-1/\beta}$ can be regarded as a reference level of strength. The values of the two parameters α and β can be obtained from experimental data, for instance from the values of the mean fibre strength and its standard deviation.

The strengths of fibre bundles have been analysed by Daniels (1945) and by Coleman (1958). In the simplest case, it is assumed that the fibres all have the same cross-sectional area and the same stress–strain curve. If the fibres differ in their values of elongation at break and the fibre strength distribution is $f(\sigma)$, then the probability that a fibre will break before the stress reaches a value σ is given by the cumulative strength distribution function,

$$F(\sigma) = \int_0^\sigma f(\sigma)\, \mathrm{d}\sigma. \tag{5.52}$$

Suppose we carry out a large number of measurements of the breaking load of individual *bundles* of these fibres. The bundles are loaded from their ends and each contains the same large number, N, of fibres of the same cross-sectional area. From the measured breaking loads of these bundles and the initial number of fibres we measure the average fibre stress at bundle failure. Daniels (1945) shows that for very large N the distribution of the average fibre stress at bundle failure, σ_B, approaches a normal distribution with mean value, or expectation,

$$\bar{\sigma}_B = \sigma_{fmax}\{1 - F(\sigma_{fmax})\}. \tag{5.53}$$

σ_{fmax}, the maximum fibre stress, is found from the condition that at failure the load borne by the bundle is a maximum. The load is the product of a the fibre stress (multiplied by the area of cross-section of a fibre) and the number of unbroken fibres. Thus σ_{fmax} is obtained from

$$\frac{\mathrm{d}}{\mathrm{d}\sigma}[\sigma\{1 - F(\sigma)\}]_{\sigma = \sigma_{fmax}} = 0. \tag{5.54}$$

The values of σ_B are characterized by the density distribution function

$$\omega(\sigma_B) = \frac{1}{\psi_B \sqrt{(2\pi)}} \exp - \left\{\frac{1}{2}\left(\frac{\sigma_B - \bar{\sigma}_B}{\psi_B}\right)^2\right\} \tag{5.55}$$

ψ_B is the standard deviation and is given by

$$\psi_B = \sigma_{fmax}[F(\sigma_{fmax})\{1 - F(\sigma_{fmax})\}]^{1/2} N^{-1/2}. \tag{5.56}$$

Thus ψ_B becomes small as N is made very large. This expresses the intuitively obvious point that the breaking strength of bundles of fibres is more highly reproducible the larger the number of fibres in each bundle. For bundles characterized by equation (5.55) we define the cumulative distribution function $\Omega(\sigma_B)$ as

$$\Omega(\sigma_B) = \int_0^{\sigma_B} \omega(\sigma_B)\mathrm{d}\sigma_B. \tag{5.57}$$

If we now take the case of the Weibull distribution we find from equation (5.54) that

$$\sigma_{\max} = (L\alpha\beta)^{-1/\beta} \tag{5.58}$$

and then from (5.53) we obtain the expected value for the tensile strength of the bundle

$$\bar{\sigma}_B = (L\alpha\beta e)^{-1/\beta}. \tag{5.59}$$

Coleman (1958) compared this value for the average fibre stress at bundle failure with that given by equation (5.47) for the average strength of fibres of the same length and showed that when there is no dispersion in the fibre strength then, as expected, the average fibre stress in the bundle is the same as the average fibre strength. As the coefficient of variation of fibre strength increases above zero the average fibre strength in the bundle approaches zero in the limit of infinite dispersion. When the coefficient of variation is 10 per cent the average fibre strength in the bundle is about 80 per cent of the average strength of the fibres; when $\mu = 25$ per cent, the strength in the bundle is 63 per cent of the average strength.

Rosen and his co-workers (Rosen 1965, 1970, Zweben and Rosen 1970) have developed theories of the tensile failure of aligned composites for the case of brittle fibres (showing a range of breaking strengths) in a non-ductile matrix (of much lower rigidity than the fibre). In his cumulative-weakening theory Rosen (1965) considers the strength of the material to be governed by the statistical accumulation of failures of individual volume elements which are *separated by barriers to crack propagation* and hence fail independently. We shall follow some of the ideas of this theory. A critique has been given by Hale and Kelly (1972). The load carried by the matrix is neglected. Increased application of the load results in individual fibre fractures occurring at loads lower than that of ultimate composite failure. An individual fibre does not render the fibre unable to carry load over its entire length but reduces the ability to carry load only near the break. The fibre stress distribution is approximated to one in which the fibre carries its full load over its entire length except for a length near the break where the load carried is zero—the *ineffective length*. The composite is considered as a series of layers, each layer being a bundle of fibre elements embedded in the matrix, with the length of the fibre element (height of the bundle) taken as equal to the ineffective length for a fibre of diameter equal to the mean diameter. With this assumption it can then be stated that if a fibre breaks within a layer the entire length of fibre *in that layer* is ineffective. Uniform strain is assumed throughout the composite, so then failure of a fibre element within a bundle will result in a uniform redistribution of stress among the remaining unbroken fibres in that bundle; stress concentrations are thus neglected. As the applied load is increased fibre fractures accumulate until at a critical load (the failure load) one bundle of fibre elements is unable to transmit any increase in load. Thus failure occurs due to the presence of a weakened cross-section. It must be noted that a length has to be chosen for lengths of the bundles. We shall take this as equal to one-quarter of the critical length, because at the end of a fibre we expect debonding to have occurred (section 5.3). Rosen (1965) took this length as that length of fibre within which the stress built up *elastically* from zero (at the end of the fibre) to 90 per cent of the undisturbed level.

To proceed quantitatively it is necessary to derive the strength distribution of (a) the fibre elements and (b) the bundles, and then use the weakest link theory to obtain the strength of the composite. In the case of fibres characterized by a Weibull distribution, the fibre element strength distribution will be

$$\omega(\sigma) = l\alpha\beta\sigma^{\beta-1} \exp(-l\alpha\sigma^\beta) \qquad (5.60)$$

where l is the length of the fibre element, i.e. the ineffective length.

The probability density function $f(\sigma_B)$ for the bundle strength can then be obtained using equations (5.52)–(5.56); the corresponding cumulative distribution function $\Omega(\sigma_B)$ will be given by equation (5.57).

The bundles are now considered as n links in a chain, and the probability $\lambda(\sigma_c)\,d\sigma_c$ of failure of the chain is obtained by multiplying the probability that one link fails at a stress between σ_c and $(\sigma_c+d\sigma_c)$ (i.e. $f(\sigma_c)$) firstly by the probability that the other $(n-1)$ links have a strength greater than $(\sigma_c+d\sigma_c)$, and then by n, the number of links in the chain.

We shall assume, as does Rosen, that the number of elements in a bundle is so large that the standard deviation of bundle strength tends to zero. It then follows that the statistical mode of the composite strength is equal to $\bar{\sigma}_B$ (equation (5.53)).

In the case of the Weibull distribution it follows from equation (5.59) that

$$\sigma_c{}^\star = (l\alpha\beta e)^{-1/\beta}, \tag{5.61}$$

and the statistical mode of the tensile strength of the composite is then given by

$$\sigma^\star = V_f(l\alpha\beta e)^{-1/\beta} \tag{5.62}$$

where V_f is the fibre volume fraction. It may be noted that l will be of the order of 10 to 100 fibre diameters and consequently very much less than the gauge lengths normally used in tests on fibres. If we compare the mean strength of a set of fibres of length L with the fibre strength which would be expected in the composites we have from equations (5.47) and (5.61)

$$\frac{\sigma_c{}^\star}{\bar{\sigma}} = \left(\frac{L}{l\beta e}\right)^{1/\beta}\frac{1}{\Gamma(1+1/\beta)}.$$

If $\beta = 5$ and $L/l = 100$ then $\sigma_c^\star/\bar{\sigma} = 1\cdot62$ and the composite will be very much stronger than would be expected from tests on individual fibres as emphasized by Rosen (1970). Since it was assumed that the standard deviation of the bundle strength was zero, the mean tensile strength of the composite is, in fact, equal to the strength of a bundle containing a large number of fibres of length l, and is independent of the length of the composite.

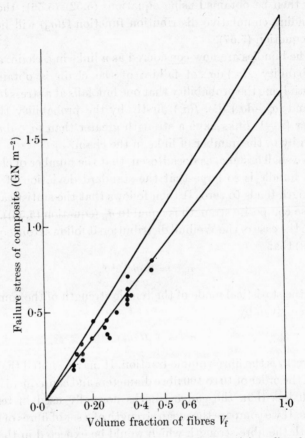

FIG. 5.14. Plot of tensile strength of a composite containing aligned boron fibres in a sintered aluminium matrix as a function of volume fraction. Data from Kreider and Leverant (1966).

The mean strength of the individual fibres, on the other hand, decreases with increasing length.

Figure 5.14 is a plot of the measured strength of composites containing aligned fibres of boron in aluminium. The fibres tested in 2·5 cm lengths, have an average strength of 3 GN m^{-2}.

The coefficient of variation of the strength is 0·2 so from equation (5.49) $\beta \sim \frac{1}{3}$. $\Gamma(1+1/\beta)$ then equals 6 and equation (5.47) yields a value of $(\alpha L)^{-1/\beta}$ of 0·5 GN m^{-2}. Further, comparing equation (5.47) for the average strength of the fibres and the average strength in a bundle, equation (5.59), we expect the average bundle strength to be 68 per cent of the average fibre strength. The average fibre strength in the composite is then 1·95 GN m^{-2} which is close to the observed outer envelope of strengths in Fig. 5.14. However, these figures all correspond to gauge lengths of 2·5 cm.

If we neglect the strength of the matrix and use equation (5.62), the value of l, the ineffective length, necessary to account for the mean slope in Fig. 5.14 is 1·7 cm. The fibres are of a diameter $\sim 125\mu$m so that this value of the ineffective length corresponds to a critical aspect ratio of about $4 \times 1\cdot7/0\cdot0125 = 540$ and so corresponds to a shear strength of the interface or matrix in equation (5.16) of about 3 MN m^{-2} (440 psi).

If we took τ in equation (5.16) as an order of magnitude larger, e.g. 30 MN m^{-2}, which is a value that would be expected if τ were to be identified with the shear strength of the aluminium matrix, then l would be reduced by an order of magnitude and the predicted strength increased by $\sim(10^{1/3})$ or 2·15. We do not know the value of τ.

Zweben and Rosen (1970) attempt to estimate the effects of local stress concentrations in reducing the strength. We discuss some estimates for these in the next section (5.5). If local stress concentrations increased the stress on the fibres by a factor $7/6 = 1\cdot17$, then the data shown in Fig. 5.14 could be accounted for with the values of τ and of the critical aspect ratio increased and decreased respectively by factors of $(7/6)^3$, i.e. to 4·8 MN m^{-2} (676 psi) and 338, respectively. The importance of stress concentrations at the ends of broken fibres are not fully understood at present.

5.5. Local stress concentrations

If one or more fibres are broken in a composite under stress the load shed by the broken fibre must be transferred through the matrix to neighbouring fibres. The magnitude of the increased stress in the unbroken fibres and in the matrix is important in considering the strengths of composites with continuous fibres breaking at different strains, and in understanding the strength of composites containing discontinuous fibres.

There have been a large number of theoretical investigations and photoelastic studies of these effects. Barker and McLaughlin (1971) have summarized many of these and carried out an elastic analysis, using a finite element method. Their results apply to a two-dimensional plane stress state and they vary the end gap t in Fig. 5.15, V_f, and (E_f/E_m). Their full elastic analysis predicts a maximum stress concentration of 1·5 in a fibre adjacent to a broken one, i.e. the maximum stress in an adjacent fibre is 1·5 times the average stress in the fibres a long way from the fibre break at a given strain of the composite. The stress concentration factors in the matrix are very much larger and increase with decreasing gap size and increasing (E_f/E_m) and (slowly) with decreasing volume fraction, e.g. 100 for a gap size of 1/10 fibre diameter, $(E_f/E_m) \sim 200$, and $V_f \sim 0.45$. These factors would only be observed in practice for extremely small strains of the composite and they apply only when both components are fully elastic. Long before the strain on the composite is such as to break a fibre, the matrix will have failed, either by shear at the interface as the analysis in section 5.3 predicts, or by plastic flow or cracking at the interface or in the matrix. Such stress concentrations cannot be applied to understanding the breaking strength of the composite without consideration of the effects of matrix or interface failure. Hedgepeth and Van Dyke (1967) have taken into account this interface failure by assuming a limiting shear stress near the end of the fibre; they assume that the matrix bears no tensile load. This type of analysis has been extended by Lockett (1971) who also takes into account the ability of the matrix to bear some tensile load. Lockett finds a maximum stress concentration factor of 1·17 for the two-dimensional case and Hedgepeth and Van Dyke a value of 1·104 for the case of a single broken fibre in an hexagonal array. This does not differ greatly from the factor of 7/6 (1·17) suggested physically for a hexagonal array, if the matrix is unable to sustain any extra load when the central fibre breaks.

5.6. Discontinuous fibres

When a composite contains discontinuous fibres the tensile stress in the fibres is not uniform but builds up from the ends.

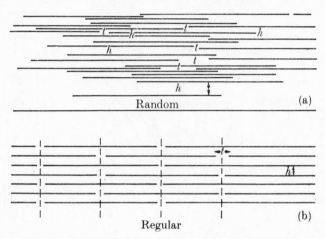

Fɪɢ. 5.15. (a) A random array of discontinuous fibres; and (b) a regular array. t is the end gap and h the lateral separation.

To take account of this effect we replace σ_{uf} in equation (5.14) by $\bar{\sigma}$ and obtain

$$\sigma_{\text{uc}} = \bar{\sigma} V_{\text{f}} + \sigma'_{\text{m}}(1 - V_{\text{f}}); \quad V_{\text{f}} > V_{\text{min}}. \qquad (5.64)$$

This equation can only be used provided that the distribution of the fibres is a truly random one. This implies that all cross-sections of the composite normal to the tensile axis are identical, i.e. that in any small length of the specimen the number of fibre-centres per unit area of cross-section must be constant, Fig. 5.15(a). Further, to avoid failure by shear, a distribution such as that in Fig. 5.16(d) must be avoided.

When the strain of the composite is such as to produce a stress in the central portion of the fibre equal to the breaking stress the *average* stress in the fibre ($\bar{\sigma}$) will be less than this.

Because failure occurs at the interface or in the matrix before a fibre can be broken the shear stress at the interface is limited (section 5.3). If, in addition, stress concentrations in one fibre due to the presence of adjacent fibre-ends can be neglected, then a first approximation to the stress distribution in the fibre for both metallic and polymer matrices (sections 5.3.1 and 5.3.2) will

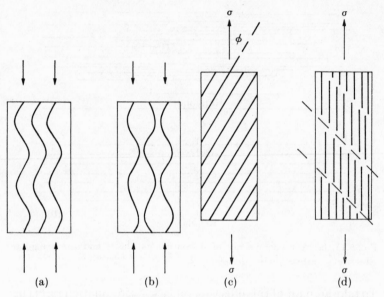

Fig. 5.16. Modes of failure of a fibre composite in compression and at an angle to the fibres. (a) and (b) illustrate possible modes of failure when the composite is compressed; (c) illustrates the notation used in section 5.9; (d) illustrates that with discontinuous fibres failure may occur by shear of the matrix on a plane at an angle to the fibres if the fibre distribution is not a truly random one.

be that shown in Fig. 5.13 with a taken as $l_{\text{crit}}/2$ and e as the breaking strain of the fibre. We then have

$$\bar{\sigma} = \sigma_{\text{uf}}(1 - l_{\text{crit}}/2l). \tag{5.65}$$

If the stress builds up from the end of a fibre in a non-linear way we can write

$$\bar{\sigma} = \sigma_{\text{uf}}\{1 - (1 - \beta))l_{\text{crit}}/l\}, \tag{5.66}$$

where β is the average stress in a fibre within a distance $l_{crit}/2$ of either end.

The ultimate strength of a composite containing uniaxially aligned discontinuous fibres which are *randomly* distributed will then be obtained from equations (5.64) and (5.66). We have

$$\sigma_{uc} = \sigma_{uf} V_f \left(1 - \frac{1-\beta}{\alpha}\right) + \sigma'_m (1-V_f); \quad V_f > V_{min} \quad (5.67)$$

where $$\alpha = l/l_{crit}$$

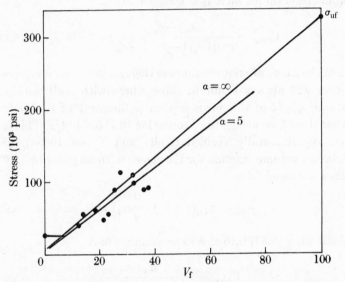

Fig. 5.17. Variations of UTS of a composite of copper reinforced with continuous and discontinuous tungsten wires of 0·005 in. diameter as a function of volume fraction V_f. The experimental points are shown only for the discontinuous wire composites. $\alpha = \infty$ is the experimental curve for continuous wires. $\alpha = 5$ is a line drawn from the experimental points by the method of least squares. (Data from McDanels *et al.* 1965).

Equations (5.14) and (5.67) show that discontinuous fibres will always strengthen a composite less than continuous ones. However, this is not important if α is large. If α equals 10, 95 per cent of the strength obtainable with continuous fibres will be obtained with discontinuous ones. Figure 5.17 illustrates this from experimental results. The approximate validity of equation

(5.67) has been established experimentally on a number of systems for values of V_f up to about 60 per cent (Kelly and Tyson 1965b, Kelly and Davies 1965). This shows that interactions between the stress distributions in adjacent fibres, for example the presence of a fibre-end affecting the rate of build-up of stress in an adjacent fibre, are found experimentally not to reduce the strength by more than 20 per cent for values of V_f less than 0·6. For discontinuous fibres of length l greater than l_{crit} the composite strength is given by equation (5.67). Thus the critical volume fraction for increased strength is

$$V_{\text{crit}} = \frac{\sigma_{\text{um}} - \sigma'_{\text{m}}}{\sigma_{\text{uf}}\{1 - (1-\beta)/\alpha\} - \sigma'_{\text{m}}} \; ; \; \alpha \geqslant 1. \qquad (5.68)$$

When the fibres are not continuous then failure at a given cross-section will always result in those fibres with ends within a distance $l_{\text{crit}}/2$ of this cross-section pulling out of the matrix rather than fracturing; the proportion of these is $1/\alpha$. This has been experimentally verified (Kelly and Tyson 1965a). The minimum volume fraction for the strength to be given by (5.67) is then obtained from

$$\sigma_{\text{uc}} \geqslant \sigma_{\text{um}}(1 - V_f) + \frac{\beta}{\alpha}\sigma_{\text{uf}}V_f. \qquad (5.69)$$

Substituting (5.67) into this expression we find

$$V_{\min} = \frac{\sigma_{\text{w}}}{\sigma_{\text{uf}}(1 - 1/\alpha) + \sigma_{\text{w}}} \qquad (5.70)$$

When $V_f < V_{\min}$,

$$\sigma_{\text{uc}} = \sigma_{\text{um}}(1 - V_f) + (\beta/\alpha)\sigma_{\text{uf}}V_f. \qquad (5.71)$$

Since σ_{uc} cannot be less than the value given by (5.71) this equation can be used to define some properties of the fibres for reinforcement to occur in the region $V_f < V_{\min}$. We must have $\sigma_{\text{uc}} > \sigma_{\text{um}}$ and therefore from (5.71),

$$(\beta/\alpha)\sigma_{\text{uf}} > \sigma_{\text{um}}. \qquad (5.72)$$

When $\quad (\beta/\alpha) \times \sigma_{\text{uf}} = \sigma_{\text{um}}$, then $V_{\text{crit}} = V_{\min}$.

Equations (5.68) to (5.71) can be used when $l = l_{\text{crit}}$, i.e. $\alpha = 1$. When this is so V_{min} equals unity and failure must occur by plastic flow of the matrix. However, in this case $V_{\text{min}} > V_{\text{crit}}$ and reinforcement of the matrix will occur provided (5.72) is satisfied. The strength of the composite is then given by (5.71) with $\alpha = 1$. This will be the strength of a composite consisting of aligned fibres broken down to the critical length by plastic flow of the matrix.

For discontinuous fibres of length $l < l_{\text{crit}}$ the strength is given by

$$\sigma_{\text{uc}} = \sigma_{\text{um}}(1 - V_{\text{f}}) + \sigma_{\text{f}}' V_{\text{f}}. \tag{5.73}$$

where σ_{f}' is the average load borne by the fibres. If the stress builds up linearly within the fibre we then have

$$\sigma_{\text{uc}} = \sigma_{\text{um}}(1 - V_{\text{f}}) + \frac{\tau l}{d} V_{\text{f}} \tag{5.74}$$

where for a metal matrix $\tau = \tau_{\text{y}}$ and for a resin matrix, according to Outwater's theory, $\tau = \mu n$.

5.6.1. Stress concentration in discontinuous fibre composites

The experimental results shown in Fig. 5.17 indicate that for composites with discontinuous fibres in a metal matrix which work-hardens, the effects of stress concentration are not important, and hence very long fibres with $l \gg l_{\text{crit}}$ will provide a composite with strength approaching that of a composite containing continuous fibres. However, if the matrix can carry no load and the fibres were regularly arranged as in Fig. 5.15(b) then a discontinuous composite would have a strength only half of that shown by a continuous one. Fig. 5.15(b) represents, of course, a weak section and its presence is to be avoided in practice. The modulus of the arrangement shown in Fig. 5.15(b) for a fully elastic composite (i.e. no failure anywhere even at the interface) is given by $(E_{\text{f}} V_{\text{f}} + E_{\text{m}} V_{\text{m}})$ for sufficiently long fibres.

However the strength predicted by a *fully elastic* analysis, which cannot apply in practice because of failure at the interface, must predict a strength of only one-half the continuous one if the matrix sustains no load or if $E_m \ll E_f$. For metallic matrices the value of $(1-\beta)/\alpha$ in equation (5.67) has values between 0·05 and 0·15 for very long fibres (Riley 1968, Bomford and Kelly 1971), so that in a metallic matrix stress-concentrating effects are detectable and of a magnitude predicted by the work in section 5.5. Bomford and Kelly's results indicate that stress concentrating effects are less important for small V_f, as expected. For discontinuous fibres in polymer materials the situation is a little less clear. The values of E_f/E_m are much larger than in the metal case and values of $(1-\beta)/\alpha$ varying from zero (Lees 1968, Hancock and Cuthbertson 1970) up to one-half (Chen 1971) for very long fibres have been reported. In addition, these last experiments were carried out with very brittle fibres of glass or of boron. Under such conditions the value to be taken for the breaking strength of the fibre needs to be defined, even for a constant length of fibre (see section 5.4). This difficulty does not occur in the case of metallic fibres. Another problem with the resin matrix systems studied to date, is the difficulty of knowing τ so that l_{crit} can be evaluated, independently of making a check on the validity of equation 5.67. It is worth noting in passing that if a specimen were showing a decreased strength due to weak sections such as that in Fig. 5.15(b) it would show a flat fracture with no pull-out.

5.7. Evaluation of the critical aspect ratio

Experimental values of the critical aspect ratio l_{crit}/d are useful in designing composites of a desired strength and a knowledge of this quantity is necessary to predict the work of fracture under certain conditions (section 5.8). When the strengths of the individual fibres vary in a given population then the value of l_{crit}/d clearly varies also.

In metallic matrices where the transfer length is determined by the shear strength of the matrix and *not* by that of the interface the values of l_{crit}/d are given within a factor of 2 simply by equation (5.16) with τ equal to the ultimate shear strength of the matrix.

An estimate of l_{crit}/d can be made by embedding a single fibre in a piece of the matrix and finding the stress on the fibre to pull it out. Some results from this type of experiment are shown in Fig. 5.18. The stress to pull out a fibre embedded to a length l, less than half the critical length, should be given by

$$\sigma = \sigma_0 + kl/d$$

where σ_0 and k are constants. k should be a constant for a given fibre and matrix, *independent* of the fibre *strength*. It is not then

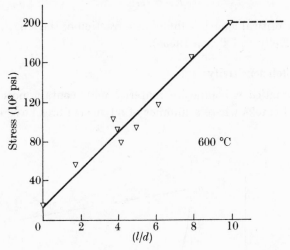

FIG. 5.18. The tensile stress required to pull a single tungsten wire out of a piece of copper as a function of the length l embedded in the copper. The closed triangle indicates fracture of the wire before pull-out. d is the diameter of the wire.

necessary to employ strong fibres in this type of experiment. k is evaluated from the slope of the line delineated by open triangles in Fig. 5.18. For a fibre of breaking stress σ_f the critical aspect ratio is given by

$$l_{\text{crit}}/d = 2\sigma_f/k. \tag{5.75}$$

When the strengths of the individual fibres do not vary very much then a value of l_{crit}/d can be found from observation of the fracture surface of a composite containing a volume fraction V_f, greater than V_{crit}, of discontinuous fibres of uniform length l, and uniform aspect ratio. All those fibres with ends within a distance $l_{\text{crit}}/2$ of the fracture surface will not be broken but will pull out of the matrix. Inspection of the fracture surface will reveal the number of fibres which have fractured n_f and the number which have pulled out, n_p.

Then

$$\frac{n_f}{n_p} = \frac{l}{l_{\text{crit}}} - 1 \qquad (5.76)$$

and the critical length is found as a fraction of the length of the fibres (Kelly and Tyson 1965b).

5.8. Notch sensitivity

In practice a composite material may contain notches or internal cracks where a number of adjacent fibres have broken

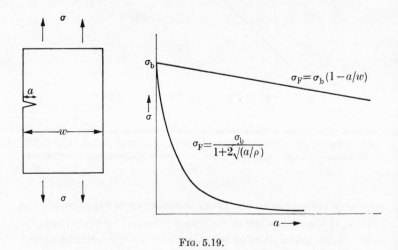

FIG. 5.19.

at the same cross-section. At these an applied stress will be concentrated and we wish to know how such stress concentrations will affect the breaking strength.

Consider a sheet of elastically continuous material of width w, to which we can apply the theory in Chapter 2 (Fig. 5.19). At the end of a sharp notch of radius of curvature ρ and depth a, the maximum tensile stress is given by $\sigma\{1+2\sqrt{(a/\rho)}\}$ for an applied stress of σ. This concentrated stress depends critically on the value of ρ. If it can reach the breaking stress σ_b of the unnotched material failure will occur under an applied stress σ very much less than σ_b. The dependence of σ_F, the applied stress necessary to produce failure, on notch depth is indicated schematically in Fig. 5.19. The behaviour of a material which is not notch sensitive is indicated by the upper curve in Fig. 5.19. Here the strength is reduced by the presence of a notch only in proportion to the reduction in width.

In a composite material complete notch insensitivity might be produced by providing an interface parallel to the fibres which is weak in tension (Cook and Gordon 1964). This model is essentially two dimensional. We note that in Fig. 2.2 the maximum value of σ_x occurs at a distance ahead of the crack tip. This stress could break the interface parallel to the fibres before the fibres fail, if the stress to break the interface in tension is much less than that required to break a fibre. We then expect a crack running transverse to the fibres to open another crack transverse to itself and to run into it. This happens for thin specimens of thickness little greater than one fibre diameter (see Plate 3). The stress concentration due to the crack may then be removed, and complete notch insensitivity could result.

Using specimens like that illustrated in Plate 3, Cooper and Kelly (1967) have demonstrated that complete notch insensitivity can be produced because splitting occurs parallel to the fibres over a distance much greater than the notch depth (a in Fig. 5.19) and removes the notch. Quantitatively they find that the transverse strength must be less than a fraction one-thirteenth of the longitudinal strength for that to occur. They also demonstrate that for a very deep notch the strength of the composite does decrease with the inverse square root of the notch depth; a necessary condition for the application of the principles of fracture mechanics. This is as expected because some parting at the crack tip or shear parallel to the fibres does not eliminate the concentration of *strain* in the composite if a *deep* notch is cut so that $a \gg l_{\text{crit}}/2$. This condition shows that whether or not a notch of given length is to be treated as sharp, depends on the value of l_{crit} for the composite considered.

If the notch is a sharp one in this sense, then fibres close to the crack tip are still more highly stressed than remoter ones. The problem of reducing notch sensitivity becomes one of ensuring a large work of fracture so that the strain energy release rate must be made large, i.e. a large value of the critical stress intensity factor K_c is required in order to make the crack run (section 4.1).

To apply fracture mechanics to a fibrous composite we must: (a) take account of elastic anisotropy in deriving expressions for the elastic strain energy released as the crack advances; (b) take account of the fact that the resistance of the material to crack propagation (i.e. the value of γ_p in section 4.1) will be different for different directions of crack path; and (c) consider the various material parameters and interactions which contribute to γ_p. We deal with these in turn.

5.8.1. *Elastic anisotropy*

If the strains ε_i are related to the stresses by elastic compliances $\varepsilon_i = a_{ij}\sigma_j$ and a stress intensity factor K_1 is *defined* as $K_1 = \sigma(a)^{\frac{1}{2}}$ where $a =$ notch depth and σ is the applied stress, then if $\mathfrak{G}$ is the work which must be done to produce unit area of crack surface (on both sides of the open crack) when the crack runs normal to the fibres, and the applied stress is parallel to the fibres, then,

$$\mathfrak{G} = \pi\sigma^2 a \left(\frac{a_{22}a_{11}}{2}\right)^{\frac{1}{2}} \left\{\left(\frac{a_{22}}{a_{11}}\right)^{\frac{1}{2}} + \left(\frac{a_{66}+2a_{12}}{2a_{12}}\right)\right\}^{\frac{1}{2}}, \quad (5.77)$$

for the case of parallel fibres lying in the plane of a thin sheet under conditions of plane stress (Sih, Paris, and Irwin 1965).†

---

† The axes are aligned with respect to the crack which runs normal to axis 2 and parallel to axis 1.

$$\varepsilon_1 = a_{11}\sigma_1 + a_{12}\sigma_2 + a_{16}\tau_{12}$$
$$\varepsilon_2 = a_{12}\sigma_1 + a_{22}\sigma_2 + a_{26}\tau_{12}$$
$$\varepsilon_3 = a_{16}\sigma_1 + a_{26}\sigma_2 + a_{66}\tau_{12}$$

The bracketed quantities replace the reciprocal of E, the Young's modulus in isotropic fracture mechanics—equations (4.1) to (4.4).

In isotropic fracture mechanics three basic types of crack extension are considered. These are illustrated in Fig. 5.20. For each of these the appropriate value of K depends only on a single stress, which is indicated in the sketches in Fig. 5.20. In the anisotropic case the appropriate K will not depend only on a

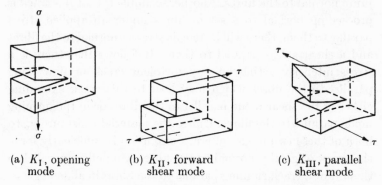

(a) K_{I}, opening mode

(b) K_{II}, forward shear mode

(c) K_{III}, parallel shear mode

FIG. 5.20. Independent modes of crack propagation.

single stress except in special cases, and the crack path will be determined both by the elastic anisotropy and by the differing resistance of the material to crack propagation in directions parallel and transverse to the fibres.

5.8.2. *Varying resistance to crack propagation*

The value of $\mathfrak{G}$ for the tensile crack opening made (Fig. 5.20(a)) for the two cases when the crack runs parallel or normal to the fibres are very different, e.g. for a glass-reinforced epoxy $\mathfrak{G}$ for a

---

Hence for a crack lying normal to the fibres, $a_{22} = 1/E$, $a_{66} = 1/G$, $a_{11} = 1/E_t$, and $a_{12} = (-\nu/E) = (-\nu'/E_t)$ in the notation of section 5.1. For the carbon-reinforced epoxy given in Appendix C, Table 4, where $E \sim 20G \sim E_t/3$, E' for a crack in this orientation is $2/5\ E$. For a crack running parallel to the fibres $E' \sim 1\cdot 3\ E_t$. Hence for a given crack length, a crack parallel to the fibres provides a much larger crack extension force for a given stress, since the material is more compliant in a direction normal to the fibres.

crack running parallel to the fibre may be as small as 10^{-1} J m^{-2} whereas for cracks normal to the fibres the value may be as large as 10^5 J m^{-2}.

The very different resistance to crack propagation in different directions and for different applied stresses means that the crack path in a stressed fibrous composite may be unexpected. If a crack is proceeding parallel to aligned fibres under combined tension normal to the fibres and shear parallel to them, it may jump normal to the fibres. Another example is that if a crack is proceeding normal to a set of fibres under an applied stress parallel to them, there will be tensile stresses normal to the fibres and a shear stress parallel to them. It follows that there is a stress intensity acting on any incipient crack or flaw lying parallel to the fibres which may lead to this crack extending either in the shear mode parallel to the fibres or in the opening mode parallel to the fibres. Unless the material resistance γ_p to both of these two modes of crack extension is sufficiently large the crack originally normal to the fibres will deflect parallel to them. For a crack running parallel to the fibres in aligned glass-reinforced plastic Wu and Reuter (1965) find critical values of K for tensile opening of 930 psi in$^{\frac{1}{2}}$ (1·03 MN m$^{-3/2}$) and for shear opening (Fig. 5.20(b)) of 3580 psi in$^{\frac{1}{2}}$ (4 MN m$^{-3/2}$); for balsa-wood in the same configuration the values are 58 psi in$^{\frac{1}{2}}$ (64 kN m$^{-3/2}$) and 145 psi in$^{\frac{1}{2}}$ (160 kN m$^{-3/2}$). Wu also established that for such cracks to propagate rapidly a critical stress which depends on crack length must be applied.

5.8.3. *Contributions to the work of fracture*

The values of $\mathfrak{G}_{Ic}$, i.e. the resistance of the material to the propagation of a crack in mode (a) of Fig. 5.20 normal to the fibres, are extremely high for a fibrous composite; much higher than may be accounted for by adding the contributions of the two components. For example, the value for glass is less than 6 J m^{-2} (section 2.5). For a polyester resin the value is less than 100 J m^{-2}, and for an epoxy, perhaps up to 200 J m^{-2}. In contrast the value for a glass-reinforced plastic may be as large as 10^5 J m^{-2}. Clearly, some interaction between the two components is responsible for this large increase. There are a number of contributions to the work of fracture: (a) the matrix must be plastically deformed as the crack is opened (Cooper and Kelly 1967); (b) broken fibres may be pulled out of their 'sockets' in the matrix on the other side of the crack (Kelly 1964, Cottrell 1964); and (c) an energy may be required to debond the fibre and matrix (Outwater and Carnes 1967). The first occurs principally in composites with ductile metal matrices. The second two processes are illustrated schematically in Fig. 5.21. The sketch in Fig. 5.21 shows that the definition of the length of the crack must be attended to with care in the case of a composite because fibre and matrix may be at all stages of failure. If the crack is regarded as having its tip at T, then unbroken fibres spanning the open faces of the crack in the matrix will resist these opening further. If this view is taken then the *work done* in breaking fibres to the left of T over the debonded length must be taken as contributing to the work of fracture, i.e. contributing to $\mathfrak{G}$. This view is taken by Mandell and McGarry (1972).

Deformation of the matrix. The work done in deforming the matrix is proportional to the work done in deforming the matrix to rupture per unit volume, U, times the volume of matrix deformed per unit area of crack surface. The volume deformed is equal to $V_m x'$, where x' is equal to $(V_m/V_f)(r\sigma_{um}/2\tau)$, (Cooper and Kelly 1967). This equation may be derived in a similar fashion to equation (5.19). It follows that the total work of fracture due to this cause is proportional to $(V_m^2 r/V_f)$, and hence increases with increasing fibre radius. V_f must be greater than V_{crit}—equation (5.14(c)).

Pull-out. For a metallic matrix we can estimate γ_p the work done in separating the material into two pieces when the stress distribution in each fibre is as shown in Fig. 5.13. In a discontinuous fibre compact when fracture occurs by the breaking of fibres then it is found experimentally that all those fibres with ends within a distance $l_{crit}/2$ of the particular cross-section at which failure occurs, and which cross the break, pull out of the matrix, instead of fracturing. The fraction of fibres pulling out will be l_{crit}/l. The work done in withdrawing a fibre whose end is within a distance x of the break, assuming the shear stress τ is maintained throughout this process, is

$$\pi r^2 \int_0^x \sigma \, \mathrm{d}x = \pi r^2 \int_0^x \frac{2\tau x}{r} \, \mathrm{d}x = \pi r \tau x^2 \qquad (5.78)$$

using equation (5.15). The total work done, per unit area of specimen cross-section, in withdrawing all those fibres which pull out is

$$W = \frac{V_\mathrm{f}}{\pi r^2} \left(\frac{l_\mathrm{crit}}{l}\right) \int_0^{l_\mathrm{crit}/2} \pi r \tau x^2 \frac{\mathrm{d}x}{(l_\mathrm{crit}/2)} = \frac{V_\mathrm{f}}{12} \left(\frac{l_\mathrm{crit}}{l}\right) \sigma_\mathrm{uf} l_\mathrm{crit}. \qquad (5.79)$$

Cottrell (1964) has emphasized that to maximize the work of fracture l_crit should be made large and the fibre length should be kept closely equal to l_crit. If $l > l_\mathrm{crit}$ the work of fracture due to this cause decreases with increasing length. If $l < l_\mathrm{crit}$ the work of fracture is obtained by setting $l_\mathrm{crit} = l$ in the integral and is

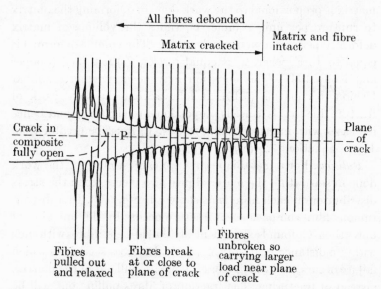

FIG. 5.21. Processes occurring close to a crack tip in a composite with brittle fibres of fracture *strain* greater than that of the matrix.

$V_f \pi r \tau l^2/12$. The variation of work of pull-out for a constant l_{crit} is plotted against l in Fig. 5.22. Such a variation is found for discontinuous fibres (Cooper and Kelly 1970). Cooper (1970) has treated the case of pull-out of continuous but flawed fibres. The treatment *will not apply* to brittle fibres; it requires some plasticity in the fibre. Pull-out involves a maximum work of fracture proportional to l_{crit} and hence a work of fracture increasing with increasing radius of the fibre from equation (5.16).

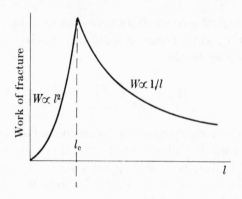

FIG. 5.22. Work of fracture due to pull-out against fibre length for a composite with discontinuous fibres.

For realization of the work of pull-out the crack faces must be separated by a distance l_{crit} (see Fig. 5.21). This total work of fracture will be that measured in an experiment which separates the specimen into two halves and this value is not necessarily all to be included in the value of $\mathfrak{G}$ obtained from a fracture mechanics test of the type described in section 4.1.

Debonding. Values of the work of debonding for a number of materials have been given by Kelly (1970); they are usually $\leqslant 500$ J m^{-2} and of the order of the interface shear strength times the failure strain of the resin. No other way of theoretically estimating the debonding energy from the properties of the components and of the interface has been given. Outwater and Murphy (1968) equate the energy of debonding with the elastic energy stored in the fibre after debonding. If this be done, the work of debonding must always be much less than the total work of pull-out, as the following argument shows. When a fibre debonds, the work done in the debonding process W_d per unit area appears as strain energy in the fibre. If W_D is the total work of debonding a fibre of diameter d, over a length x, then

$$W_D = W_d \pi \, dx = \frac{\pi d^2}{8E_f} \int_0^x \left(\sigma - \frac{4\tau x}{d} \right)^2 dx \qquad (5.80)$$

The maximum value occurs if σ reaches the breaking strength of the filament σ_{uf} which occurs at a distance $\sigma_{uf} d/4\tau$. Substituting this value of x we obtain

$$W_D = \frac{\pi d^2}{24} \left(\frac{\sigma_{uf}}{E_f} \right) \sigma_{uf} x. \qquad (5.81)$$

The maximum work to be done in pulling out a fibre is $\pi d^2 \sigma_{uf} x/8$. Hence the work of pull-out is $3(E_f/\sigma_{uf})$ times the work of debonding. (E_f/σ_{uf}) is always much greater than unity and normally much greater than 50; its smallest value is in the case of silica glass, when it is about 10. If

$$W_d \geqslant (\sigma_{uf} d)/8E_f, \qquad (5.82)$$

the fibre breaks rather than debonds so the maximum work of debonding again increases with fibre diameter as does the maximum work of pull-out.

Mandell and McGarry (1972) in a series of elegant experiments demonstrate that crack propagation normal to the fibres in unidirectional glass-reinforced epoxy can be described by the fracture mechanics approach, and that if the crack length is defined as the length of crack in the matrix (see Fig. 5.21) the crack is stable and can only propagate further into the matrix if the unbroken fibres linking the crack surfaces in the matrix are strained to failure. They find that the dominant contribution to the value of $\mathfrak{G}$ is the work done in deforming these linking fibres to failure over the debonded length. This work greatly exceeds the debonding work and there can be no pull-out since the fibres fail at the plane of the crack in the matrix. The work of fracture must again increase with diameter of the fibres (or of the yarn in this case) since the debonded length increases with diameter. In these experiments the crack length is much the same size as the specimen dimensions and the failure strain of the fibres is much greater than the failure strain of the matrix so that the crack is introduced with the fibres very lightly loaded compared with their UTS. It is not at all clear that work done in straining the fibres to failure contributes to $\mathfrak{G}$ in the case of a crack whose length is large compared with the debonded length in a specimen which is large compared with the crack length. All of the processes contributing to $\mathfrak{G}$ for a crack running normal to a set of fibres in opening mode (a) of Fig. 5.20 show an increase in $\mathfrak{G}$ with increase in fibre diameter (or of yarn diameter if the individual fibres are not well separated).

5.9. Orientation effects

In sections 5.2 and 5.4 we discussed the tensile strength of composites consisting of aligned fibres when stress is applied parallel to the fibres. In this section we consider first failure in compression, when a stress is applied parallel to the fibres, and then we discuss the breaking stress in tension when the stress is applied at some angle ϕ to the axis of the fibres.

5.9.1. *Failure in compression*

No satisfactory theory has yet been given for the failure stress of an aligned composite compressed parallel to the fibres. An elastic analysis has been given by Rosen (1965). This follows in detail the treatment given by Timoshenko (1936) for the buckling of a column by end loads, when the column is laterally supported by elastic members uniformly spaced along the length; the lateral support is taken to represent the matrix. This mode may apply if adjacent fibres buckle 'out of phase', as in Fig. 5.16(b); 'in-phase' buckling of the fibres results in a shear deformation of the matrix (Fig. 5.16(a)). The quantitative treatment for both modes is developed for a two-dimensional model so that the fibres are treated as plates. The tensile load borne by the matrix is neglected. If this is done then when failure occurs according to the model in Fig. 5.16(a) the stress on the composite is

$$\sigma_c = \frac{G_m}{V_m}, \tag{5.83}$$

and when failure occurs according to Fig. 5.16(b)

$$\sigma_c = 2V_f \left(\frac{V_f}{V_m} \frac{E_m E_f}{3} \right)^{\frac{1}{2}}. \tag{5.84}$$

As V_f tends to zero, (5.84) shows that σ_c tends to zero and as V_f tends towards unity (5.84) becomes very large. Equation (5.84) should therefore be followed at small V_f and equation (5.83) at large V_f. If, as usually obtains, $E_f \gg E_m$, and $\nu_m \sim \frac{1}{3}$, the transition is predicted to occur at $(E_m/10E_f)^{1/3}$ or at $V_f = 10$ per cent for $(E_f/E_m) \sim 100$ and 22 per cent for $E_f/E_m \sim 10$. The restriction of the analysis to reinforcement in the form of plates is serious. For example, for the mode shown in Fig. 5.16(b), if one follows Timoshenko's method but considers a rod to represent the fibre rather than a plate then the variation of σ_c with volume fraction is close to $V_f^{5/4}$ rather than $V_f^{3/2}/(1-V_f)^{1/2}$ as in equation (5.84). Composites of boron fibres in an epoxy matrix provide an example; here the variation of composite strength with volume fraction follows equations (5.83) and (5.84) with a transition at the appropriate volume fraction between the two modes (Lager and June 1969). However, the absolute values of the compressive strength are 63 per cent of those predicted.

These expressions involve only the elastic constants of the matrix and of the fibre, and the stresses given by equations (5.83) and (5.84), for a value of V_f of 0·5, are very large. For a metallic matrix the values of σ_c from both equations are several million pounds per square inch. Even for a resin with $G_m = 2 \times 10^5$ psi equation (5.83), yields a value of σ_c of 4×10^5 psi. The strain of the composite at failure must therefore be several per cent. Plastic flow of a metallic matrix and anelastic effects in resins must be considered. Figure 5.5(b) shows the compressive strength of a composite of tungsten wires in copper as a function

of volume fraction. The behaviour in tension is shown in Fig.
5.5(a). A linear dependence of σ_c on V_f is obtained so that equation (5.14) is obeyed within experimental error. Failure of the copper–tungsten specimens occurred by buckling and by splitting of the tungsten wires down their centres.† These failure modes are consistent with the failure modes predicted. Plastic flow of the matrix always occurred before failure. It is clear that strengths in compression at least as great as those obtained in tension are being demonstrated. This is also found in many other systems, provided care is taken over the method of testing.

5.9.2. *Fibre orientation*

When a composite containing aligned fibres is stressed in tension at an angle to the fibre direction three quantities become of importance. These are the stress σ_c required to produce failure by flow parallel to the fibres and given by equation (5.14) or (5.67); the shear stress τ_u required to produce failure by shear of the matrix or at the fibre–matrix interface, or at an interface in the matrix parallel to the fibres; and σ_u the tensile stress required to produce failure of the composite in a direction normal to that of the fibres. σ_u will be controlled either by the plastic flow of the matrix in plane strain in which case

$$\sigma_u = \sigma_{ult}(1 - V_f) \tag{5.85}$$

where σ_{ult} is the UTS of the matrix in plane strain, or σ_u may be controlled by the tensile strength of the fibre–matrix interface, in which case

$$\sigma_u = \sigma_i V_f \tag{5.86}$$

where σ_i is the tensile strength of the fibre–matrix interface or of an interface parallel to the fibres, in plane strain.

---

† A review of some of the effects in other systems has been given by Moncunill de Ferran and Harris (1970) and very recently an improved theoretical analysis has been made by Lanir and Fung (1972). However this has not yet been subjected to experimental test. As Argon (1972) emphasizes, if fibres are not exactly parallel to the axis of compression, failure may occur by shear parallel with the fibres as occurs analogously in tension for misaligned fibres (Figure 5.16(c).

Let ϕ be the angle between the fibre axis and the direction of an applied tensile stress σ (Fig. 5.16(c)). Failure of the composite by fracture of the fibres requires a tensile stress

$$\sigma = \sigma_{uc} \sec^2 \phi. \tag{5.87}$$

Failure by shear in the direction of the fibres on a plane parallel to the fibres requires an applied tensile stress

$$\sigma = 2\tau_u \operatorname{cosec} 2\phi. \tag{5.88}$$

τ_u will often be the failure stress in shear of the matrix. The appropriate value will be higher than the value measured in a test on the matrix alone, without fibres, because of constraints due to the fibres, by analogy with the failure of thin brazed joints. Metallic matrices show an appreciable failure strain in shear. During failure by this means the value of ϕ will decrease as the matrix shears and the value of σ will increase. ϕ must then be understood to indicate the appropriate angle when the ultimate shear stress of the matrix is attained. If τ_u is the shear strength of the fibre–matrix interface little change of ϕ is expected.

Failure by flow of the matrix transverse to the fibres, or failure of the fibre–matrix interface in tension requires an applied stress

$$\sigma = \sigma_u \operatorname{cosec}^2 \phi \tag{5.89}$$

We assume that whichever of the above failure modes requires the lowest applied stress, given by equations (5.87), (5.88), and (5.89) will be the one which occurs.

Figure 5.23(a) shows the variation of σ the tensile stress required to produce failure with angle ϕ, measured on a composite containing aligned silica fibres in an aluminium matrix by Jackson and Cratchley (1966). The solid lines indicate the predicted failure stress according to the above analysis using the measured values of σ_{uc}, σ_u, and of τ_u. The theory is quite well obeyed, when account is taken of the expected change in ϕ when (5.88) controls failure and the observed modes of failure agree with those predicted.

There is a critical angle ϕ_{crit} given from equations (5.87) and (5.88) by

$$\phi_{\text{crit}} = \tan^{-1} (\tau_u/\sigma_{uc}) \tag{5.90}$$

above which the strength falls off. For the case shown in Fig. 5.23(a) the predicted value is about 3·5°. Thus the strength of a fibrous composite is markedly anisotropic.

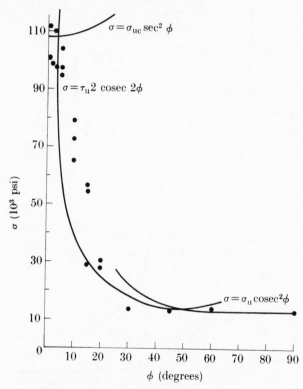

FIG. 5.23(a). Measured variation of tensile strength σ with angle between aligned continuous fibres and the tensile axis. The specimen consisted of 50 per cent by volume of silica fibres in a matrix of pure aluminium. The three curves are the theoretical predictions from equations (5.87), (5.88), and (5.89),

The analysis of the strength of the composite as a function of orientation, which we have just presented, assumes that failure will occur when a certain stress is reached. Although obeyed by experiment in the case quoted it has the disadvantage that the transition between the different modes of failure is discontinuous. An alternative suggestion, which has the advantage of providing

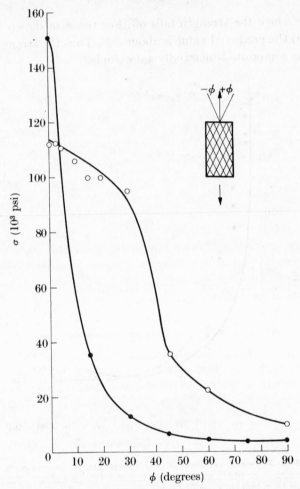

FIG. 5.23(b). Measured variation of tensile strength σ with angle ϕ for specimens consisting of a number of alternate layers of fibres. The fibres in each layer are parallel and continuous. Alternate layers are at $+\phi$ and at $-\phi$ to the tensile axis. Open circles represent data for a volume fraction of 40 per cent of silica fibres in aluminium. Full circles represent data for a volume fraction of 66 per cent of E glass fibre in an expoxy resin. The data for silica in aluminium is replotted from Jackson and Cratchley (1966) and that for glass in an epoxy resin from S. W. Tsai (1965) *N.A.S.A. Report CR*-224.

a smooth variation of strength with orientation, is that of Azzi
and Tsai (1965) who specialize a suggestion of Hill for the case
of plane stress, and assuming transverse isotropy for the properties of an aligned composite propose that failure occurs when
the stress state satisfies the condition

$$\sigma_x^2 - \sigma_x \sigma_y + \frac{\sigma_{uc}^2}{\sigma_u^2} \sigma_y^2 + \frac{\sigma_{uc}^2}{\tau_u^2} \tau_{xy}^2 = \sigma_{uc}^2 \qquad (5.91)$$

where σ_x is the applied stress parallel to the fibres, σ_y that normal
to the fibres and τ_{xy} the shear stress parallel and perpendicular
to the fibres. σ_c, σ_u, and τ_u are the strengths in these directions
as we have employed them. Any stress state inside the surface
given by equation (5.91) represents an elastic deformation of
the composite and any stress state outside is inadmissible.
Equation (5.91) has the advantage of providing an analytic form
which is easily used in calculation, for instance in the strength of
laminates. The difference from the criterion given above
(equations 5.87 to 5.89) is not large in practical cases.

The extreme sensitivity of the strength of a fibrous composite
to the angle ϕ can be reduced by bonding together laminated
sheets each containing aligned fibres. This is a much better
method than that of arranging fibres randomly in a plane since
large values of V_f can still be obtained. Figure 5.23(b) shows
results for silica fibres in aluminium when alternate layers with
fibres at angles $+\phi$ and $-\phi$ to the tensile axis are bonded
together. A large value of the tensile strength is maintained up to
values of ϕ of about 25°. This is because for angles ϕ less than 45°
shear parallel to the fibres in one layer requires a displacement
at the interface between layers which has a component parallel
to the fibres in the adjacent layer. The maintenance of the tensile
strength of the composite as ϕ increases is then controlled by the
shear strength of the matrix. Composites made in this way with
metallic matrices, maintain their strength at quite large angles
since τ_u is at least several thousand pounds per square inch.
Composites made with resin matrices do not maintain their
strength at such large values of ϕ as Fig. 5.23(b) shows. Here
again, however, the strength is maintained at larger angles in

composites made with alternate layers at $+\phi$ and at $-\phi$ than if a single layer is used.

Planar isotropy of strength can be obtained by bonding together sheets each consisting of uniaxially aligned fibres. This is similar to the method employed in the construction of plywood.

5.10. Design of a strong fibrous composite

We have seen that if a large number of strong fibres are bound together with a suitable matrix then we can prepare a usable material with a tensile breaking strength in the direction of the fibres of approximately $\sigma_f V_f$. Even brittle fibres may be used provided adequate attention is paid to the properties of the matrix and to those of the fibre–matrix interface. Values of V_f of 0·5 are quite possible and so from the values of the strength of the various glasses, fibres, and metal wires listed in Appendix A and mentioned in the earlier chapters, solids which are very strong in tension and very stiff in tension can be made.

What is usually most important to an engineer in designing a structure is not solely static strength. The weight and stiffness of a member are at least as important. In tension the important properties are specific strength which we shall take as ultimate tensile strength divided by specific gravity (σ/ρ) and specific stiffness (E/ρ). Support for a load in bending over a given length l may be accomplished with least weight for a given deflection provided $\rho/E^{1/3}$ is a minimum.† Support for a load in compression by a given length of support is accomplished with least weight provided $\rho/E^{\frac{1}{2}}$ is a minimum.† In these two cases the importance of decreasing density for a given stiffness is seen. Fibrous composite materials may be constructed of lower density than conventional materials for the same value of the modulus.

---

† Deflection of a cantilever of length l, thickness d and of unit width, supporting a load W at its end is

$$\delta = 4Wl^3/Ed^3.$$

The mass of material required for the beam is ρdl and this mass may be written $\rho(4W/E\delta)^{1/3}l^2$. Similarly, the buckling load of a strut in compression with pin-jointed ends is $W = \pi^2 EI/l^2$ where I is the second moment of area. For a circular cross-section we then obtain the mass as $2\rho(W/\pi E)^{1/2}l^2$ since I is equal to $\pi d^4/64$ where d is the diameter.

Values of the maximum specific strength and of E/ρ for the whiskers and fibres in Tables 1 and 2 of Appendix A show that the possible improvement of specific strength, with respect to steel wire, is greater than 3 for alumina, about 5 for SiC, and about 3 for boron, again assuming $V_f = 0.5$ and a matrix of the same density as the fibre. Assuming zero elastic modulus for the matrix, graphite whiskers can produce a value of E/ρ about six times that of steel and this value is closely approached by graphite filaments (Appendix A, Table 2). An added advantage is that if stiffness rather than strength is important, values of V_f greater than 0.5 could be used. The only metal showing a value of E/ρ which approaches the values shown in Table 1 of Appendix A is beryllium with the outstanding value of 25×10^6 psi.

To obtain the highest values of E_c continuous fibres are necessary. The breaking strength parallel to the fibres is then independent of the transfer length. Values of l_{crit} can be made long but this will reduce the transverse strength. If only discontinuous fibres are available l_{crit} should be made short so that for a given length, l, of the fibres l/l_{crit} is as large as possible. Two-dimensional strength can be obtained by lamination, i.e. binding together sheets each consisting of uniaxially aligned fibres.

There are essentially two types of matrix possible: metallic matrices and polymer matrices. To obtain the highest values of E/ρ and of σ/ρ a polymer matrix is best. Most materials can be glued with resins and there is a well-developed technology for fabricating composites with this type of matrix. The disadvantage of resin matrices is the low value of shear modulus which resins possess and hence large values of l_{crit} are expected if the resin does not fail at the fibre ends (section 5.3). If failure occurs at fibre ends l_{crit} is controlled by the breaking strength of the resin and the coefficient of friction between fibre and resin. Hence values of l_{crit} are much greater than for metals at room temperature. At present polymers for use at temperatures above 200°C are not available.

Ductile metal matrices can deform plastically and relieve stress concentrations at fibre ends. At room temperature values of l_{crit} are small and controlled by the shear strength of the metal, provided an adequate bond can be made to the fibre. Metals can be used at high temperatures and possess good oxidation resistance. The yield strength can be controlled by alloying and so l_{crit} can be varied. The strengths of non-metallic fibres do not exceed the strengths of metals by so much as they do of polymers and hence it must be borne in mind that minimum fibre concentrations are necessary to produce marked increases in strength in metals which work-harden (section 5.2). Plastic flow of the metal can contribute to the fracture toughness of a composite but at the same time cyclic stressing of a metallic matrix will lead to fatigue. This is the chief disadvantage of the metal; the other is that the normally high density prevents the achievement of high values of specific strength and stiffness.

The stiffness and strength of an array of aligned fibres can be adequately predicted from the properties of the fibre and matrix; as we have seen the fracture toughness of such arrays is not fully understood, but it is known that fracture toughness is usually directly proportional to the fibre diameter, for a given volume fraction and properties of the fibre and matrix. The properties of an aligned array are highly anisotropic. This anisotropy must be either removed or adequately predicted and controlled by the engineer. If a small volume fraction of fibres is used in a matrix, say to improve the properties of the matrix, e.g. in cement, then a random planar mat of fibres may be sufficient to give isotropy in a plane or a three-dimensional felt could give three-dimensional isotropy. For random mats or felts there are severe practical limitations on the volume fraction attainable if the fibres are randomly arranged in direction. High volume loadings are achieved by stacking together laminae within each of which the fibres are parallel and as closely packed as possible. Most of the design studies carried out with fibrous composites involve such a geometry.

The basic elastic theory of laminated composites is given for instance in Calcote (1969) and a very readable introduction by Ashton, Halpin, and Petit (1969). The laminate consists of a series of layers (Fig. 5.24). Each layer is an aligned composite and is treated as an orthotropic elastic continuum in a state of plane stress; each layer then has just four elastic constants since zero stress is always assumed in the direction parallel to the thickness. The constitutive equations of the laminate are worked out from the individual elastic properties of the layers and the orientations of the fibres in each layer. Since the individual layers are thin and the laminate will also be thin, the most convenient form of the constitutive equations enables one to write both the

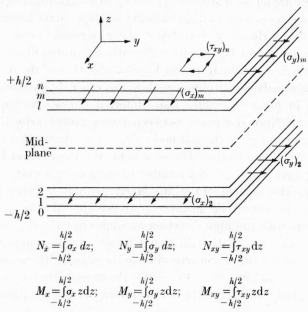

$$N_x = \int_{-h/2}^{h/2}\sigma_x\,dz; \quad N_y = \int_{-h/2}^{h/2}\sigma_y\,dz; \quad N_{xy} = \int_{-h/2}^{h/2}\tau_{xy}\,dz$$

$$M_x = \int_{-h/2}^{h/2}\sigma_x\,z\,dz; \quad M_y = \int_{-h/2}^{h/2}\sigma_y\,z\,dz; \quad M_{xy} = \int_{-h/2}^{h/2}\tau_{xy}\,z\,dz$$

Fig. 5.24. The basis of simple laminate theory. The stress resultants N_x, N_y, N_{xy} represent the components of the total force per unit length acting at the mid-plane. The moment resultants M_x, M_y, M_{xy}, represent the components of the bending and twisting moment with respect to the mid-plane per unit length along the mid-plane parallel to the axis of the component.

resultant total stresses on the laminate N_x, N_y, N_{xy} (Fig. 5.24) and the resultant total movements on the laminate M_x, M_y, M_{xy} (Fig. 5.24) in terms of the strains at the mid-plane of the laminate (which are functions of the displacement at the mid-plane) and of the curvatures of the laminate (functions of the displacement in the z direction). Basically the procedure is to transform the stress–strain relation of each layer from the principal axes of the layer to the principal axes of the laminate and then to integrate through the thickness in order to obtain the resultant force and resultant moment. The strains in each layer are written in terms of the strain at the mid-section of the laminate and the curvatures at the mid-section of the laminate, neither of which is assumed to vary with z and so is the same for each layer. The laminate has six elastic constants in general.

There are no shear stresses τ_{xz} and τ_{yz} in a single isolated layer and none are assumed within an individual layer in the laminated composite. However interlayer shear stresses must arise between adjacent layers with differently orientated fibres as in the experiments illustrated in Fig. 5.23(b). One of the uses of laminate analysis is to minimize these and other stresses between layers in order to reduce these internal stresses within the laminate. Normal stresses between layers cannot arise if the assumption of plane stress is maintained. This assumption is not a good one close to the edges of a laminate. Pagano and Pipes (1971) have investigated a number of cases using a more exact theory. The sequence in which layers are put together then becomes important. For instance, if stress is applied to a sequence of layers with the fibre direction at angles of $90° + 45°$, $-45°$, $-45° + 45°$, $90°$ to the (in-plane) tensile stress, compressive stresses in the z direction arise close to the edges. If the sequence is $+45°$, $-45°$, $90°$, $90° - 45°$, $+45°$ the stresses are tensile and tend to cause splitting between the layers, i.e. delamination.

REFERENCES

A. S. ARGON (1972). *Treatise on Materials Science and Technology* 1, p. 79. Academic Press, New York.

J. E. A. ASHTON, J. C. HALPIN, and P. H. PETIT (1969). *Primer on Composite Materials: Analysis*, Technomic Publishing Co., Stamford, Conn.

J. AVESTON, G. A. COOPER, and A. KELLY (1971). Single and Multiple Fracture. In *Properties of Fibre composites; Conference Proceedings N.P.L.*, p. 15. I.P.C. Science and Technology Press, Guildford.

V. D. AZZI and S. W. TSAI (1965). *Exp. Mech.* 5, 283.

R. M. BARKER and T. F. MACLAUGHLIN (1971). *Jnl. compos. Mater.* 5, 492.

J. M. BLOOM and H. B. WILSON Jr. (1967). *Jnl. compos. Mater.* **1**, 268.

M. J. BOMFORD and A. KELLY (1971). *Fibre Sci. and Tech.* **4**, 1.

L. R. CALCOTE (1969). *The Analysis of Laminated Composite Structures*, Van Nostrand Reinhold, New York.

C. C. CHAMIS and G. P. SENDECKYJ (1968). *Jnl. compos. Mater.* **2**, 332.

P. E. CHEN (1971). *Polym. Eng. and Sci.* **11**, 51.

B. D. COLEMAN (1958). *J. Mech. Phys. Solids* **7**, 60.

J. COOK and J. E. GORDON (1964). *Proc. R. Soc.* A**282**, 508.

G. A. COOPER (1970). *J. mater. Sci.* **5**, 645.

—— and A. KELLY (1967). *J. Mech. Phys. Solids* **15**, 279.

—— and A. KELLY (1970) *Mechanics of Composite Materials* (Eds. F. W. WENDT, M. LIEBOWITZ and N. PERRONE) p. 653. Pergamon Press, Oxford.

—— and J. SILLWOOD (1972). *J. mater. Sci.* **7**, 325.

A. H. COTTRELL (1964). *Proc. R. Soc.* A**282**, 2.

H. L. COX (1952). *Br. J. appl. Phys.* **3**, 72.

I. M. DANIEL and A. H. DURELLI (1961). 16th Conference, Society of Plastics Industry, Paper 19A.

H. E. DANIELS (1945). *Proc. R. Soc.* A**183**, 405.

N. F. DOW (1963). *General Electric Co. Report* R 63SD61.

D. K. HALE and A. KELLY (1972). *Ann. Rev. mater. Sci.* **2**, 405.

P. HANCOCK and R. C. CUTHBERTSON (1970). *J. mater. Sci.* **5**, 762.

Z. HASHIN (1965). *J. Mech. Phys. Solids* **13**, 119.

—— (1970). *Mechanics of Composite Materials* (Eds. F. W. WENDT, H. LIEBOWITZ, and N. PERRONE), p. 301, Pergamon Press, Oxford.

—— and B. W. ROSEN (1964). *J. appl. Mech.* **31**, 223.

J. M. HEDGEPETH and P. VAN DYKE (1967), *Jnl. compos. Mater.* **1**, 294.

R. HILL (1963). *J. Mech. Phys. Solids* **11**, 357.

—— (1964). *J. Mech. Phys. Solids* **12**, 194, and 213.

P. W. JACKSON and D. CRATCHLEY (1966). *J. Mech. Phys. Solids* **14**, 49. See also G. A. COOPER (1966). *J. Mech. Phys. Solids* **14**, 103.

A. KELLY (1964). *Proc. R. Soc.* A**282**, 63.

—— (1970). *Proc. R. Soc.* A**319**, 95.

—— (1971). *Strengthening Methods in Crystals* (Eds. A. KELLY and R. B. NICHOLSON) p. 433, Elsevier, London.

—— and G. J. DAVIES (1965). *Metall. Rev.* **10**, 1.

—— and W. R. TYSON (1965a). *High Strength Materials* (Ed. V. F. ZACKAY) p. 578, Wiley, New York.

—— and W. R. TYSON (1965b). *J. Mech. Phys. Solids* **13**, 329.

K. G. KREIDER and G. R. LEVERANT (1966). *Advanced Fibrous Reinforced Composites* S.A.M.P.E. 10, Society of Aerospace Material and Process Engineers, San Diego, California.

J. R. LAGER and R. R. JUNE (1969). *Jnl. compos. Mater.* **3**, 48.

Y. LANIR and Y. C. B. FUNG (1972). *Jnl. compos. Mater.* **6**, 387.

J. K. LEES (1968). *Polym. Eng. and Sci.* **8**, 195.

F. J. LOCKETT (1971). Strength of Composites with Discontinuous Reinforcement. In *Properties of Fibre Composites; Conference Proceedings N.P.L.*, p. 85 I.P.C. Science and Technology Press, Guildford.

J. F. MANDELL and F. J. MCGARRY (1972). *Fracture Toughness Studies of Fibre Reinforced Plastic Laminates*, Faraday Society Discussion, Nottingham..

D. L. MCDANELS, R. W. JECH, and J. W. WEETON (1960). *Metal Prog.* **78**, 118.

——, R. W. JECH, and J. W. WEETON (1965). *Trans. Am. Inst. Min. metall. Petrol. Engrs* **233**, 636.

S. T. MILEIKO (1969). *J. mater. Sci.* **4**, 974.

E. MONCUNILL DE FERRAN and B. HARRIS (1970). *Jnl. compos. Mater.* **4**, 62.

J. F. MULHERN, J. G. ROGERS, and A. J. M. SPENCER (1967). *J. Inst. Math. and its Appl.* **3**, 21.

J. O. OUTWATER Jr. (1956). *Mod. Plast.* **33**, 156.

—— and W. O. CARNES (1967). *Final Report Contract* No. DAAA 21–67–C–0061 –AD659363.

—— and M. C. MURPHY (1969). 26th Annual Conference, Society of Plastics Industry (Reinforced Plastics–Composites Division), Paper 11C.

N. J. PAGANO and R. B. PIPES (1971). *Jnl. compos. Mater.* **5**, 50.

V. RILEY (1968). *Jnl. compos. Mater.* **2**, 436.

B. W. ROSEN (1965). *Fiber Composite Materials*, p. 37, Am. Soc. Metals.

—— (1970). *Proc. R. Soc.* A**319**, 79.

G. C. SIH, P. C. PARIS and G. R. IRWIN (1965). *Int. J. fracture Mech.* **1**, 189.

G. E. SMITH and A. J. M. SPENCER (1970). *J. Mech. Phys. Solids* **18**, 81.

W. H. SUTTON, B. W. ROSEN, and D. G. FLOM (1964). *S.P.E. Jl.* **20**, 1.

S. TIMOSHENKO (1936). *Theory of Elastic Stability*, McGraw-Hill, New York.

W. R. TYSON (1964). Ph.D. Thesis, Cambridge.

J. H. WHITNEY and M. B. RILEY (1966). *AIAA J.* **4**, 1537.

E. M. WU and R. C. REUTER Jr. (1965). *Crack Extension in Fiberglass Reinforced Plastics Report*, No. 275, Dept. of Theoretical and Applied Mechanics, University of Illinois.

C. ZWEBEN and B. W. ROSEN (1970). *J. Mech. Phys. Solids* **18**, 189.

6

STRONG FIBROUS SOLIDS

THE purpose of this chapter is to describe some of the processes which have been used, or might be used, to make fibres and to incorporate them into a matrix. The scientific principles will be emphasized. A most useful summary of the technology has recently appeared (Parratt 1972). We shall distinguish between fibres and whiskers as possible reinforcements. We consider a fibre to be a long, thin rod with a length of at least several centimetres whether it be of circular cross-section or not and whether it be polycrystalline, amorphous or a single crystal; a metal wire or a glass filament are examples. A whisker will be taken to mean a single crystal produced by filamentary growth with a diameter not exceeding 10 μm and with a large ratio of length to diameter. Whiskers will always provide a discontinuous reinforcement. Fibres may be used to provide a continuous reinforcement or they may be chopped up to provide a discontinuous one.

We dealt with the properties required of fibre and matrix, in order to obtain efficient reinforcement, in section 5.10. Section 6.1 deals with the properties of glass-reinforced resins and with the types of glass fibre available. Because asbestos may also be introduced into resin matrices, section 6.1 includes a description of the properties of asbestos. Section 6.2 deals with the production of strong fibres and 6.3 with some of the relevant properties of whisker crystals. With metallic matrices the possibility arises of producing the reinforcement directly *in situ* in the matrix. This is dealt with in section 6.4.

6.1. Reinforced plastics

Strong glass fibres were first studied accurately by Griffith in 1920. They have been used to reinforce a resin matrix in commercial materials for nearly thirty years. Normal glass-reinforced plastics are composite materials consisting of glass fibres in a plastic of the thermosetting type. Newer ones contain thermoplastic materials as the binder. The glass can be unidirectionally arranged, as for example in a fishing rod, but generally the stronger types contain the glass in the form of a woven fabric. The random mat and chopped strand form is cheaper. The strength is directly proportional to the volume of the glass used.

6.1.1. *The matrix*

The most widely used binder is a thermosetting resin of the polyester type, although other thermosetting resins such as phenolics, epoxies, and silicones are used, and in some cases thermoplastic binders such as polystyrene and polyvinylchloride. The cross-linked polymers include epoxy, polyester, and phenolic resins all of which are infusible, insoluble solids in which the polymer chains have been linked together in the 'curing' process to form a three-dimensional network. The stress–strain curve for a typical resin of this type is non-linear but there is no sharp division into elastic and plastic behaviour as with a metal. At low stresses, the behaviour is elastic and the stress–strain behaviour shows only a small time-dependence compared with the thermoplastics.

The *epoxy resins* have the important advantage that volatiles are not liberated during cure. They have low shrinkage (1–5 per cent), good adhesive properties, and can be cured at room temperature if required. Disadvantages are their high viscosity (over 6–7000 cP at 25°C with a conventional epoxy resin) and, in general, their higher cost compared with polyesters. They are cured by reaction through the epoxy sites $(-C\overset{\displaystyle O}{\overbrace{\hspace{1.5em}}}C-)$ with, for example, diethylene triamine when the curing agent becomes part of the cross-lined network.

Typical properties of epoxies are: specific gravity 1·1–1·2; tensile strength 35–100 MN m^{-2}; tensile modulus 2·4–5·0 GN m^{-2}; ultimate elongation 2–9 per cent; compressive strength 90–220 MN m^{-2}; and cure shrinkage 1–5 per cent. At room temperature, cross-linked epoxies are brittle and the work required for crack propagation ranges from $1 \cdot 5-9 \times 10^2$ J m^{-2} depending on the curing agent. Considerable increase in the toughness of epoxies can be achieved by the incorporation of a butadiene–acrylonitrile copolymer (e.g. McGarry 1970), resulting in values up to 2×10^3 J m^{-2}. These high values are similar to the fracture surface work of high impact polystyrene.

Most of the resins used for the manufacture of glass-reinforced plastics are *polyesters*. Like the epoxies, these have the advantage that volatiles are not liberated during cure. The polyesters are, in general, lower in cost than the epoxy resins and their low viscosity (800–2300 cP at 25°C) is also an advantage. Disadvantages are their high cure shrinkage (5–12 per cent) and poor adhesion to glass.

A typical polyester is represented by the condensation product of an unsaturated dicarboxyclic acid, e.g. fumaric acid with a dibasic alcohol, e.g. ethylene glycol. Cross-linking can take place through the reactive double bonds. The unsaturated polyester is usually dissolved in a polymerizable monomer such as styrene; this leads to the additional possibility of cross-linking through styrene monomer units. By using promoters in conjunction with peroxide catalysts, cross-linking can be effected at ordinary temperatures. Details of a wide variety of polyesters and catalyst systems are given in the literature (Morgan 1961, Rubin 1969, Parkyn 1970).

Typical properties of cured polyesters are: specific gravity $1 \cdot 1-1 \cdot 25$; tensile strength 34–70 MN m^{-2}; tensile modulus $2 \cdot 1-4 \cdot 8$ GN m^{-2}; ultimate elongation 1–8 per cent; compressive strength 70–240 MN m^{-2}; and cure shrinkage 5–12 per cent.

A recent development is the introduction of polyester bulk moulding compounds in which two-phase heterogeneous resin systems are used. These consist of unsaturated polyesters modified by thermoplastics such as polystyrene, polyethylene or polymethylmethacrylate. This modification eliminates shrinkage during cross-linkage of the polyester.

The *phenolic resins* have the advantages that they are rather cheaper than the polyesters and that by using solutions (e.g. in alcohol or, in some cases, in water) reinforcements in the form of paper or cloth can be easily impregnated. A major disadvantage (which is shared with the melamine–formaldehyde resins) is that volatiles are liberated during the curing process and relatively high pressures have to be used during fabrication. Phenol and melamine–formaldehyde resins are, however, still widely used for laminate manufacture.

The fibre reinforcement of thermoplastics has been assuming steadily increasing importance and a wide variety of thermoplastics containing from 10–50 per cent glass fibre reinforcement is commercially available. The addition of glass fibre leads to substantial improvements in tensile strength and modulus; the advantage of the thermoplastic, its ease of fabrication, is retained.

The strength of unfilled thermoplastics (not oriented) ranges from about 7–13 MN m^{-2} for low density polyethylenes, up to 70–85 MN m^{-2} with, for example, the nylon polymers. Elongations range from a few per cent with polystyrene and ABS (acrylonitrile–butadiene–styrene) polymers up to several hundred per cent with the polyethylenes and polypropylenes. The tensile moduli are generally less than 3·5 GN m^{-2}. Unlike the cross-linked polymers, the stress–strain behaviour is markedly time- and temperature-dependent and rates of creep and stress relaxation are high.

With many of the thermoplastics, adhesion between the fibre and matrix is poor and this is thought to lead to an inefficient transfer of stress between the fibre and matrix. Adhesion can be improved by the use of coupling agents as, for example, suitable silanes with glass-reinforced polypropylenes. Alternatively, modified polymer matrices which can form a chemical bond with the fibre surface may be used. Examples are the use of a modified polypropylene, or ethylene–acrylic acid copolymers with glass fibre reinforcements.

6.1.2. *The glass*

The glass is usually a soda-free calcia–alumina–borosilicate glass known commercially as 'E' glass. This is drawn from the molten state at speeds up to 2×10^3 cm s^{-1} to diameters of between 5 μm and 20 μm and a surface treatment, called a size, is usually applied as the filaments are gathered. If a yarn is to be made, or the filaments are to be woven, a lubricating size is usually applied. The tensile strength of the glass after drawing averages 400 000 psi (2·86 GN m^{-2}) with a Young's modulus of about $10 \cdot 5 \times 10^6$ psi (70 GN m^{-2}), a Poisson's ratio of 0·22 and a specific gravity of 2·55 (bulk glass of the same composition is slightly denser with a specific gravity of 2·58). The freshly formed glass has a great affinity for water and the adsorption of water leads to a loss in strength (section 2.5). The glass is used either as continuous strands wound together into what are called rovings, or woven cloths, or else the glass is cut up into chopped strands which are available as random mats.

The composition and some properties of glasses which may be drawn into fibres are shown in Table 6.1. The E glass composition is the most widely used for glass fibres—the composition is based on the eutectic in the CaO–Al$_2$O$_3$–SiO$_2$ system which occurs at 62 per cent SiO$_2$, 14·7 per cent Al$_2$O$_3$ and 23·3 per cent CaO. The composition given may be regarded as an average one. Total alkali content (K$_2$O+Na$_2$O) is kept below 2 per cent to ensure corrosion resistance and a high electrical surface resistivity. B$_2$O$_3$ decreases the liquidus temperature and provides a larger temperature range within which a glass may be worked without devitrification. Soda-lime glass is the cheap glass used commercially to make windows or bottles; it can be fiberized to produce coarse fibres. There is usually some sulphur present in it. C glass is one developed for corrosion resistance and is better than E glass in acids though poorer in alkalis. M glass was designed specifically to attain a high Young's modulus, without losing the ability to draw the glass and without increasing the toxic hazard by using too much BeO. As well as the elements listed in the table, M glass also contains 2 per cent Li$_2$O and 3 per cent CeO$_2$. The temperature-dependence of the Young's modulus is greater than that of E glass and the strength at room temperature about the same. S glass was specially developed for the U.S. Air Force as a commercially fiberizable glass with a

TABLE 6.1

Composition and properties of glass filaments

Name	SiO_2	Al_2O_3	CaO	MgO	B_2O_3	BeO	Na_2O	K_2O	ZrO_2	TiO_2	Fe_2O_3	ρ	E	ν	n	α	T_1
E	54·4	14·4	17·5	4·5	8·0						0·4	2·54	72·4	0·2	1·548	4·9	616
Soda-Lime	72·0	0·6	10·0	2·5			14·2	0·5				2·50			1·512		695
C	65·0	4·0	14·0	3·0	5·5		8·0	0·5				2·54	69·0		1·541	4·0	552
M†	53·7	12·9		9·0		8·0			2·0	7·9	0·5	2·89	112		1·635	3·2	
S	65·0	25·0		10·0								2·48	85·6		1·523	1·6	760
Fused Silica	100											2·2	73·1	0·16	1·458	0·31	1070

Compositions are in weight per cent.

ρ = density in 10^3 kg m^{-3}; E = Young's modulus before compaction in GN m^{-2}; ν = Poisson's ratio

n = refractive index at 550 nm; α = linear expansion coefficient at 25°C to 100°C in 10^{-6} per °C.

T_1 = temperature in °C at which viscosity is $10^{14.5}$ poise—Appendix E.

† Contains also 3 per cent CeO_2 and 2 per cent Li_2O.

Sources: Lowrie (1967) and Hutchins & Harrington (1966).

higher strength and elastic modulus than E glass and with a
greater retention of strength at high temperatures; it contains
nothing but SiO_2, Al_2O_3, and MgO. The strength of S glass at
room temperature is $\sim$5·0 GN m^{-2} (700 000 psi). Its corrosion
resistance is far superior to E glass in all but strong alkali
solutions. Glass fibres produced with a low dielectric constant
for use in radomes usually have a lower Young's modulus than
E glass ($\leqslant$56 GN m^{-2}) and the strength is lower, while the
density is only a little less (2·16 g cm^{-3}).

Fused silica may be produced in fibrous form. The elastic
modulus is much the same as that of E glass but the strength at
room temperature is a good deal greater, $\sim$5·4 GN m^{-2}, and the
strain point, listed as T_1 in Table 6.1, very much higher. The
conditions under which very high strength is obtained have been
closely specified (Morley, Andrews, and Whitney 1964). Silica
fibres can be drawn continuously and coated with a proprietary
aluminium alloy so that an average strength of 540 000 psi
(3·8 GN m^{-2}) is obtained (Arridge, Baker, and Cratchley 1964).
The fibre diameter is about 50 μm and the aluminium coating
10 μm thick. Composites may be made simply by pressing the
aluminium-coated fibres together. The resulting volume fraction
of silica is $\sim$50 per cent. Some damage to the fibre is produced
in pressing. The pressures and temperatures which must be used
(12 000 psi at 450°C) are very much greater than those used in
making glass-reinforced plastics. Strengths up to 180 000 psi
have been obtained at room temperature and 60 000 psi at 400°C
for aligned fibres (Cratchley and Baker 1964). The average
strength at room temperature is $\sim$115 000 psi. Aluminium and
silica have very similar values of Young's modulus so that at
very small strains the modulus is 10^7 psi. However, at stresses
greater than 10^4 psi the matrix yields plastically and the modulus is reduced to 6 $\times$ 10^6 psi (section 5.2). The average strength
of this material and the value of Young's modulus are similar to
those of glass-reinforced plastics at room temperature. Above
room temperature the properties are better than those of glass-
reinforced plastics. The silica-reinforced aluminium maintains
the strength shown at room temperature up to 300°C and has

a UTS of 60 000 psi at 400°C in a short time tensile test. This is a factor of about 9 greater than that of a commercial aluminium alloy at 400°C. The long term strength at temperatures greater than about 400°C is affected by reaction between the silica and the aluminium.

The great drawback to any material using silica as a reinforcement, is the low value of Young's modulus of the silica and the decrease in the strength of silica at temperatures above 300°C. Silica is so easily drawn that many attempts have been made to produce silica-based glasses with higher values of Young's modulus. Results of these experiments are reported by Loewenstein (1961). It is found that oxides generally accepted as glass formers, e.g. Si, Al, B, P reduce Young's modulus. Ions of high field strength introduced into the interstices of the glass network, e.g. Be, Ti, Zr, raise the value of Young's modulus. Beryllium is outstanding and moduli up to 20×10^6 psi (140 GN m^{-2}) can be obtained by addition of Be. However, its use introduces a toxic hazard during drawing. Without using Be values up to 17×10^6 psi (120 GN m^{-2}) can be obtained.

6.1.3. *Properties of glass-reinforced plastics*

The combination of fibrous glass and liquid polyester is moulded to shape. This is a simple operation involving pressing to shape and curing the polyester. Curing is the reaction between the polyester and a material, such as styrene, to form the crosslinked structure characteristic of a thermosetting resin. This can be carried out at very low temperature, less than $\sim$120°C, and since the pressure required is also low, $\lesssim$250 psi (1·7 MN m^{-2}), the glass is incorporated without drastic loss of strength.

The strength characteristics of commercial glass-reinforced plastics conform well to the principles of Chapter 5. The strength is a linear function of V_f for both parallel strands and for random mats. The strength of a random mat in any direction, in the plane of the mat, is proportional to Young's modulus in that direction. Continuous roving has a tensile strength parallel to the fibres of $\sim$130 000 psi ($\sim$1 GN m^{-2}) when $V_f \sim 0$·5. The strength of the glass fibres in the resin thus appears to be

$\sim$260 000 psi (1·7 GN m^{-2}). The specific gravity of a composite is $\sim$1·9 for $V_f = 0$·5 and so σ/ρ is 7×10^4 psi, or about the same as steel wire. The elastic modulus is $\sim$5 $\times 10^6$ psi (35 GN m^{-2}), so E/ρ is 2·6 $\times 10^6$ psi, which is less than that of steel. The energy absorbed in breaking an unnotched specimen, in an impact test, is $\sim$20 ft lb in^{-2} ($\sim$4·5 $\times 10^7$ mJ m^{-2}). Specimens containing a mat of fibres, which show uniform elastic properties in a plane, have values of E and of the breaking stress, of about half the values shown by material containing parallel strands, but about the same energy is required to break them. At resin contents of less than 50 per cent the properties of glass-reinforced plastics begin to deteriorate. The strength varies with temperature as does that of the glass and falls by a factor of 3 between 77 K and 200°C. The strength at 77 K is about twice that at room temperature.

The strength of a specimen containing parallel strands is greatest for continuous fibres and falls rapidly for fibre lengths of less than about 1·5 cm (Sonneborn 1954). This corresponds to an aspect ratio of 750 for fibres of 20 μm diameter. This is consistent with the theory of Chapter 5. We expect the strength to be decreased substantially if $l/d \lesssim 5l_{crit}/d$. From equation (5.45), with $\sigma_{uf} = 260\ 000$ psi (1·7 GN m^{-2}) and $\mu n = 1000$ psi (7 MN m^{-2}) gives $5l_{crit}/d \sim 650$ which is close to that observed.

Glass-reinforced plastics are easily made and show large values of σ/ρ and quite adequate impact resistance at room temperature. They have demonstrated for a number of years the feasibility of the principles of fibre-reinforcement. The chief failings of this type of material are: the very low Young's modulus, so that the strength is only developed at elastic strains of 3–4 per cent; the loss of strength in the presence of water, which is connected with a reaction at the glass–matrix interface (see Ashbee and Wyatt (1969) for some of the effects); and the poor fatigue life. After 10^7 cycles at room temperature the flexural strength of a polyester reinforced with 50 per cent of woven fibre is only 15 000 psi (105 MN m^{-2}). The static strength is about $\sim$65 000 psi (400 MN m^{-2}). A commercial aluminium alloy of high strength will show a fatigue life of 10^8 cycles under a stress of 22 000 psi (154 MN m^{-2}). Glass-reinforced plastics also show fatigue at room temperature and cannot be used at temperatures greater than 250°C.

A marked increase in the Young's modulus of reinforced plastics may be achieved by the introduction of low density fibres other than glass which are of high strength, and also of high elastic modulus. Asbestos has been used in place of glass for a number of years and stiff fibres of carbon and boron, are available today. These can be satisfactorily bonded with commercial epoxy and polyester resins. Production of carbon and boron fibres is dealt with in section 6.2.

6.1.4. *Asbestos fibres*

Asbestos has been used as a diluent and a filler for thermoplastics for many years but its potential as a fibre reinforcement has only recently been fully appreciated. Asbestos fibres occur naturally and are cheaper than glass fibres; they can also be stronger and they possess larger values of Young's modulus. Asbestos minerals are fibrous silicates. 90 per cent of that used commercially is chrysotile—$Mg_3 (Si_2O_5)(OH)_4$—and the others are all amphiboles of which those having asbestiform varieties are shown in Table 6.2.

Chrysotile is a hydrated magnesium silicate. The individual fibres consist of fibrils which are single crystals, each of which is a hollow tube in cross-section comprising alternate sheets of silica and of magnesium hydroxide rolled up like a 'Swiss roll'.

TABLE 6.2

Varieties of asbestos

Name	Formula	Density (10^3 kg m^{-3})	Young's modulus (GN m^{-2})	Tensile Strength (GN m^{-2})
Chrysotile	$Mg_3(Si_2O_5)(OH)_4$	$2 \cdot 5_5$	169	3·1
Crocidolite	$Na_2Fe_3{}^{II}Fe_2{}^{III}Si_8O_{22}(OH)_2$	3·4	170	2·1
Amosite	$Mg_2Fe_5{}^{II}Si_8O_{22}(OH)_2$	3·2	177	1·7
Actinolite	$Ca_2Fe_5{}^{II}Si_8O_{22}(OH)_2$		159	1·9
Tremolite	$Ca_2Mg_5Si_8O_{22}(OH)_2$		149	0·4
Anthophyllite	$Mg_7Si_8O_{22}(OH)_2$	2·95–3·2	153	1·2

A small individual fibre would be of diameter ~10 μm and the fibrils are ~0·1 μm in diameter. Crocidolite or blue asbestos is a hydrated sodium iron silicate with carcinogenic properties which restrict its use. Anthophyllite and amosite are usually found containing both iron and magnesium, though the composition of anthophyllite given in Table 6.2 is one without iron; the composition of anthophyllite is more variable than that of amosite. Amosite occurs only in South Africa and anthophyllite in both India and Finland. It retains its strength after heating to higher temperatures better than do the other amphiboles. Amphiboles can be synthesized under extreme hydrothermal conditions, e.g. 3000 bars (1 bar = 10^5 Pa—see Appendix D) at 700°C (see Gier, Cox, and Young 1964).

A recent review of the attempts to use asbestos as an aligned reinforcement has been given by Hollingsworth (1969). New methods of processing the minerals must be developed in order to prevent the degradation of the fibres to short lengths which usually occurs when the natural mineral is ground for use as a filler.

The strength of asbestos has been discussed by Aveston (1969), who has investigated the strength of fibres of asbestos as a function of length and of cross-sectional area of the specimen. His figures for the tensile strengths of the natural minerals at room temperature, extrapolated to zero cross-section, are shown in Table 6.2. Apart from that of tremolite, the strengths are very similar. Aveston concluded that the variations in strength with cross-sectional area reported variously by previous workers was not statistically significant.

Natural asbestos loses a large fraction of the strength at room temperature if it is heated to between 300°C and 500°C; there is no obvious change in crystal structure. In the case of chrysotile, the strength is reduced by one-third, and in the case of crocidolite by one-half as well as the specimen becoming extremely brittle.

Aveston has had some success in explaining the strength of asbestos by regarding it in effect as a fibrous composite, with a volume fraction of essentially 100 per cent of fibres which are flawed, so that individual fibres will show a strength/length effect. The fibrils (the fibres of the notional composite) are coupled by interfibrilar friction. The sliding friction provides a shear strength parallel to the fibrils of between 10 and 20 $MN\,m^{-2}$, or less than one-hundredth of the tensile strength. The strength of tremolite is low because the microstructure consists of short and somewhat poorly aligned fibrils. The fracture of chrysolite and of the fibrous amphiboles in the natural condition is a typically fibrous one, and in the case of chrysolite the 'Swiss-roll' structure of the fibrils must also be taken into account. This structure usually leads to failure at the outer surface of a specimen before there is failure at the inside, as in the case of graphite whiskers. After heating any of the asbestos minerals listed in Table 6.2 the strength is much reduced, but only a very small amount of the physically combined water is eliminated and there is no change of crystal structure. Aveston has demonstrated that heating in fact leads to an increase in the interfibrilar shear strength, and an increased resistance to longitudinal cleavage, and that when this occurs the mode of fracture changes so that cracks run normal to the fibrils for many fibril diameters. To account for the absence of a strength/diameter effect but the presence of a strength/length effect in natural asbestos (excluding tremolite) as well as for the decrease in strength on heating, it is suggested that asbestos consists of bundles of continuous (but flawed) fibres in which the interfibrilar adhesion is low for chrysotile, somewhat higher for the amphiboles, and very much higher for the heat-treated amphiboles. The decrease in strength on heating is then due to the bundles of fibres becoming more notch-sensitive due to the increased adhesion. It follows that industrial treatment designed to prevent the dispersion of the rock into component fibrils of too small a diameter will in general lead to a decrease (though perhaps tolerable) in strength.

6.2. Production of fibres

The largest values of the strength and of the elastic modulus of a fibrous material are obtained if it can be made of parallel and continuous fibres. Continuous fibres are easily arranged parallel to one another and high packing fractions can be obtained.

6.2.1. *Metals*

Metals are easily produced in the form of wire by cold drawing. We dealt with this in Chapter 4. Strong metal wires are useful reinforcing materials. The strength is due to cold work and increases with increasing reduction in area, but high strength cannot be maintained at high temperatures at present. However, materials such as internally-oxidized copper alloys which contain a dispersion of an extremely stable phase do not re-crystallize or show a decrease in hardness at temperatures very close to the melting temperature (Preston and Grant 1961). There is therefore no theoretical reason why the range of temperature could not be greatly increased, over which heavily drawn metal wires retain their strength.

With the use of pure materials there seems no reason to doubt that steel wire with a strength of 10^6 psi (7 GN m^{-2}) and β-titanium wire with a strength of 5×10^5 psi (3·5 GN m^{-2}) at room temperature can be made. Beryllium wire has a value of E/ρ of 25×10^6 psi which is greater than that of boron fibres and has been experimentally exceeded only by graphite fibres and by *whiskers* of graphite and silicon carbide. Beryllium shows a smaller temperature dependence of the modulus than most metals. The strengths produced in beryllium wire so far are not large, up to about 200 000 psi, but there is no reason to suppose that this cannot be increased by conventional means. A composite material can be made of beryllium wire in aluminium, in which there is no mutual solid solubility (according to the latest phase diagrams—A. Moore, private communication), with a specific gravity of 2·35 for 50 per cent Be.

6.2.2. *Taylor wires*

Fine metal wires can also be produced by drawing a hollow silica tube containing molten metal (Taylor 1924, 1931). The theoretical reason why pure metals produced in this form should be very strong is not clear. If whisker dimensions are approached then just from experience high strengths might be expected. Ulitovskiy (1957) has been able to claim the production of really strong wire by the Taylor method ($1 \cdot 4 \times 10^6$ psi for cast iron and 350 000 psi for manganin, a copper base alloy) and Nixdorf and his co-workers (Nixdorf 1970) have had success in producing fine wires by this method. Marageing steel wires, even with a high content of embrittling components (e.g. molybdenum) have been transformed into fine wires with maximum values of tensile strength up to 5 GN m^{-2} (750 000 psi). The diameters of the wires are very uniform and the scatter in strength small compared with that of E glass filaments.

The Taylor method offers promise for the production of high strength fibres of non-metals which melt at less than 2200°C or so, e.g. silicon. Silicon is strong if the surface is smooth (section 3·2) and provided there is no reaction with the silica glass during drawing a strong solid should be produced. Nixdorf (1970) has made filaments of the silicides of titanium, iron, and vanadium as well as of a ceramic containing a high content of aluminium oxide. Materials which melt at temperatures greater than 2000°C have been drawn in silica (see McCreight, Rauch, and Sutton 1965) and eutectic mixtures of two inherently strong solids might possibly be drawn.

There is no other glass which rivals silica in both strength and ease of drawing. Glasses draw and do not neck, as a metal does, because, in the range of temperatures in which drawing is possible, the tensile stress, σ, necessary to elongate a rod is proportional to the rate of change of true strain with time.

$$\sigma = 3\eta\dot{\varepsilon}, \qquad (6.1)$$

where η is the coefficient of viscosity. If the area of a rod is A, $d\varepsilon = -dA/A$ and the drawing force $F = \sigma A$. Substituting in (6.1),

$$F = -3\eta\dot{A}.$$

Thus the rate of change of area is proportional to the drawing *force* and hence a rod containing sections of differing area of cross-section will maintain this difference as drawing proceeds (Nadai and Manjoine 1941).

Glasses are conveniently drawn when the coefficient of viscosity is about 100 poise. However, quite wide variations are possible depending upon conditions and values of η between 10 poise and 10^5 poise can be used. As well as a convenient value of η a suitable variation of η with temperature is necessary if drawing is to be easy.

When a normal solid melts the change in η is discontinuous from a value greater than 10^{15} poise, usually taken as the conventional definition of a solid, to a value of less than 10^{-1} poise, so that drawing is not possible. The application of pressure to change the viscosity of a given liquid to that appropriate for drawing is possible in principle, but clearly very difficult for materials of high melting point. Silica retains a high viscosity at temperatures well above its melting point according to this conventional definition of a solid. The coefficient of viscosity is still equal to 10^5 poise at temperatures in excess of 2000°C, and it is for this reason that a number of materials with melting points nominally greater than that of silica can, in fact, be drawn in a silica sheath.

6.2.3. *Boron fibres*

The established polymorphs of boron are α-B the low temperature rhombohedral form, a tetragonal form, and the high temperature β-rhombohedral form. The α-B and the tetragonal form are simpler structures and these are closely related to that of boron carbide. This phase has a composition range from the theoretical $B_{12}C_3$ to at least B_7C. B_4C, α-B, and the tetragonal phase contain boron atoms arranged at the corners of a regular icosahedron (the figure formed by twelve equilateral triangles meeting in groups of 5 at each vertex) but in the case of rhombohedral boron this entity is not recognized.

α-B is usually obtained at temperatures between 750°C and 1200°C and is the only form thought stable below 1000°C. Above 1200°C α-transforms to β-rhombohedral. All transformations are sensitive to the presence of impurities. So far as the author is aware no measurements have been made of the elastic moduli of single crystals of any of the forms of boron.

A useful and up-to-date account of the production and some of the properties of boron filaments has been given by Wawner (1967). The original process is due to Talley (1959). The density of boron is $2 \cdot 34 \text{ g cm}^{-3}$, the Young's modulus $> 420 \text{ GN m}^{-2}$, and the melting point 2050°C. Filaments can be prepared by deposition from either halide or hydride systems. The first method involves reduction of a halide, e.g. BCl_3, by hydrogen gas according to the reaction

$$2BCl_3 + 3H_2 = 2B + 6HCl.$$

Chlorine may be replaced by bromine or by iodine. In the second method the boron hydride is decomposed by heat, and the method is most effective if carried out at low pressure. In both methods, a heated substrate is required which must remain at the vapour deposition temperature, usually >1200°C. Tungsten wire of $\sim 12 \ \mu m$ diameter has been most successful. The temperature of deposition is critical, but the pressure less so, in the halide system. If the temperature is too low, the rate of deposition is slow; if too high, large crystals are produced in parts of the filament and this leads to a low strength. Boron filaments produced on a routine basis have diameters between $35 \ \mu m$ and $125 \ \mu m$. The residence time in the reaction chamber is 1–2 min. Continuous lengths up to several miles have been routinely produced. The boron deposit grows in cones that originate at the substrate surface, in a similar fashion to pyrolytic carbon and some forms of silicon carbide. Filaments produced by successive depositions in a number of reaction chambers have a layered structure due to quenching in passing between the chambers.

During deposition the tungsten substrate is converted into various tungsten borides, WB, W_2B_5, and WB_4. All three reaction products occur, and the time for complete reaction with the tungsten is about one minute. After long deposition or annealing times WB_4 is the only phase present. During deposition the boron diffuses into the core more rapidly than the tungsten diffuses outward, so that the reaction occurs within the area of the original cross-section of the tungsten. Sometimes voids have been detected at the interface. X-ray measurements show that the core is highly stressed in compression, and there is a tensile stress in the deposited layers next to the original substrates. This leads to the presence of radial cracks in most boron filaments.

There has been some controversy over the crystalline texture of boron filaments. The presence of the β-rhombohedral structure appears certain with an extremely small crystallite size, which may be as small as 20 Å. This does not constitute the whole of the filament and the rest is composed of an 'amorphous' or 'glassy' arrangement. At deposition temperatures below 1400°C it is claimed that the boron is amorphous, and that deposition between 1400°C and 1500°C produces β-tetragonal boron, while above 1500°C β-rhombohedral boron is formed. Between 1400°C and 1500°C the initial deposit is amorphous and becomes crystalline later with the production of large columnar grains.

As in all brittle materials, the strength of boron filaments depends on the length tested. Average strengths of as much as 4·5 GN m^{-2} have been reported with a standard deviation of $\sim$1 GN m^{-2} but the average strength produced in a routine run is usually $\sim$2·3 GN m^{-2} for a gauge length of the specimen tested of 2·5 cm. The Young's modulus of the filament produced is consistently close to 420 GN m^{-2}. The shear modulus is 180 GN m^{-2} so that the calculated Poisson's ratio is $\sim$0·2. Like graphite fibres and SiC filaments, etching does improve the strength of boron filaments but the effect is much less marked with those filaments showing high strength in the as-deposited condition. The strength is much less sensitive to surface handling than is that of glass. Some indication of the reasons for the high strength are given in section 3.5, but it is not adequately explained.

Galasso, Salkind, Kuehl, and Patarini (1966) investigated the temperature-dependence of the strength of boron fibres produced by deposition on a tungsten substrate. Fibres heated (for one hour) up to 500°C in air did not show a large change in strength but at higher temperatures the decrease in strength was catastrophic. A decrease in strength also occurs on heating in argon. That occurring in air is due to oxidation and to the low melting point of boric oxide, B_2O_3. Boron rapidly oxidizes in air and is soluble in most metals.

The properties in fatigue, at room temperature, of single filaments of boron have been described by Salkind and Patarini (1967). The life exceeded 10^8 cycles at a stress of $2 \cdot 0$ GN m^{-2}, but an effect of fatigue is observed at higher stresses. At the strains reached in these experiments, a fibre of tungsten would have undergone fatigue damage and so the fatigue effect may be produced by the tungsten core.

6.2.4. *Miscellaneous methods*

There are many possible variants of coating procedures which may be used to make continuous filaments. Small diameter, and very light threads of natural and artificial textiles are available on which deposition can be carried out at low temperature. Metals are available for high temperature deposition. Deposition at a low temperature has not been much explored. Deposition on to a heated wire by decomposition of a volatile compound of the desired coating material, or by reduction of a compound, has been successful in a number of cases. Using such methods, polycrystalline filaments of boron, boron carbide, silicon carbide, titanium boride, titanium carbide, beryllium oxide, and beryllium and others have been made (see McCreight *et al.* 1965 for details and references). The elastic moduli and strengths of some of the products are quite low and they are also porous. However, the possibility of annealing or rapid melting and solidifying or continuous flame polishing of the filaments are obvious ones for improving the properties.

Silicon carbide filaments produced by vapour deposition on a tungsten wire have a Young's modulus in the range 350–450 GN m^{-2} and strengths at room temperature up to 4 GN m^{-2} are quoted. There is a small dependence of the strength on the length of the specimen and quite a wide spread in strength. Failure is usually ascribed to internal flaws. In tensile tests of a few minutes duration, SiC fibres produced by deposition on tungsten show very little reduction in strength at temperatures up to 1000°C in air and the elastic modulus is unchanged. Longer time tests, either in air or *in vacuo*, show a reduction in strength to occur quite rapidly above 700°C and Aveston (1970) has shown that this is due to reaction between the SiC and the tungsten core.

Very fine-grained polycrystalline zirconia (ZrO_2 with $\sim$6 per cent CaO) can be produced in a continuous form by a technique in which extremely small particles of the oxide (less than 1 μm in diameter) are mixed with an organic binder and extruded. The problems are those of shrinkage during drying and firing. Strengths of 200 000 psi to 500 000 psi at room temperature have been obtained with a Young's modulus of 45×10^6 psi. The fibres are only of about 2 μm diameter and cannot apparently be used at temperatures above 1000°C because of grain growth.

Fibres of polycrystalline alumina can also be made by extrusion of a plastic mass of alumina particles in ammonium alginate, followed by sintering at temperatures up to 1900°C (Kliman 1962). These have strengths of 100 000 psi at room temperature and 75 000 psi at 1050°C. At the high temperature Young's modulus is 43×10^6 psi. Such fibres, perhaps with polished surfaces can provide reinforcement at high temperatures. Nabarro–Herring creep occurs in polycrystalline alumina at temperatures of greater than 1200°C. Creep in single crystals of alumina occurs at lower temperatures but is reduced by solute additions (see section 3.2).

Single crystal sapphire filaments may be produced from the melt in lengths up to 30 m and diameters between 150 μm and 500 μm, with an average tensile strength of 2 GN m^{-2} (300 000 psi) and Young's modulus of 460 GN m^{-2} (64×10^6 psi) (Mlavsky and Labelle 1970).

6.2.5. *Carbon fibres*

Single crystal graphite has a density of 2·26 g cm^{-3} with strong bonding due to σ-hybridization within the layer planes and weaker π-bonding linking them together. It is, consequently, highly anisotropic. The value of C_{11} is 1015 GN m^{-2} and of C_{33} only 35 GN m^{-2}. Diamond has a higher density (3·5 g cm^{-3})

and a value of Young's modulus parallel to $\langle 111 \rangle$ slightly greater than C_{11} of graphite (1030 GN m^{-2}). Since graphite is the stable form of carbon at room temperature any useful graphite fibre must either be a single crystal with layer planes parallel to the fibre axis, or else a polycrystal of very high preferred orientation.

Many fibrous forms of carbon and graphite are produced which have neither high elastic moduli nor great strength (see e.g. Carroll-Porczynski 1969). The graphitization at high temperature of polymers such as polyacrylonitrile leads to a preferred orientation and a value of Young's modulus of 120 GN m^{-2} (17×10^6 psi) (Shindo 1961). This value is much larger than that of normal polycrystalline graphite.

Very stiff graphite fibres with moduli greater than 140 GN m^{-2} (20×10^6 psi) can be produced from a variety of textiles such as α-cellulose (Bacon and Tang 1964) or polyacrylonitrile (PAN) (Watt, Phillips, and Johnson 1964, 1966). The need is for a fibre which can be carbonized without melting. Textile fibres contain assemblies of long chain molecules between 0.1 and 1.0 μm in length when fully extended; any pendant side groups are small to allow close chain packing. In wet spinning of PAN,

$$(-[CH_2CHCN]-)_n$$

(see Fig. 6.2), the fibre is first formed by squirting a solution of the polymer as a fine jet into a coagulating-bath where precipitation of the polymer as a fibre occurs. The fibre is then stretched by between 4 and 8 times at an elevated temperature (say in steam) to align and order the chains along the fibre axis. At this stage, the fibres are of tensile strength about 0.5 GN m^{-2} and show an elongation at fracture of ~ 25 per cent, with an initial Young's modulus of 10 GN m^{-2}. Figure 6.1 shows schematically what must be accomplished in converting an all-carbon backbone polymer into an ordered carbon fibre. It is important that in going from 6.1(b) to 6.1(c) its microstructure will not revert to 6.1(a) as it normally would do when heated above the stretching temperature. In the RAE process for the conversion of PAN, tows of fibres are wound on to frames so that they are restrained from shrinking, and heated in an air oven at 220°C for a few

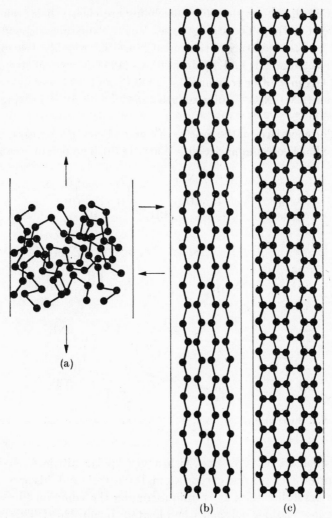

(a)

(b) (c)

Fig. 6.1. Schematic illustration of the conversion of a polymer into an oriented carbon fibre (after Watt 1970).

hours when they turn black. The fibres are then cut off and carbonized at 1000°C in an inert atmosphere and then heated to temperatures between 1500°C and 2500°C. The shrinkage of the fibre is very anisotropic, being 13 per cent in length but ∼42 per cent in diameter; the polymer chains are clearly being pulled closer together. The strength and Young's modulus depend on the final temperature of treatment. Speaking roughly, two main types emerge: (1) high modulus fibres (420 GN m^{-2}) of strength $\sim$2 GN m^{-2} after treatment at 2000°C; and (2) lower modulus fibres (220 GN m^{-2}) of strength 3·5 GN m^{-2} after heating to $\sim$1500°C.

The chemistry of the process of conversion of PAN to graphite fibre has been summarized by Watt (1970). The polymer can be

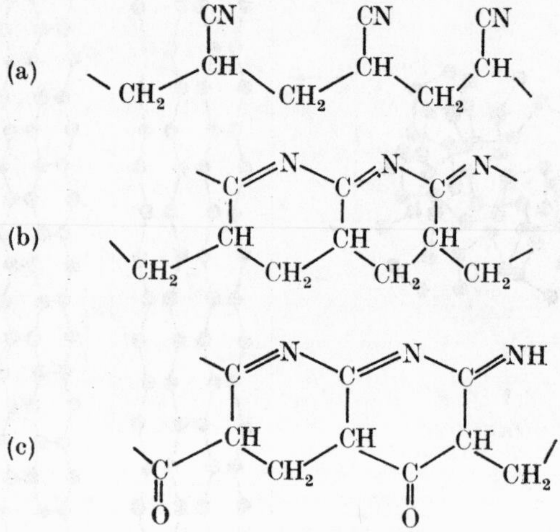

FIG. 6.2. Structures of (a) PAN. (b) PAN ladder polymer; and (c) oxidized PAN.

regarded as polyethylene with a very polar nitrile (—C≡N) group on every second carbon atom. It is atactic and this prevents true crystallization. It is unique among the common fibres in forming a ladder polymer when heated to 200–220°C. This consists of linked hydrogenated naphthypyridine rings (Fig. 6.2) which arise from the formation of a chain of

$$(-\overset{|}{C}=N-\overset{|}{C}=).$$

This increases the thermal stability of the polymer since it prevents the easy formation of small volatile fragments. When the fibres are heated in air at 220°C, ketonic groups are formed on the ladder polymer by oxidation of the —[CH_2]— groups (Fig. 6.2). This also happens in polyethylene but not nearly so rapidly as in PAN. It was at one time thought that the oxidation stage in the preparation of high modulus carbon fibres from PAN led to (—O—) links between chains but this is no longer thought to be the case—the argument which depends essentially on the plasticity of the oxidized fibre is given by Watt.

When the oxidized polymer is heated to a higher temperature in an inert atmosphere intermolecular reactions occur giving cross-linking. Water is eliminated by interladder reactions at 300°C to 500°C, and nitrogen is lost by a similar type of reaction. The elimination of nitrogen does not depend on the presence of oxygen so that it can occur in an unoxidized polymer. The interladder linking gives rise to the increase in modulus. At temperatures up to 1000°C the elimination of water, nitrogen, and other low molecular weight products is time- and temperature-dependent, the elimination becoming complete at any one temperature and starting again when the temperature is raised.

Very high modulus fibres can be obtained by stretching at temperatures where plastic flow of graphite can occur, e.g. 2700°C, so that with RAE fibres, moduli of ~700 GN m^{-2} may be obtained after a stretch of ~30 per cent. Much lower modulus fibres (70 GN m^{-2}) made from highly crystalline rayon can also be stretched at a very high temperature in order to increase their modulus to much the same figure, but of course the extensions required are very much larger (~300 per cent) and correspondingly more difficult to produce. Fibres based on pitch are amenable to the same treatment.

The Young's modulus of graphite fibres is a function of the preferred orientation of the basal planes, increasing with increasingly perfect orientation. In high modulus fibres, small crystallites are present, of dimensions in the basal plane (L_a) 80 Å and normal to this ~60 Å. Such crystallites seem to be present in strings derived from the parent fibres, with long narrow pores between them. The detailed structure of carbon fibres has been discussed by Ruland (see Fourdeux, Perrot, and

Ruland 1971) who draws conclusions from many examinations, e.g. using X-ray small angle scattering, electron microscopy and experiments involving the formation of intercalation compounds. He finds that there is little sp^3 bonding in carbon fibres and the crystallites consist of turbostratic graphite with sheets of carbon atoms extending over large distances so that the measured L_a values probably correspond to kinks or bends in the layer planes

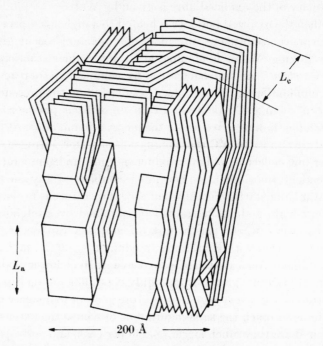

FIG. 6.3. Structure of carbon fibre.

rather than high angle boundaries—a view confirmed by electron microscopy. These ideas lead to the schematic picture of the structure in Fig. 6.3.

The strength of the fibres is affected by flaws between and within the crystallites and these flaws can be inherited from the parent fibre. The strength observed depends upon the length, being smaller for larger lengths, e.g. mean strength increasing from $1\cdot86$ GN m^{-2} for 100 mm lengths to $2\cdot8$ GN m^{-2} at 5 mm.

There is evidence of some non-Hookean behaviour in the stress–strain curve which indicates that some plastic shear may occur on layer planes during extension of a fibre. If this is so, a smaller crystallite size will increase the strength once pyrolysis has produced an essentially graphitic structure. High modulus graphite fibres do not appear to suffer a loss of strength when rubbed together so that the strength is not highly sensitive to surface perfection although small increases in strength can be produced by etching.

A number of different types of carbon fibre are now available, differing in detail. Those produced from rayon have a fluted cross-section and those from PAN a circular one; the diameters are similar—7 μm. Strengths at room temperature are between 1·5 and 3·5 GN m^{-2} (200 000–500 000 psi) and Young's moduli between 200 and 500 GN m^{-2} (30–70 × 10^6 psi). Modulus and strength do not change on heating up to 600°C. On heating in air oxidation occurs at higher temperatures.

6.2.6. *Properties of boron and of carbon fibre composites*

Epoxy resin composites containing boron or carbon fibres produce materials of very high strength and stiffness, which are stronger and stiffer than glass-reinforced plastics and which have densities much lower than the strong metals. For example a 50 per cent boron epoxy composite with aligned fibres has a strength parallel to the fibres of 1·7 GN m^{-2} (255 000 psi), a modulus of 210 GN m^{-2} (30 × 10^6 psi), a compressive strength of 3·1 GN m^{-2}, and a strength normal to the fibres of 0·13 GN m^{-2}. The shear strength for shear parallel to the fibres is 0·1 GN m^{-2}. The density is ~1·8 g cm^{-3} (1·8 × 10^3 kg m^{-3}) so E/ρ is four times that of steel measured parallel to the fibre and σ/ρ about twice that of steel wire. A carbon fibre epoxy resin composite with $V_f \sim 0.6$ yields a slightly lower density of 1·5 g cm^{-3} (1·5 × 10^3 Kg m^{-3}), a strength and modulus parallel to the fibres of 1·10 GN m^{-2} and 360 GN m^{-2} respectively, a compressive strength of 1·1 GN m^{-2}, and a shear strength parallel to the fibres of 0·06 GN m^{-2}. These properties are superior to those of the boron composite but greater care in production is necessary to attain alignment with the much more flexible carbon fibres. In order to obtain the best properties in the composite a resin must be chosen to match the fibre. For instance Fairbairn, Dominic, and Garnish (1971) find that the best and most consistent properties of carbon fibre–epoxy resin composites are found when the resin is chosen with a strain to failure some three or four times that of the fibre, and with an equal strength both in bending and in tension.

6.3. Whiskers

Detailed references to the growth and properties of whisker crystals can be found in the books edited by Doremus, Roberts, and Turnbull (1958) and by Gilman (1963). A recent review is given in the book edited by Levitt (1970).

Whisker crystals are the strongest solids known and graphite whiskers show the largest known values of σ/ρ and of E/ρ (see Appendix A). Whisker growth is related to dendritic growth of crystals in a liquid, but is generally understood to mean the filamentary growth of a solid which produces unbranched hair-like crystals. These crystals are very strong and show an increase in the maximum observed values of breaking strength with decrease in diameter. An example of the variation of breaking strength with size is shown in Fig. 6.4 for whiskers of sapphire. The whiskers are not circular in cross-section and the parameter to describe the size is taken as the square root of the area of cross-section. A rapid increase in the maximum strength occurs for whiskers of diameter less than about 10 μm. If instead of measured strength the ordinates in Fig. 6.4 were converted to fraction of the modulus, very similar curves would be found for all whiskers of metals and non-metals which do not possess cleavage planes parallel to the whisker axis. This includes the majority of materials. For those with a well-developed cleavage plane parallel to the whisker axis the strength is much less sensitive to size (Cook and Gordon 1964).

Most whiskers, of both metals and non-metals, show only elastic deformation before failure in tension. However, sometimes whisker crystals of metals and of ionic solids show plastic deformation. In the case of some metal whiskers, e.g. copper and zinc, the onset of plastic deformation is usually accompanied by a very large yield drop. If the whisker crystals are initially perfect and dislocations are introduced at the upper yield point a very large yield drop is naturally expected, since once dislocations are introduced they should be able to move at very low stresses in a perfect metallic lattice.

The reason for the high strength of whisker crystals, up to about $0.05 E$, is not properly understood. It is certainly connected with the absence of gross imperfections and with the smoothness of the surface of whiskers of those inherently strong crystals which have (roughly) isotropic elastic properties. Figure 6.4 is typical of the results shown by many whiskers and it can be clearly seen that as the size decreases, both the maximum strength and the spread in the values of the measured strength, increases. A small diameter does not guarantee a strong crystal.

Careful selection by hand can result in sorting out only crystals without inclusions and with an apparently perfect surface. These also show an increase in strength with decrease in diameter (Sutton and Chorné 1965). This point is very important when considering the use of whisker crystals as a means of producing consistently strong specimens of a material to be used as a reinforcement. When discussing the strength-size effect in whiskers the dotted line in Fig. 6.4 is often drawn to represent the results. What is measured is a large increase in the variability of the strength as the size decreases, as shown by the full lines in Fig. 6.4.

However, if whisker crystals of sapphire are selected by hand and polished in, say, orthophosphoric acid, the scatter in strength is largely removed (Bayer and Cooper 1967). The curve marked with crosses in Fig. 6.4 represents results obtained by Grenier and Kelly (1968). An increase in strength at effective diameters less than 5 μm still occurs. The line for larger diameters extrapolates to 700 000 psi ($\sim$5 GN m^{-2}) for diameters of about 1 cm which corresponds well with values found for large carefully polished sapphire crystals. For all clean crystals the strength decreases inversely (to some fractional power) with the surface

area. Grenier and Kelly (1968) found that the weaker crystals
always showed non-linear stress–strain curves and that the
strong ones were elastic to fracture.

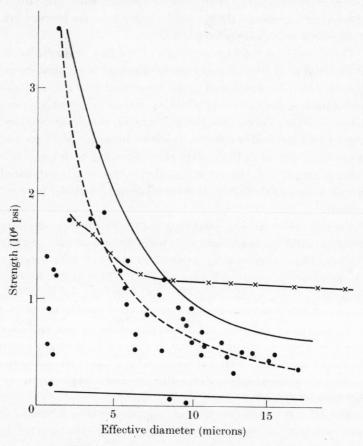

FIG. 6.4. A plot of the measured strengths of sapphire (α-Al_2O_3) whiskers as
a function of the square root of the cross-sectional area. (The data is replotted
from R. L. Mehan, W. H. Sutton, and J. A. Herzog (1965). *General Electric
Company Report* No. R65SD28). The curve marked with crosses corresponds
to carefully polished whiskers (Grenier and Kelly 1968).

When used as a reinforcement whisker crystals must be grown
in sufficient quantity in a reproducibly strong form, and these
must be harvested and aligned and put into a matrix. There is

no point whatsoever in considering whiskers of the face-centred cubic metals as a reinforcement because their theoretical shear strengths are low and any dislocations introduced into them will lead to a catastrophic loss of strength. Whiskers of the body-centred cubic transition metals can be very strong with strengths up to about 2×10^6 psi. These strengths can also be developed after they have been grown in a metallic matrix (Hertzberg and Kraft 1963). Provided dislocations in the matrix do not easily pass into them, these whiskers can therefore provide substantial reinforcement.

The whiskers offering most promise are those of the inherently strong solids because they possess high strength, a high Young's modulus, and low density. Whiskers of alumina, and boron carbide, have been produced in quantities of a few grams at the time of writing, and silicon nitride and silicon carbide in somewhat larger quantities. The methods of growth have involved production of the whiskers from the vapour, usually by a reaction in the vapour phase. Detailed references to the method of production and the quantities produced as well as some of the properties can be found in McCreight, Rauch, and Sutton (1965), and Levitt (1970).

Most whiskers produced from the vapour are produced in the form of a tangled wool. Experiments on reinforcement have been made with this but to produce very strong materials the whiskers must be sorted and aligned. Parratt (1964) has described a semi-automatic method for sorting of the whiskers by dispersing them in ethylene glycol and rapidly stirring the suspension. The whiskers are then passed through columns of water to remove debris and passed through screens to sort them into a variety of lengths. A random mat of whiskers is produced.

Conventional processes for aligning short fibres developed in the textile industry such as combing and carding are satisfactory provided tough and flexible materials are being used. They are generally unsatisfactory for stiff, brittle whiskers or for short fibres whose strength may be lost if rubbed together. Special processes must be developed in order to deal with very short whiskers, e.g. silicon carbide whiskers less than 1 mm long and <1 μm diameter which are too short to be spun. Techniques developed in the paper-making industry do not in general provide sufficient packing density of the fibres. Very satisfactory processes have been developed in recent years for handling these small whiskers by dispersing in a fluid, e.g. glycerine, in dilute suspension to avoid damage, and then elongating the medium to provide alignment and finally removing the fluid to achieve a high density of packing (Bagg, Dingle, Edwards, Evans, and Ziebland 1970).

Experiments on the reinforcement of materials with strong whiskers have demonstrated the potential (Sutton and Chorné 1965). In these, alumina whiskers have been introduced into metallic matrices and also into epoxy resin. Whiskers of Al_2O_3, produced by reacting aluminium vapour with oxygen in a stream of hydrogen at 1300–1500°C have been selected by hand and incorporated into silver after coating the whiskers with nickel or platinum (Sutton and Chorné 1965). The whisker strengths depend upon the size and also upon the crystallographic orientation. A large number of results have been obtained. The breaking strengths of composites containing whiskers of uniform size show a variation with volume fraction which follows equation (5.64). If $\bar{\sigma}$ is put equal to the measured arithmetic mean strength of the whiskers of a particular size before incorporation, then the strengths are between 80 and 97 per cent of the value given by equation (5.64), at room temperature. Values of l/d of between 100 and 2600 have been used. The strongest composite made had a breaking strength of $2·3 \times 10^5$ psi ($1·6$ GN m^{-2}) at room temperature and contained a volume fraction of $0·24$ of whiskers of mean breaking strength $1·1 \times 10^6$ psi ($7·7$ GN m^{-2}); values of l/d were between 1300 and 2600. Tensile tests have also been carried out at high temperatures after a short time at the elevated temperature. Values of the breaking stress of a composite of greater than $0·8 \times 10^5$ psi ($0·6$ GN m^{-2}) at 870°C ($0·93$ of the melting temperature of the matrix) and of $0·25 \times 10^5$ psi ($0·18$ GN m^{-2}) at $0·98$ T_M were obtained. These experiments demonstrate conclusively the feasibility of reinforcing a metal with whiskers at room temperature and, at least for short periods, at temperatures close to the melting temperature of the matrix, provided great care is taken in the selection of the whiskers.

The incorporation of similar whiskers into an epoxy resin has also been shown to produce effective reinforcement (Sutton, Rosen, and Flom 1964). A value of $V_f = 0.14$ of aligned whiskers produced a breaking strength of greater than 113 000 psi in a composite of specific gravity 1·64, giving a value of σ/ρ of $>0.7\times10^5$ psi. The elastic modulus of these composites was discussed in section 5.3.2.

6.4. Metallic matrices

A metallic matrix containing strong fibres provides a very efficient medium for transferring stress to the fibres by plastic flow of the matrix. The plastic flow contributes to preventing notch-sensitivity of the composite. The disadvantage is that because the metal flows plastically at low stresses the matrix makes little contribution to the elastic modulus of the composite and is liable to failure by fatigue.

Because of the possibility of dissolving many elements in a metallic matrix at high temperature, and precipitating these at low temperature, the possibility arises of producing reinforced composites solely by heat treatment.

To attain high strengths in such composites several conditions are necessary (Davies 1965, Kelly and Davies 1965). The ductile metal which is to form the matrix must be the continuous phase and the reinforcement, unless produced as parallel rods without branches, must be discontinuous. It must be possible to produce a sufficiently large volume fraction of the reinforcing phase and this must be produced in an aligned fibrous form with a sufficiently large value of l/d to enable efficient transfer of stress to the reinforcement. It is well established that intermetallic compounds and other small crystals extracted from metallic matrices show strengths equal to those of whiskers (see section 4.4 and Salkind, Lemkey, and George 1970).

Production of fibrous microstructures by a transformation in the solid state has not been much exploited. The possible volume fraction of strong phase is often small (see section 4.3) and a strong phase is usually produced in a variety of orientations, corresponding to the different crystallographically equivalent variants. However, in the production of hard magnetic materials preferential alignment in a particular one of these can be obtained by the application of a magnetic field during the transformation (see, for example, de Vos 1964), and there is also the possibility of applying a compressive or tensile stress or other physical constraint to affect this in other cases.

Growth of fibrous microstructures from the melt has been accomplished successfully by a number of workers who have used alloy systems, possessing a eutectic (see Plate 2). The aluminium–nickel system has been studied in great detail. Uniaxially aligned whiskers of Al_3Ni of diameter a few microns and providing a value of V_f of about 0·1 have been produced in an aluminium matrix. The strengths of the Al_3Ni whiskers are 300 000–400 000 psi and such composites obey closely the principles outlined in Chapter 5 (Herzberg, Lemkey, and Ford 1965).

This method of production of a composite offers the possibility of producing directly, structures containing inherently strong materials such as graphite, silicon, beryllium, and boron in metallic matrices. Of course the strong phase may occur in the form of discrete plates. This is not a suitable form since a plate may contain a long crack on a plane normal to that of the plate and thus its strength will be much reduced.

For alloys of eutectic composition the tendency is to form rods only when one phase has a low volume fraction (<30 per cent at most). This unfortunately sets a limit to the volume fraction of reinforcement possible since the matrix must be the continuous phase. Attempts to overcome this restriction depend on varying the rate of cooling and the rate of solidification and are influenced by the impurities, particularly those segregating to the solid–liquid interfaces.

A number of aligned eutectics of high melting point materials have been produced with high strengths at elevated temperatures but with insufficient long-term stability or resistance to oxidation to be likely to replace heat-resistant metals described in section 4.7. The Ta–Ta$_2$C and the Nb–Nb$_2$C systems both contain ~30 per cent by volume of carbide whiskers in the refractory metal matrix, and show a strength at room temperature of more than 1 GN m^{-2} (145 000 psi) and of 0·2 GN m^{-2} (~30 000 psi) at 1600°C. Sometimes an intermetallic can be produced in a metal, e.g. 40 per cent of NiMo *lamellae* in a nickel matrix, and sometimes a metal in an intermetallic, e.g. $V_f = 0·11$ of Mo in NiAl by solidifying the NiAl–Mo eutectic (see Salkind, Lemkey, and George 1970).

The possibility of using ternary systems or those with higher numbers of components raises a very large number of possibilities, but the existence of eutectics cannot be predicted. In the Ni–Al–Nb system plates of Ni$_3$Al, i.e. the γ'- phase (section 4.7), may be grown in a matrix of Ni$_3$Nb (Thompson and Lemkey 1969). The rupture strength at elevated temperature is illustrated in Fig. 4.7. The strength is very high at elevated temperature but the composite possesses very poor oxidation resistance, and having reinforcement in the form of plates and without a ductile matrix is not at all tough.

In order to produce an aligned eutectic, the ratio of the temperature gradient in the liquid at the solid–liquid interface to the rate of freezing must be controlled. In order to produce the solid at an economic rate there is a lower limit to the rate of solidification. It may be argued that this rate is as much as 3 m hr^{-1} which may demand unattainably steep temperature gradients.

Growth of fibrous structures from the melt is not only possible with eutectic melts. Dendritic growth can also be utilized (Davies 1965). By utilizing dendritic and eutectic solidification to grow fibres *in situ*, the fibres produced are stable at the melting point of the metallic matrix. The fibres will also retain their form for long periods at temperatures close to the melting point of the metal and therefore do in fact offer promise for use at high temperature. Instability at high temperatures of a phase produced by precipitation in the solid state is one of the chief difficulties encountered in the production of a fibrous microstructure by unidirectional mechanical deformation (see Kelly and Davies 1965).

In Chapter 1 we remarked that oxides and other ionically bound solids possess lower surface energies than do the common metals. This means that the equilibrium contact angle between liquid metals and such solids is usually high ($>90°$) and therefore arrays of whiskers or fibres of the ceramic are not easily infiltrated by molten metals to make a composite. To overcome this, fibres can be covered by a thin film of a metal of very much higher melting point than the infiltrant, prior to infiltration. This can be done, for example, by sputtering. Also, to assist infiltration control of the atmosphere can be exercised during infiltration and specific additives can be made (Kelly and Davies (1965) give references to these methods). Carbides have lower contact angles with metals than do oxides, and bundles of such fibres are more easily infiltrated.

One of the features of the metallic matrix is the variety of means by which it can be fabricated as well as by casting it around the fibres. Powder metallurgical methods may be used, where fibres and a metal powder are pressed and sintered. A composite may also be produced by continuous electrodeposition, by electroless deposition and by spraying. The technological importance of reinforced metals is likely to centre on their use at elevated temperatures. Glenny (1970) has considered the possibilities of producing materials for use at temperatures above 800°C, in highly stressed situations.

REFERENCES

R. G. C. ARRIDGE, A. A. BAKER, and D. CRATCHLEY (1964). *J. scient. Instrum.* **41**, 259.

K. H. G. ASHBEE and R. C. WYATT (1969). *Proc. R. Soc.* **A312**, 533.

J. AVESTON (1969). *J. mater. Sci.* **4**, 625.

—— (1970). *Nature, Lond.* **226**, 146.

R. BACON and M. TANG (1964). *Carbon* **2**, 221.

G. E. G. BAGG, L. E. DINGLE, H. EDWARDS, M. E. N. EVANS, and H. ZIEBLAND (1970). British Plastics Federation 7th International Reinforced Plastics Conference, Brighton, Paper 6.

P. D. BAYER and R. E. COOPER (1967). *J. mater. Sci.* **2**, 347.

C. Z. CARROLL-PORCZYNSKI (1969). *Advanced Materials*, Asted Publishing Co., Guildford.

J. COOK and J. E. GORDON (1964). *Proc. R. Soc.* A **282**, 508.

D. CRATCHLEY and A. A. BAKER (1964). *Metallurgia* **69**, 153.

G. J. DAVIES (1965). *High Strength Materials* (Ed. V. F. ZACKAY), p. 603, Wiley, New York.

K. J. DE VOS (1964). *Proc. Int. Conf. Magnetism* p. 772, Inst. of Physics and Phys. Soc., London.

R. H. DOREMUS, B. W. ROBERTS, and D. TURNBULL (1958). (Eds.). *Growth and Perfection of Crystals*, Wiley, New York.

G. FAIRBAIRN, C. J. DOMINIC and E. W. GARNISH (1971). International Conference on Carbon Fibres and their Application, Paper 24, The Plastics Institute, London.

A. FOURDEUX, R. PERROT, and W. RULAND (1971). International Conference Carbon Fibres and their Composites, Paper 9, The Plastics Institute, London.

F. GALASSO, M. SALKIND, D. KUEHL, and V. PATARINI (1966). *Trans. Am. Inst. Min. metall. Petrol. Engrs* **236**, 1748.

T. E. GIER, N. L. COX, and H. S. YOUNG (1964). *Inorg. Chem.* **3**, 1001.

J. J. GILMAN (1963). (Ed.). *The Art and Science of Growing Crystals*, Wiley, New York.

R. J. E. GLENNY (1970). *Proc. R. Soc.* A**319**, 33.

P. GRENIER and A. KELLY (1968). *C.r. hebd. Séan. Acad. Sci., Sér. B. Paris*, **266**, 859.

R. W. HERZBERG and R. W. KRAFT (1963). *Trans. Am. Inst. Min. metall. Petrol. Engrs* **227**, 580.

——, F. D. LEMKEY, and J. A. FORD (1965). *Trans. Am. Inst. Min. metall. Petrol. Engrs* **233**, 342.

B. L. HOLLINGWORTH (1969). *Composites* **1**, 28.

J. R. HUTCHINS and R. V. HARRINGTON (1966). *Encyclopedia of Chemical Technology* **10**, 533.

A. KELLY and G. J. DAVIES (1965). *Metall. Rev.* **10**, 1.

M. I. KLIMAN (1962). *Watertown Arsenal Technical Report* WAL TR 371/50.

A. P. LEVITT (1970). (Ed.). *Whisker Technology*, Wiley, New York.

K. L. LOEWENSTEIN (1961). *Physics Chem. Glasses* **2**, 69, and 119.

R. E. LOWRIE (1967). *Modern Composite Materials* p. 270 (Eds. L. J. BROUTMAN and R. H. KROCK), Addison Wesley, Reading, Mass.

L. R. McCREIGHT, H. W. RAUCH Sr., and W. H. SUTTON (1965). *Ceramic and Graphite Fibres and Whiskers*, Academic Press, New York.

F. J. McGARRY (1970). *Proc. R. Soc.* A**319**, 59.

A. I. MLAVSKY and H. E. LA BELLE Jr. In *Whisker Technology*. (Ed. A. P. LEVITT) p. 121, Interscience, New York.

P. MORGAN (1961). (Ed.). *Glass Reinforced Plastics*, 3rd Edit. Iliffe, London.

J. G. MORLEY, P. A. ANDREWS and I. WHITNEY (1964). *Physics Chem. Glasses* **5**, 1.

A. NADAI and M. J. MANJOINE (1941). *J. appl. Mech.* **8**, A-77.

262   STRONG FIBROUS SOLIDS

J. NIXDORF (1970). *Proc. R. Soc.* A**319**, 17.

B. PARKYN (Ed.) (1970). *Glass Reinforced Plastics* Iliffe Books, London.

N. J. PARRATT (1964). *Powder Metall.* **7** (14), 152.

—— (1972). *Fibre Reinforced Materials Technology.* Van Nostrand Reinhold, London.

O. PRESTON and N. J. GRANT (1961). *Trans. Am. Inst. Min. metall. Petrol. Engrs* **221**, 164.

M. RUBIN (1969). *Handbook of Fiberglass and Reinforced Plastic Composites* (Ed. G. LUBIN), p. 23, Van Nostrand Reinhold, New York.

M. J. SALKIND, F. D. LEMKEY, and F. D. GEORGE (1970). *Whisker Technology* (Ed. A. P. LEVITT) p. 343, Wiley, New York.

—— and V. PATARINI (1967). *Trans. Am. Inst. Min. metall. Petrol. Engrs* **239**, 1268.

A. SHINDO (1961). *Rep. Gov. Ind. Res. Inst. Osaka* No. 317.

R. H. SONNEBORN (1954). *Fiberglass Reinforced Plastics*, Reinhold Publishing Corp., New York.

W. H. SUTTON and J. CHORNÉ (1965). *Fibre Composite Materials*, p. 173, American Soc. Metals, Cleveland, Ohio.

——, B. W. ROSEN, and D. G. FLOM (1964). *S.P.E. Jl.* **20**, 1.

C. P. TALLEY (1959). *J. appl. Phys.* **30**, 1114.

G. F. TAYLOR (1924). *Phys. Rev.* **23**, 655 and (1931); U.S. Patent No. 1,739,529.

E. R. THOMPSON and F. D. LEMKEY (1969). *Trans. Am. Soc. Metals* **62**, 140.

A. V. ULITOVSKIY (1957). *Pribory Tekh. Éksp.* **3**, 115.

W. WATT (1970). *Proc. R. Soc.* A**319**, 5.

——, L. N. PHILLIPS, and W. JOHNSON (1964). British Patent No. 1,110,791.

——, L. N. PHILLIPS, and W. JOHNSON (1966). *The Engineer* **221**, 815.

F. E. WAWNER Jr. (1967). In *Modern Composite Materials* Eds. L. J. Broutman and R. H. Knock p. 244. Addison Wesley, Reading, Mass.

APPENDICES

APPENDIX A

TABLE 1

Tensile strengths of whiskers at room temperature

Material	Maximum tensile strength (σ) (10^6 psi)	(GN m^{-2})	Young's modulus (E) (10^6 psi)	(GN m^{-2})	Specific gravity (ρ)	$\dfrac{\sigma}{\rho}$ (10^5 psi)	$\dfrac{E}{\rho}$ (10^6 psi)	Melting temperature (°C)
Graphite	2·8	19·6	98[a]	686	2·2	12·7	45	sub 3000
Al$_2$O$_3$	2·2[b]	15·4	76 (max)	532	4·0	5·5	19	2072
Al$_2$O$_3$ large crystal	1·0[c]	7·0	76 (max)	532	4·0	2·5	19	2072
Iron	1·8[b]	12·6	28	196	7·8	2·3	3·6	1540
Si$_3$N$_4$	2[d]	14·0	55[e]	385	3·1	6·5	18	sub 1900
SiC	3[d]	21·0	100 (max)	700	3·2	9·4	31	sub 2200
Si	1[d]	7·0	26	182	2·3	4·3	11	1450
Si large crystal	0·52[f]	3·5	26	182	2·3	2·1	11	1450
BeO	1·0[g]	7·0	51	357	3·0	3·3	17	2520
AlN	1·0[h]	7·0	50	350	3·3	3·0	15	sub 2000
NaCl	0·14[i]	0·98						

a. Measured value of $1/S_{11}$. See R. BACON (1960). *J. appl. Phys.* **31**, 283; and C. BAKER and A. KELLY (1964). *Phil. Mag.* **9**, 927.

b. S. S. BRENNER (1958). *Growth and Perfection of Crystals*, p. 157, Wiley, New York.

c. J. G. MORLEY and B. A. PROCTOR (1962). *Nature, Lond.* **196**, 1082; F. P. MALLINDER and B. A. PROCTOR (1966). *Phil. Mag.* **13**, 197. Strengths measured in a bend test.

d. C. C. EVANS, J. E. GORDON, D. M. MARSH, and J. N. PARRATT (1961). *Tube Investments Res. Lab. Report No. 133.*

e. J. E. GORDON (1964). *Proc. R. Soc.* **A282**, 16.

f. W. C. DASH (1958). *Growth and Perfection of Crystals*, p. 189, Wiley, New York.

g. P. L. EDWARDS and R. J. HAPPEL, Jr. (1962). *J. appl. Phys.* **33**, 943.

h. T. J. DAVIES and P. E. EVANS (1965). *Nature, Lond.* **207**, 254.

i. Z. GYULAI, E. HARTMANN, and B. JESZINSKY (1961). *Phys. Stat. Solidi* **1**, 726.

TABLE 2

Strong non-metallic fibres

Material	Tensile strength (σ) (10^6 psi)	(GN m^{-2})	Young's modulus (E) (10^6 psi)	(GN m^{-2})	Specific gravity (ρ)	$\dfrac{\sigma}{\rho}$ (10^5 psi)	$\dfrac{E}{\rho}$ (10^6 psi)	Melting temperature (°C)
Asbestos (crocidolite)	0·85[a]	5·9	27	189	3·4	2·5	8	Loses water at 300
Mica	0·45[b]	3·2	33	231	2·7	1·7	12	Loses water at ~400
Etched soda glass	0·4 (mean)[c]	3·0	9·8	68·6	2·5	1·6	3·9	
	0·5 (max)[c]	3·5	,,	,,	,,	2·0	,,	
Drawn silica	0·86 (mean)[c]	6·0	10·5	73·5	2·5[h]	3·5	4·2	1660
Silica in air	1·5 (max)[c]	10·5	,,	,,	,,	6·0	,,	,,
Silica in vacuo	1·2 (mean)[c]	8·4	,,	,,	,,	4·8	,,	,,
Silica at 77 K	2·0 (mean)[c]	14·0	,,	,,	,,	8·0	,,	,,
Boron filaments deposited on tungsten	1·0[d]	7·0	55	385	2·6	3·8	21	2040
High tenacity Nylon 66	0·15[e]	1·05	0·7[g]	4·9	1·1	1·4	0·6	sub 3000
Graphite filaments	0·45[f]	3·2	70[f]	490	1·9	2·4	37	
PRD-49 (Kevlar)	0·4	2·8	19	133	1·5	2·7	13	—

a. R. ZUKOWSKI and R. GAZE (1959). *Nature, Lond.* **185**, 35.

b. E. OROWAN (1933). *Z. Phys.* **82**, 235.

c. J. G. MORLEY, P. ANDREWS, and I. WHITNEY (1964). *Physics Chem. Glasses* **5**, 1; see also J. G. MORLEY (1964). *Proc. R. Soc.* A**282**, 43.

d. C. P. TALLEY (1959). *J. appl. Phys.* **30**, 1114; and C. P. TALLEY and W. J. CLARK (1962). AD 296575.

e. F. C. FRANK (1964). *Proc. R. Soc.* A**282**, 9.

f. W. W. WATT and W. JOHNSON, Private communication. See also W. WATT, L. N. PHILLIPS, and W. JOHNSON (1966). *The Engineer* **221**, 815.

g. J. E. GORDON (1952). *Jl R. aeronaut. Soc.* **56**, 704.

Strong crystals

(Yield stress deduced from hardness measurements at room temperature)

Material	Indentation hardness (kg mm^{-2})	Yield stress (σ) (10^6 psi)	Young's modulus (E) (10^6 psi)	Specific gravity (ρ)	$\dfrac{\sigma}{\rho}$ (10^5 psi)	$\dfrac{E}{\rho}$ (10^6 psi)	Melting temperature (°C)
C							
Diamond	8400[f]	7·7	150[a]	3·5	22	43	Transforms
WC	2100[g]	1·0	104	15·8	0·63	6·5	2755*
TiB$_2$	3400[h]	2·0	94[b]	4·5	4·5	21·0	2900
TiC	2900	2·9	72[b]	4·9	5·9	14·7	3250
B$_4$C	2400	1·7	66[c]	2·5	6·8	26	2470
B	2500	1·9	64[d]	2·3	8·3	28	2300
BeO	1300	1·0	51	3·0	3·3	17	2520
AlN	1225	0·9	50[d]	3·3	2·7	15	2300†
TiN	1994	2·0	50[d]	5·4	3·7	9·3	2950
TaC	1800	1·0	91[e]	14·5	0·69	6·3	3880
Al$_2$O$_3$	2600[f]	1·6	57	4·0	4	14	2072

* decomposes   † sublimes

The Vickers Hardness numbers are taken from *Handbook of High Temperature Materials, Materials Index* (P. T. B. SHAFFER, Plenum Press, 1964) except where reference is given.

a. ⟨111⟩ direction.

b. Taken from single crystal measurements, J. J. GILMAN and B. W. ROBERTS (1961). *J. appl. Phys.* **32**, 1405.

c. J. J. GILMAN (1961). *Mech. Engng* **83**, p. 55.

d. J. E. GORDON (1964). *Proc. R. Soc.* A**282**, 16

e. S. M. LANG (1960). *NBS Monograph* No. 6.

f. B. W. MOTT (1956). *Microindentation Hardness Testing*, Butterworth, London.

g. Maximum value parallel to ⟨0001⟩. T. TAKAHASHI and E. J. FREISE (1965). *Phil. Mag.* **12**, 1.

h. C. T. LYNCH, S. A. MERSOL, and F. W. VAHLDIEK (1965). *Trans. Am. Inst. Min. metall. Petrol. Engrs* **233**, 631.

TABLE 4

Tensile strengths of metal wires

(at room temperature except where stated)

Material	Composition (%)	Diameter (10^{-3} in)	Tensile strength (σ) (10^6 psi)	($GN\ m^{-2}$)	Young's modulus* (E) (10^6 psi)	($GN\ m^{-2}$)	Specific gravity (ρ)	$\dfrac{\sigma}{\rho}$ (10^5 psi)	$\dfrac{E}{\rho}$ (10^6 psi)	Melting temperature (°C)
Patented steel	0·9C	4	0·6[a]	4·2	30	210	7·9	0·77	3·8	1300
Patented steel at 260°C after 30 min	"	"	0·46[a]	3·2	—	—	—	—	—	—
Stainless steel	18Cr-8Ni-0·8Mo	2	0·3[a]	2·1	29	203	7·9	0·38	3·7	—
René 41	19Cr-11Co-10Mo-3Ti-1·7Al balance Ni	4	0·33[a]	2·3	32	224	8·2	0·40	3·9	—
René 41 at 800°C after 30 min	"	"	0·2[a]	1·4	—	—	—	—	—	—
Ti(β)	13V-11Cr-3Al	6	0·32[b]	2·3	17	119	4·6	0·70	3·7	—
W	99·95	1	0·55[a]	3·9	50	350	19·3	0·28	2·6	3390
Mo	99·9	6	0·3[b]	2·1	49	343	10·3	0·29	4·8	2610
Be	Commercial purity	6	0·18[c]	1·3	45	315	1·8	1·00	25·0	1284
Al	High purity	6	0·024[b]	0·17	10	70	2·7	0·09	3·7	660

* Bulk values. Young's modulus may be different in drawn wire due to preferred orientation.

a. D. A. ROBERTS (1961). *DMIC Memorandum* 80.
b. W. E. RUMBLES, S. F. WATANABE, E. J. HAYES, and E. N. PETRICK (1961). *Proc. S.A.M.P.E. Filament Winding Conference*, p. 122.
c. R. J. FULAP (1962). *Mater. Des. Engng* 55, 10

TABLE 5

Bond dissociation energies

Bond	Energy (kcal mole^{-1})†	Bond	Energy (kcal mole^{-1})†
Si–C	78	C_{aliph}–C_{aliph}	83
Si–Si	53	C_{aliph}–O	93
Si–O	106	C_{aliph}–H	97
Si–F	135	C –Cl	80
B–N	105	C_{aliph}–N	82
B_{arom}–N_{arom}	115	C_{arom}–N	110
B–C_{aliph}	89	C_{arom}–C_{arom}	98
B–C_{arom}	100	C_{arom}–O	107

These values are taken principally from

C. E. H. BAWN (1964). Proc. R. Soc. A282, 91 following L. PAULING (1960). The Nature of the Chemical Bond, 3rd ed., Cornell University Press, and T. L. COTTRELL (1958). The Strength of Chemical Bonds, 2nd ed., Butterworth, London.

† 1 kcl = 4·186 kJ.

Table 6

Properties of some commercially available fibres (after J. AVESTON (1970). *Composites* **1**, 296.)

Fibre	Melting point (°C)	Density (10³ kg m⁻³)	Strength (GN m⁻²)†	Young's modulus (GN m⁻²)	Specific‡ strength (GN m⁻²)	Specific§ modulus (GN m⁻²)	Coefficient of thermal expansion at room temperature (10⁻⁶ °C⁻¹)	Producer	Approximate cost July 1970 (£ kg⁻¹)
Continuous and semi-continuous									
E glass	700	2·55	3·5	72	1·4	28	4·9	Generally available	0·5
S glass	840	2·50	4·6	84	1·8	34	1·6	Owens Corning	1·0
Silica	1660	2·19††	6·0	72	2·7	33	0·31	General Electric	28
Alumina, single-crystal	2072	3·96	2·0	470	0·5	118	7·9	Tyco	72 000
Carbon type I	3000(sub)	1·90	2·0	390	1·1	204	−1·0	Courtaulds	60
Carbon type II	3000(sub)	1·90	2·6	240	1·4	126		Courtaulds	50
Boron nitride	2980	1·90	1·4	90	0·7	47		Carborundum	280
Boron/tungsten	2040	2·63	2·8	380	1·1	145	8·3	United Aircraft	270
Silicon carbide/boron/tungsten	2300	2·70	2·8	380	1·0	140		United Aircraft	400
Silicon carbide/tungsten	2200(sub)	3·35	2·3	470	0·7	140	4·9	General Technologies	2700
Boron carbide/tungsten	2450	2·36	2·3	470	1·0	200		General Technologies	NA
Titanium diboride/tungsten	2980	4·48	1·0	510	0·2	114	2·7	General Technologies	NA
Tungsten wire	3390	19·3	4·0	410	0·2	210	5·5	General Electric	90
Beryllium wire	1284	1·83	1·3	240	0·7	131	16	Beryllium Corporation	9000
Discontinuous and whiskers									
Chrysotile asbestos	loses H₂O ~500	2·55	4·5	164		64		Turner Bros Asbestos	0·1
Crocidolite asbestos	loses H₂O ~300	3·87	2·8	180		53		Cape Asbestos	0·1
Alumina whiskers	2072	3·96	2–20	470		118		Thermokinetic Fibres	7000
Silicon carbide whiskers	2200(sub)	3·17	2–20	470		150		Carborundum	100
Silicon nitride whiskers	1900(sub)	3·18	1–10	380		120		ERDE	NA

† 1 GN m⁻² = 145 000 lbf in⁻²
†† Density of bulk silica. Density of fibres not measured.
‡ Strength divided by density
§ Young's modulus divided by density

TABLE 7

Resistance to crack propagation of various materials

$$K = \sqrt{(EG)} = \sigma\sqrt{c} \qquad ; \qquad G = K^2/E \qquad (1)$$

$$1 \text{ J m}^{-2} = 10^3 \text{ ergs cm}^{-2} \qquad\qquad 1 \text{ GN m}^{-2} = 145\,000 \text{ lbf in}^{-2}$$

Material	G (J m^{-2})	E (GN m^{-2})	E (10^6 psi)	†	K_c MN m^{-2} m$^{1/2}$ $\simeq$	ksi in$^{1/2}$
Copper	5.10^4	126	18	→	79	79
Dural	$1\cdot4.10^5$	70	10	→	100	100
Cast Iron	4.10^3	210	30	→	29	29
Ti 6·4 (β)	5.10^4	119	17	←	80	80
18 Ni Maraged Steel	5.10^4	196	28	←	100	100
Al–7075	10^4	70	10	←	27	27
Teak Wood	6.10^3	10	1·4	→	7·7	7·7
Alumina	40	280‡	40‡	→	3·9	3·9
Graphite (Reactor)	100	14	2	→	1·2	1·2
Polystyrene (toughened)	4.10^3	3·5	0·5	→	3·7	3·7
Epoxy Epon 828 (untoughened)	100	4·2	0·6	0·65 →	1·6	1·6
Glass FRP (50% epoxy) parallel fibres	10^{-1}	35	5	←	0·06	0·06
Carbon FRP (50% epoxy) normal to fibres	5.10^4	175	25	→	93	93

† The arrowhead points away from the value of K_c if the experimenter determined K_c and the value G has been derived from this using the equation (1). If G was measured the arrowhead points towards the value of K_c. In the case of Epoxy Epon 828 K_c and G were both determined. The value of K_c derived from the measured value of G is $0\cdot65$ MN m$^{-3/2}$.

‡ porous material.

APPENDIX B

TABLE 1

Glide elements of crystals

(room temperature)

Crystal	Class	Lattice	Direction	Plane	Notes
f.c.c. metals and solid solutions	m3m	F	$\langle 1\bar{1}0\rangle$	{111}	
Si, Ge, C	m3m	F	$\langle 1\bar{1}0\rangle$	{111}	
InSb, α-ZnS	$\bar{4}$3m	F	$\langle 1\bar{1}0\rangle$	{111}	
CaF$_2$, UO$_2$	m3m	F	$\langle 1\bar{1}0\rangle$	{001}	
				{110}	
				{111}	
NaCl, MgO, and others with the rocksalt structure†	m3m	F	$\langle 1\bar{1}0\rangle$	{110}	Wavy glide at high temperature
				{001}	
PbS, PbTe	m3m	F	$\langle 1\bar{1}0\rangle$	{001}	
			$\langle 001\rangle$	{110}	
b.c.c. metals	m3m	I	$\langle 1\bar{1}1\rangle$	{110}	Wavy glide
CsCl structure	m3m	P	$\langle 001\rangle$	{110}	
β-Sn	4/mmm	I	$\langle 001\rangle$	{110}	
				{100}	
Rutile (TiO$_2$)	4/mmm	P	$\langle 10\bar{1}\rangle$	{101}	
			$\langle 001\rangle$	{110}	
Bi	$\bar{3}$m	R	$\langle 10\bar{1}\rangle$	(111)	α < 60°*
Hg	$\bar{3}$m	R	$\langle 100\rangle$	{110}	60°<α<90°*
Graphite, MoS$_2$	6/mmm	P	$\langle 11\bar{2}0\rangle$	(0001)	
α-Al$_2$O$_3$	$\bar{3}$m	P	$\langle 11\bar{2}0\rangle$	(0001)	
				{10$\bar{1}$0}	
Zn, Cd, Mg	6/mmm	P	$\langle 11\bar{2}0\rangle$	(0001)	
				{10$\bar{1}$1}	
				{10$\bar{1}$0}	
			$\langle 11\bar{2}3\rangle$	{11$\bar{2}$2}	
Be, AgMg	6/mmm	P	$\langle 11\bar{2}0\rangle$	(0001)	
				{10$\bar{1}$0}	
Ti	6/mmm	P	$\langle 11\bar{2}0\rangle$	{10$\bar{1}$0}	
				{10$\bar{1}$1}	
				(0001)	

* α is the angle of the rhombohedral unit cell.
† TiC, with this structure, slips as do f.c.c. metals.

TABLE 2

Independent glide systems in crystals

Slip system		Class	Number of independent systems	Example
$\langle 1\bar{1}0 \rangle$	{111}	m3m	5	f.c.c. metals and diamond structure
$\langle 1\bar{1}1 \rangle$	{110}	m3m	5	b.c.c. metals
$\langle 1\bar{1}0 \rangle$	{110}	m3m	2	NaCl structure
$\langle 10\bar{1} \rangle$	{101}	4/mmm	4	TiO_2
$\langle 001 \rangle$	{110}	m3m	3	CsCl structure
$\langle 1\bar{1}0 \rangle$	{001}	m3m	3	CaF_2, UO_2 which also slip as does NaCl
$\langle 11\bar{2}0 \rangle$	(0001)	6/mmm	2	Graphite
$\langle 11\bar{2}0 \rangle$	{10$\bar{1}$0}	6/mmm	2	Zr and Te which also slip as does graphite
$\langle 11\bar{2}0 \rangle$	{10$\bar{1}$1}	6/mmm	4	Zn, Cd, Ti
$\langle 11\bar{2}3 \rangle$	{11$\bar{2}$2}	6/mmm	5	Zn, Cd, Mg

APPENDIX C

TABLE 1

The single crystal elastic constants used in this book come from the most recent determination quoted in the following summaries. Since these summaries appeared values for graphite, magnesium oxide, titanium carbide, corundum, and iridium have been determined.

K. S. ALEKSANDROV aud T. V. RYZKOVA (1961). *Soviet Phys. Crystallogr.* **6**, 228.

H. B. HUNTINGTON (1958). *Solid St. Phys.* **7**, 213.

R. F. S. HEARMON (1956). *Adv. Phys.* **5**, 323; (1946) *Rev. mod. Phys.* **18**, 409.

G. SIMMONS (1965). *J. Grad. Res. Center* **34**, 1.

MgO D-H. CHUNG (1963). *Phil. Mag.* **8**, 833.

TiC J. J. GILMAN and B. W. ROBERTS (1961). *J. appl. Phys.* **32**, 1405.

Graphite G. B. SPENCE (1962). *J. appl. Phys.* **33**, 729; C. BAKER and A. KELLY (1964). *Phil. Mag.* **9**, 927.

Al₂O₃ J. B. WACHTMANN, Jr., W. E. TEFFT, D. G. LAM, Jr. and R. P. STINCHFIELD (1960). *J. Res. Nat. Bur. Stds.* **64***A*, 213.

TABLE 2

Values of Poisson's ratio at room temperature

Material	Polycrystals	$-S_{12}/S_{11}$	$-S_{13}/S_{33}$	$-S_{13}/S_{11}$
Aluminium	0·34	0·38		
Lead	0·44	0·46		
Copper	0·34	0·42		
Gold	0·42	0·46		
Silver	0·38	0·43		
Iridium	0·26	0·30[f]		
Nickel	0·31	0·36[g]		
α-Iron	0·28	0·36		
Tungsten	0·29	0·28		
Glass	0·25	—		
Silicon	0·27	0·28		
Germanium	0·28	0·25		
Magnesium oxide	0·18[a]	0·23[a]		
Titanium carbide	0·19[b]	0·19		
Aluminium oxide	0·20[c]	0·30	0·17	0·15
Quartz	0·17[d]	0·14	0·13	0·10
Graphite	0·16[e]	0·05	0·78	(2·3)
Diamond		0·10		

For metals the values for polycrystals are from W. Köster and H. Franz (1961). *Metall. Rev.* **6**, 1.

a. D-H. Chung (1963). *Phil. Mag.* **8**, 833.
b. P. T. B. Shaffer (1964). *Handbook of High Temperature Materials, Materials Index*, Plenum Press.
c. Data from General Electric Co. Glass Technology Laboratory.
d. Fused quartz. See reference e.
e. H. B. Huntington (1958). *Solid St. Phys.* **7**, 213.
f. H. G. Purwins, H. Hieber, and R. Labusch (1965). *Phys. Stat. Solidi* **11**, K63.

TABLE 3

Some elastic properties of cubic crystals

Material	C_{11}	C_{44}	C_{12}	Bulk Modulus $\frac{1}{3}(C_{11}+2C_{12})$	Bulk Modulus† at 10^{11} Pa	$4 \cdot 10^{11}$ Pa
	Units of $10^{10} \mathrm{N\,m^{-2}} = 10^{10}$ Pa					
Diamond	107·6	57·6	12·5	44		
Silicon	16·6	8·0	6·4	10		
Copper	16·8	7·5	12·1	13·7	54	157
Gold	18·6	4·2	15·7	16·6	64	174
Silver	12·4	4·6	9·3	10·4	54	166
Tungsten	50·1	15·1	19·8	29·9	66	156
α-Iron	22·8	11·7	13·2	16·4	55	168
Lead	5·0	1·5	4·2	4·5	40	124
Sodium	0·73	0·42	0·63	0·66		
Magnesium Oxide	28·9	15·5	8·8	15·5		
Titanium Carbide	50·0	17·5	11·3	24·2		

† Mean values from H. TAKEUCHI and H. KANAMORI (1966). *J. geophys. Res.* **71**, 3985.

TABLE 4

Elastic moduli for an orthotropic material with transverse isotropy

$$
\begin{pmatrix} \sigma_1 \\ \sigma_2 \\ \sigma_3 \\ \tau_{23} \\ \tau_{13} \\ \tau_{12} \end{pmatrix} =
\begin{pmatrix}
C_{11} & C_{12} & C_{13} & 0 & 0 & 0 \\
C_{12} & C_{11} & C_{13} & 0 & 0 & 0 \\
C_{13} & C_{13} & C_{33} & 0 & 0 & 0 \\
0 & 0 & 0 & C_{44} & 0 & 0 \\
0 & 0 & 0 & 0 & C_{44} & 0 \\
0 & 0 & 0 & 0 & 0 & C_{66}
\end{pmatrix}
\begin{pmatrix} \varepsilon_1 \\ \varepsilon_2 \\ \varepsilon_3 \\ \gamma_{23} \\ \gamma_{13} \\ \gamma_{12} \end{pmatrix}
$$

where $C_{66} = \frac{1}{2}(C_{11}-C_{12})$.

The unique direction (fibre axis) is taken parallel to axis 3. Then,

$$E = E_3 = C_{33} - \left(\frac{2C_{13}^2}{C_{11}+C_{12}} \right),$$

$G = G_{13} = G_{23} = C_{44}$,
$K = \frac{1}{2}(C_{11}+C_{12})$,
$G_{12} = \frac{1}{2}(C_{11}-C_{12}) = \dfrac{E_2}{2(1+\nu_{12})}$.

E_3 and E_1 $(= E_2 = E_t)$ are Young's modulus in the fibre direction and in the transverse direction respectively.

K is the plane strain bulk modulus for lateral dilation without contraction parallel to the fibres.

G is the shear modulus in a direction parallel to the fibres.

$$v_{12} = \frac{-\varepsilon_1}{\varepsilon_2}; \; v = \frac{-\varepsilon_1}{\varepsilon_3} = \left(\frac{C_{13}}{C_{11}+C_{12}} \right) = \frac{1}{2} \left(\frac{C_{33}-E}{K} \right)^{\frac{1}{4}}.$$

The five independent moduli or compliances are:

C_{33}	$S_{33} = 1/E$
$C_{22} = C_{11}$	$S_{22} = S_{11} = 1/E_t$
$C_{32} = C_{13}$	$S_{32} = S_{31} = -v_{13}/E$
C_{12}	$S_{12} = -v_{12}/E_t$
$C_{44} = G$	$S_{44} = 1/G$

$C_{66} = \frac{1}{2}(C_{11}-C_{12})$ $\qquad\qquad$ $S_{66} = 2(S_{11}-S_{12}) = 1/G_{12}.$

Experimental values for a carbon fibre epoxy resin composite:

$C_{11} = \quad 12{\cdot}9 \, \text{GN m}^{-2}$	$E = 112{\cdot}5 \, \text{GN m}^{-2}$
$C_{33} = 115{\cdot}9 \, \text{GN m}^{-2}$	$G = \quad 5{\cdot}3 \, \text{GN m}^{-2}$
$C_{12} = \quad 6{\cdot}3 \, \text{GN m}^{-2}$	$G_{12} = \quad 3{\cdot}3 \, \text{GN m}^{-2}$
$C_{13} = \quad 5{\cdot}7 \, \text{GN m}^{-2}$	$v = \quad 0{\cdot}3 \, \text{GN m}^{-2}$
$C_{44} = \quad 5{\cdot}3 \, \text{GN m}^{-2}$	$K = \quad 9{\cdot}6 \, \text{GN m}^{-2}$
	$E_t = \quad 15{\cdot}7 \, \text{GN m}^{-2}$.

APPENDIX D

Units

Standard acceleration due to gravity is defined (3rd CGPM, 1901) as $980 \cdot 665$ cm s^{-2} = $32 \cdot 1740$ ft s^{-2}.

Stress

    Fundamental units

        1 dyn = 10^{-5} Newton (N)

        1 Newton m^{-2} = 10 dyn cm^{-2} = 1 Pascal (Pa)

        1 bar = 10^5 N m^{-2} = 10^5 Pa. 1 hectobar = 100 bars = 10^8 dyn cm^{-2}

        1 kilobar = 10^8 N m^{-2} = 10^9 dyn cm^{-2}

    Practical units

        1 mm Hg (conventional) = 1 torr = $133 \cdot 322$ Pa = $133 \cdot 322$ N m^{-2}

        1 kgf mm^{-2} = $9806 \cdot 65$ kN m^{-2} = $9806 \cdot 65$ kPa = 100 atmospheres

        1 kgf cm^{-2} = $98 \cdot 0665$ kPa = 1 atmosphere

        1 lb in^{-2} = $6 \cdot 89476$ kN m^{-2} = $6 \cdot 89476$ kPa

        1 kgf cm^{-2} = 1 kp cm^{-2} = $14 \cdot 2233$ lb in^{-2}

        10^6 psi = 10^6 lb in^{-2} = $6 \cdot 89476$ GN m^{-2} = $6 \cdot 89476$ GPa

        1 GN m^{-2} = 145 000 psi

        10^3 kg = 1 tonne. 1 ton = 1 long ton = 2240 lb

                                         1 short ton = 2000 lb

                                         1 ton in^{-1} = $15 \cdot 4443$ MPa

Density

        1 g cm^{-3} = $62 \cdot 4280$ lb ft^{-3} = $0 \cdot 0361$ lb in^{-3}

        1 lb in^{-3} = $27 \cdot 68$ g cm^{-3}. 1 g cm^{-3} = 10^3 kg m^{-3}

Energy per unit of surface

        1 erg cm^{-2} = 1 mJ m^{-2} = 10^{-3} J m^{-2}

        10^8 erg cm^{-2} = $47 \cdot 68$ ft lb in^{-2} = $572 \cdot 16$ psi in

Fracture Mechanics

        1 psi in$^{1/2}$ = 1 lbf in$^{-3/2}$ = $1 \cdot 11$ kN m$^{-3/2}$ = $1 \cdot 11$ kN m^{-2} m$^{1/2}$

        1 ksi in$^{1/2}$ = $1 \cdot 11$ MN m^{-2} m$^{1/2}$

        1 kgf mm^{-2} mm$^{1/2}$ = $3 \cdot 16 \times 10^4$ N m^{-2} m$^{1/2}$

Viscosity

        1 poise = $0 \cdot 1$ Pa s = $0 \cdot 1$ Nm^{-2} s

        1 GN m^{-2} s = 10^{10} poise

Stress to weight ratio (under terrestrial gravity)

        10^{11} dyn cm^{-2}/g cm^{-3} = $1 \cdot 02 \times 10^8$ cm = $4 \cdot 03 \times 10^7$ in

Stress to density ratio

        10^{11} dyn cm^{-2}/g cm^{-3} = 10^{11} cm^2 s^{-2} = 10^7 m^2 s^{-2}

        10^6 psi/lb in^{-3} = 10^6 in^2 s^{-2}.

Textile Physics

The cross sectional area of a fibre of 1 denier is such that 9 km of fibre weighs 1g. So

$$1\text{g/denier} = 8{\cdot}82 \times 10^8 \, \rho \text{ dyn cm}^{-2} \text{ where } \rho = \text{density in g cm}^{-3}$$
$$= 8{\cdot}82 \times 10^4 \, \rho \text{ N m}^{-2} \text{ where } \rho = \text{density in Kg m}^{-3}.$$

APPENDIX E

Definitions used in glass manufacture

Strain Point. Temperature at which the coefficient of viscosity is $10^{14 \cdot 5}$ poise. At this temperature any internal strain is reduced to an acceptable limit within four hours.

Annealing point. Temperature at which viscosity is 10^{13} poise and so internal strains are reduced sufficiently within about fifteen minutes.

Softening Point. Temperature at which viscosity is $10^{7 \cdot 5} - 10^{8}$ poise. This temperature depends upon the mode of testing. With this viscosity a glass article elongates under its own weight at roughly 3 per cent second.

AUTHOR INDEX

SUBJECT INDEX